MARION TODD

Old bones lie

CANELOCRIME

First published in the United Kingdom in 2022 by

Canelo
Unit 9, 5th Floor
Cargo Works, 1–2 Hatfields
London, SE1 9PG
United Kingdom

A CIP catalogue record for this book is available from the British Library.

Print ISBN 978 1 80032 730 6
Ebook ISBN 978 1 80032 104 5

Look for more great books at www.canelo.co

Printed and bound in Great Britain by Clays Ltd, Elcograf S.p.A.

1

To my Witches.

You know who you are.

Saturday

Prologue

'Alexa, play seventies disco music.'

'Here's a station from Amazon you may like,' the robotic voice intoned. The cascading 'Disco Inferno' intro began playing and Kim jumped up from the cream leather sofa.

'God, I love this.' She kicked off her shoes and began to dance. 'Come on.' She reached out to grab her friend's hand but Debbie sank back into the sofa, flexing her toes.

'If you'd spent the week on your feet you'd be glad to put them up for a bit.'

'Dunno why you stay in that job,' Kim said, dancing over to the window. 'Alexa, volume up.'

'Fifty per cent discount helps.'

Kim danced back towards the sofa and scrutinised her friend. 'It's a nice dress. From the Christmas collection?'

'Winter Wearables.' Debbie reached to the side and picked up her glass, sipping from it. 'Want me to get you one?'

The sitting room door was kicked open and Alan entered bearing a tray laden with plates and cutlery.

'We okay eating on our knees?'

'Definitely.' Kim shimmied up to him but he dodged round her, setting the tray down on the coffee table.

Gav came in behind him with a six pack of cans and another bottle of Prosecco. 'Time's the food coming?'

Kim glanced at her watch. 'Should be here any time now.'

Gav set the cans down, pulling one from the plastic ring. He held it out to Alan who took it, tugging at the ring pull. Kim danced up to her husband again.

'C'mon, Alan. Dance with me.'

A shrill ring cut through the music. Alan laughed and put a hand on his wife's shoulder, pushing her gently back. 'Saved by the bell, eh?'

'Make sure it's right this time,' Kim called after him.

Minutes later he returned with a brown carrier bag. He put this down on the coffee table and Gav began handing out plates.

Alan gave Kim a bag of prawn crackers. Then he studied the writing on the top of each container as he unpacked the carrier. 'I think this is the bean curd and peppers.'

'Mine,' Debbie said, easing herself forward on the sofa.

'They'd better not have forgotten my egg fried rice,' Kim said.

'They won't.' He dug further into the bag. 'Sweet and sour.' He handed the tub to Gav, who peeled off the lid and tipped it onto his plate. 'And this must be your egg fried… oh.'

'Don't tell me.' Kim affected a huge sigh. 'I thought you told them.'

'I did, babe,' he said. 'I reminded them specially.'

'You know what, Alan? Next time I'll go and collect the bloody order myself. And I'll check it before I pay.'

'It's only a tub of rice, for fuck's sake. Have another glass of Prosecco and you won't know what you're eating.'

Debbie threw Gav a glance and he took the cue.

'I've only had a couple of sips of this,' he said, indicating the beer can. 'I'll nip along and pick you up a portion, Kim.'

The scowl vanished and she leaned across the coffee table, planting a kiss on Gav's cheek. 'Would you, Gav? That's so sweet.'

'And the rest of this will be stone cold by the time he gets back,' Alan pointed out. 'Look, babe, just eat what you've got and next time we'll pick it up ourselves.'

She glared at him. 'I'm not one of your bloody prisoners,' she said. 'You can't order me about.'

He opened his mouth to protest but the doorbell rang again. 'There,' he said. 'See? He's realised his mistake and he's come back with your rice.'

'He'd bloody better have.'

'That's your chicken,' Gav called to Alan. 'Want me to—'

'Yeah. Stick it on a plate, Gav. I'll just get madam's rice.' There was a click as Alan opened the front door.

'Give him a bloody bollocking,' Kim called. She reached into the bag of crackers and took one out. 'Anyone else?' She held the bag out but the sitting room door opened again and Alan backed slowly into the room. He was followed by two figures clad in black, wearing balaclavas.

'What the fu...' Kim's voice died away as she saw the glint of metal held against her husband's chest and she dropped the bag of crackers.

'Sit!' the one with the gun said. He was tall, muscular-looking in his black jacket and he dominated the room, a malevolent presence among the warm lighting and neutral tones. He jerked his head towards the sofa. 'There.'

Alan did as he was told, sitting down slowly. The man gestured towards the others and they joined Alan on the sofa.

'Hands where I can see them.'

Alan and Gav exchanged glances and the man shook his head slowly.

'Don't even think about it, lads. In case you're in any doubt this *is* loaded and I *will* use it. So, hands...'

Gav held his hands out, his eyes trained on the gun and the others followed suit. 'Maybe just tell us what you want,' he said.

'Disco Inferno' gave way to 'YMCA' and the man jerked his head towards the speaker. 'You can stop that fuckin' racket for a start.'

Kim cleared her throat. 'Alexa, stop.'

The music ceased and the man acknowledged this. He watched them carefully. 'Here's how this is going to play out.' He waved his gun towards Kim and Debbie. 'The ladies here are going to be leaving in a minute.'

3

Alan stiffened. 'I don't think so.'

'Easy tiger.' He trained the gun on Alan. 'You're in no position to negotiate.'

Alan held his glance but the man went on. 'Like I say, the ladies are coming with us. Just for a day or two.'

Gav cleared his throat. 'What's this about? Money?' He glanced at the others. 'Take it. Take the lot. Take it and get out. We'll say nothing, will we?'

Kim and Debbie shook their heads violently. Debbie was shivering now and she leaned against Gav. He turned his head slightly, eyes still on the man and kissed the side of her face gently.

'Like I say,' the man went on, 'the ladies are coming with us.'

Alan's eyes narrowed. 'Where are you taking them?'

'Doesn't matter. All you need to know is they'll be released unharmed when you've done what we want.'

'Which is?'

The man's eyes rested on Kim. He nodded to his companion who reached into his pocket and took out a cable tie. Stepping forward he grabbed Kim's arm, jerking her to her feet. He was smaller than the gunman, more slightly built, but he still towered over Kim, her feet shoeless.

Alan made to rise but the man with the gun pushed him back. 'Don't make me use this, son. It'll make a hell of a mess of the carpet.'

A sob escaped from Kim's mouth as the man spun her round, pulling her hands behind her. In seconds he had secured them with the cable tie. 'Shoes,' he said, nodding at the floor and Kim stepped obediently into her black wedges, wobbling a little without the use of her hands. He watched as she did this, then turned back, nodding at Debbie. She glanced at Gav, then she too rose from the sofa. The man grabbed her hands, clipping them together with another tie. Then he took a strip of cloth and tied it roughly over Debbie's eyes.

'If you hurt her,' Gav growled.

The gunman laughed. 'Oh we've not even started, son. Trust me on that.' He nudged his companion. 'Stick a blindfold on the other one and check them for phones. Let's get them in the van. Soon as it's clear.'

The women were bundled out of the room while the gunman remained in front of the men, his weapon trained on them. From the hall they heard the door open. Another voice, gruff and throaty, said, 'All clear.'

They heard the footsteps receding and the sound of a van door being slid back. Seconds later there was a whispered conversation. Then the man who had taken the women out reappeared.

'Okay?' the one with the gun said and the other nodded.

'Safely stowed.'

'Good.' He turned back to Alan and Gav. 'So, to business.' He reached into his pocket with a gloved hand and withdrew a small Nokia phone. 'There's one number stored in this. It's the only one you'll need.'

Gav flicked a glance at the men and ran his tongue round his lips. 'For what?'

'You'll see. Now, lads, there's a wee job we need you to do for us. But, before we get into that, some ground rules.'

Gav and Alan exchanged glances. Alan said, 'Pretty sure we can guess.'

'I'm sure you can. And I'm sure you lads have a protocol to follow in cases like this. All that prison officer training.' He shook his head. 'You'll no' be doing anything like that, lads. Not this time. No phone calls, no emergency signals, none of that *under duress* malarkey. You'll do exactly what we tell you. No more, no less.'

Alan cleared his throat. 'And if we don't?'

The man laughed. 'Oh, I think you know the answer to that, son, don't you?'

Alan said nothing. Even through the balaclava he could see the man's eyes narrow.

'For the avoidance of doubt,' the man went on, 'if you don't do exactly as we say, if you lift the phone to call this in, or you deviate from our instructions in any way at all…' He broke off, letting his words sink in. 'If anything goes wrong with this plan, be in no doubt. We will damage those women beyond repair. We'll hand them back to you so damaged they won't even recognise themselves in the mirror.' He looked from one to the other. 'Got it?'

Gav stared at the men for a moment, then he closed his eyes and let his head droop. Alan threw him a glance and mumbled that they understood.

'Good. So, let me tell you about our plan.'

–

They waited until the sound of the van drawing away grew fainter, then Alan jumped to his feet.

'Woah,' Gav said. 'Where the fuck are you going?'

'I'm going after them.'

'You're not, you know?'

Alan's lips thinned. 'I'm going after them and I'm going to find the girls. And when I find that gun-toting bastard I'm going to punch his fucking lights out. Gun or no gun.'

Gav stood barring the way. 'Alan, think for a minute. You heard him. He said they'd be watching us. There's probably one of them watching the house right now. Maybe someone at my gaff too. You saw that gun. He wasn't pissing about.'

Alan's face darkened but he said nothing.

'We can't call it in,' Gav went on. 'We can't send any messages; we can't do fuck all. Cos if we do...'

'How do you know you can trust them? For all we know they might be putting a bullet in the girls' heads right now.'

Gav shook his head. 'No,' he said. 'I don't think they will.'

'You trust these guys?'

Gav shrugged. 'There's far more chance of us recognising them than Debs and Kim. They were shit scared.'

Alan's head drooped. 'They were, weren't they?' His jaw tightened. 'I'll get those bastards, Gav. You see if I don't.' He sat silent for a moment, then moved to a side table and opened a drawer. He took out a notepad and pen, then sat back down on the sofa.

Gav raised an eyebrow.

Alan stabbed the pad with his pen. 'We're going to write down every fucking thing we remember about those men so we can pick them out of a line-up.'

'Balaclavas, though…'

'Yeah but the face is only part of it. So let's make a start. The lad with the gun first. Height?'

Monday

Chapter 1

'I can't decide between Dawn Light and County Stone,' DI Clare Mackay said, shoving the paint chart across the kitchen table. 'What do you think?'

DCI Alastair Gibson flicked a glance at it. 'Which ones?'

'Those.' Clare stabbed the chart with her finger. 'Look, I've marked them.'

He peered at it. 'Both look cream to me. You choose and I'll slap it on the walls.'

She snatched the chart back. 'You're absolutely hopeless.'

He sipped his coffee. 'Clare, it's a spare room. Not the Sistine Chapel. Does it honestly matter?'

'I want it nice – for James – when he comes to stay.'

'Your nephew? Clare, he's three! He wouldn't care if the walls were tartan.' He drained his cup. 'I'd better go. I've a meeting at nine.'

'Leave the dishes,' she said. 'I'm on a late.'

He rose from the table and carried his plate over to the sink. 'Sure?'

She nodded. 'On you go.'

She waited until he'd gone then filled the kettle to make a fresh pot of coffee. Benjy, her English bull terrier, was systematically licking the kitchen floor clean of crumbs and she tore a bit off her toast and offered it to him. 'Do not tell Al,' she said, and Benjy responded with a wag of his tail. As she waited for the kettle to boil she studied her garden through the kitchen window.

9

They'd tidied it up for winter at the weekend and it was looking neater than Clare could ever remember. Just one of the benefits of Al Gibson moving in, semi-permanently. She found she was smiling at this. 'Careful, Clare,' she told herself. 'You're in danger of settling down, here.'

The kettle came to the boil with a hiss of steam and she scooped the coffee grounds out of the cafetiere into her compost bin. Maybe it was time she settled down – whatever that meant. She had the cottage, the dog and now the man. And she was preparing to decorate her spare bedroom. 'There's no hope for me,' she told Benjy. 'It'll be two-point-four children before we know it.'

She poured fresh water into the cafetiere and stirred the coffee, considering this. She'd never thought about children. Not until now. Her sister had James and another baby on the way. Was it time that she, too, began thinking about it? It wasn't like they'd discussed it. She wasn't even sure she wanted children. But she wasn't getting any younger.

She drank her coffee, moving her chair so it caught the morning sun. A few more weeks and it would be too low in the sky. Time to have the chimney swept for the winter. She drew a notepad across the table and began to make a list.

–

'All quiet,' Jim said as Clare entered the station. As if on cue the phone began to ring.

'That'll teach you,' she said, heading for her office. She switched on the computer and waited for her inbox to load. A minute later Jim poked his head round the side of the door.

'Jim?'

He came in, notepad in hand. 'Might be something and nothing. A prison van possibly missing.'

Clare's brow creased. 'Possibly?'

'Aye. They're not sure. It was due back three or four hours ago. But no sign of them.'

'G4S?'

He shook his head. 'No, one of their own vans. Couple of officers taking a prisoner to a funeral down in Pittenweem.'

'Who was he?'

Jim scanned his notepad. 'Paul Devine. Doing six years for armed robbery.'

Clare raised an eyebrow. 'And they sent him in an ordinary van? No security staff?'

'Apparently he was considered low risk.'

'Hmm. Okay.' Clare rose. 'Let's look at the map in the incident room.'

The room was quiet, just a couple of officers tapping away at laptops. The blinds had been angled so the afternoon sun streamed in the windows, warming the air. Clare shrugged off her jacket and moved to the large map of Fife, a permanent fixture on the wall. 'Pittenweem, you say?'

'Aye.' Jim indicated the village, still an active fishing port on the East Neuk of Fife, now popular with holidaymakers. It sat on the north side of the Firth of Forth, an estuary straddled by three iconic bridges, the water feeding into the North Sea.

Clare studied the map. 'Looks like there's lots of little roads running between the villages. Where would they have gone?'

'That's the problem. Normally I'd say they'd take the B942 but it's closed just now for roadworks. There's any number of ways they could have gone.'

'Best guess then?'

'According to the tracker on the van they headed east to Anstruther.'

Clare frowned. 'But surely they'd be better going north, along this road,' and she tapped the map.

Jim rubbed his chin. 'Funeral was at midday. Probably over by one. I'm guessing they'd not had their lunch. Could be they decided to stop in Anstruther for fish and chips.'

'Not exactly following regulations,' Clare said, 'but it's pretty hard to pass the fish bar. What does the tracker say now?'

'That's just it. The prison radioed the officers to say the tracker was going off and on. Some intermittent fault. The men agreed to keep in touch by radio and that's the last they heard.'

'Hmm. Do trackers often play up?'

Jim shrugged. 'No idea. Most prison transport's a bit more secure. I'm guessing they don't generally need to rely on the trackers.'

'Okay. Last known location?'

'Dunino. Five or six miles south of here.'

Clare found Dunino on the map. 'Not much there by the looks of it.'

'No, just a few houses. Pretty spot, though.'

'Okay, Jim. Let's get a couple of cars out there. Make sure they have the van details. Better get a photo of the prisoner too.'

'Want the press office alerted?'

She considered this. 'Maybe leave it until the cars have had a look round. I presume Perth cops are checking from their end?'

He nodded. 'ANPR cameras too.'

'Hopefully there's a straightforward explanation.'

'Hope so.' He turned to go but Clare suddenly realised she hadn't seen her DS and she forestalled him.

'Chris?'

'Erm, nipped out I think. Want me to call him back?'

'Nah, don't worry. I'll catch up with him.' She turned back to her inbox and the emails which seemed to accumulate faster than she could attend to them. She worked on steadily, stopping occasionally to check for news of the missing van. By six o'clock with no sign of the van or its occupants she decided to call Suzi Bishop, the Press Officer.

'Clare,' the familiar voice said. 'How are you?'

'I'm well thanks, Suzi. You?'

The pleasantries dispensed with, Clare got to the point. 'Perth's had a prison van go missing, probably in Fife. It's been gone since lunchtime and there's no sign of the prison officers either, so I think we need to go public.'

'Want the officers named?'

Clare considered this for a moment. 'Not yet. Not until I've spoken to their next of kin.'

'Okay, Clare. Give me the prisoner's details and I'll get something out today.'

As she ended the call her office door opened and her detective sergeant, Chris West came in.

'Ah,' she said, 'the wanderer returns. Where have you been?'

He shrugged. 'Out on enquiries.'

'It's always the same when I'm on a late. Remind me to give you a list of jobs for tomorrow.'

He ignored this. 'Much happening?'

She looked at her notepad. 'Might be. We have a missing prison van.'

'Since when?'

'Early afternoon. Prisoner returning from a funeral down in the East Neuk. The van's tracker was playing up. Last known location was close to Dunino. I've had a couple of cars out but no sign. Just spoken to Suzi. She's going to get something out within the hour. Hopefully get it on the ten o'clock news.'

Chris frowned. 'Dangerous?'

'Potentially. He's doing a stretch for armed robbery. Held up a jeweller's shop in the town a year or so ago.'

'That big one? Along South Street?'

'Think so.'

'I remember it. You were on a course. We picked up one of the gang pretty quickly.' He wrinkled his brow. 'Think it was Paul somebody.'

'Devine. Well remembered.'

'It's amazing what we get done when you're not around.' He dodged out of the way as Clare flicked her hand at him. 'So Devine's gone missing, eh? What about the POs?'

Clare scanned her notepad again. 'They're missing too. Just the two male officers. Gavin Gates and Alan Carter.'

'Eh?' The colour drained from his face.

'What? What is it, Chris?'

'Alan. He's my cousin.' He felt in his pocket and pulled out his phone. 'I'd better call Kim. She'll be frantic if she sees it on the news.'

Clare put out a hand. 'No, Chris. Not yet.'

'Clare, it's family. We – I mean, he's like a brother to me. I've got to speak to Kim. She'd never forgive me.'

She shook her head. 'We'll call round. Do it properly. Anyway, Suzi's only naming the prisoner, for now.' She studied him for a moment. 'Maybe I should take someone else.'

'Like hell you will. Come on – let's get round there before Suzi has it all over the news.'

Clare hesitated, then she saw the expression on Chris's face and her heart melted. 'Okay. But if I judge there's a conflict of interest...'

'Yeah, I know.' He jingled his car keys. 'Coming?'

–

Alan and Kim Carter lived in a semi-detached bungalow in the Bogward Estate. The house was in darkness as they drew up and Clare took a moment to study it. A red-painted front door stood between two windows, and she crossed a square of grass and peered in. The house was in darkness except for a small red light which she assumed was coming from a TV.

'That's their front room,' Chris said, walking ahead of her. He jerked his head to the other side of the door. 'Dining room there. Bedrooms to the back.' He pressed the front doorbell, keeping his finger on it for a few moments. They heard it ring out but there was no sign of life from within. Clare began walking along the side of the house, past a single garage finished in a grey render. She stopped to peer in a small window. 'Don't think the car's here.' She stepped back from the window. 'What about Kim? Do they have a car each?'

Chris was striding past her, round the back of the house now. 'Just the one car,' he said. 'Kim works in an office. Somewhere in the town. Not sure where, though.'

As they rounded the house a security light came to life, illuminating the back garden. Clare took it in. There was a fence down one side separating the house from its neighbour and a tall hedge on the other. A shed stood at the end of the garden and she walked down to investigate this. The door was bolted but there was no padlock and she fished out a pair of gloves before drawing the bolt back. The door swung open to reveal a lawn mower and an assortment of garden tools. She bolted the door again and walked back towards the house. Chris was shading his eyes from the security light trying to see through the windows.

'Come on,' she said. 'Obviously no one at home. I'll get Jim to track down Kim's work while we check the other officer's house.'

'I'm going to try her mobile,' Chris said, tapping at his phone.

'Say nothing to panic her.'

'I do know that. I'm not stupid.'

Clare threw him a look, but he was too intent on his phone to notice. 'I'll drive,' she said, holding her hand out for the keys. He handed them over and they climbed back into the car, Chris with the phone clamped to his ear. She pulled away, heading towards Strathkinness. After a few seconds Chris ended the call.

'No reply?'

'Nope.'

The trees were turning from green to gold now. A coppery leaf fluttered down as they drove along and stuck on the windscreen. She slowed a little as they neared Daisy Cottage, her home for the past few years. Glancing left as they passed she saw there were lights on, the front room curtains drawn against the darkness. A Ford Focus, now so familiar, was parked in the drive – DCI Alastair Gibson's car. He'd been Clare's boss at one time and she still referred to him as *the DCI*. But these days their relationship was on quite a different footing.

Despite the urgency of their mission, she found herself smiling.

'He's moved in then.'

'He has.'

'Working out okay?'

'Pretty much.'

'It's starting to look permanent.'

Clare shrugged. 'Maybe. Maybe not. We'll see.'

'Would it kill you to make a commitment?'

'Probably. Never mind that, now. Check my notepad please. See what Jim found out about the other officer.'

Chris turned on the interior light and squinted at the pad. 'Your handwriting's shocking. It looks like Gareth Gates.'

'Gavin. Address?'

He peered at the pad again. 'I know it. It's Guardbridge. Turn right at the roundabout and I'll direct you.'

Five minutes later Clare drew up outside Gavin Gates's house. As with Alan's, it was in darkness. 'I'm starting to see a pattern here,' she said.

Chris moved to the front door and, seeing no bell, rapped sharply on it. While he waited, Clare walked round to the back returning a few minutes later. 'No sign of life.'

'Nothing here, either.'

Clare stood, looking at the house. 'Get onto Jim now, will you? See if he can find out where Kim works; and if there's a Mrs Gates.'

Clare waited, tapping the steering wheel while Chris spoke to Jim. Eventually he ended the call.

'Kim's a data operator for a bank in South Street.'

Clare looked at him. 'A bank?'

'Yeah.'

'Reckon that's anything to do with it?'

'Dunno. I doubt it, to be honest. Bank security's pretty tight these days.'

'You're probably right.' She turned the key in the ignition and the car came to life. 'What about Gavin Gates?'

'According to Jim, he's married too. Wife's Debbie. She works in Eccentricity.'

'That shop in Market Street?'

'Think so.'

'No point in chasing up their workplaces tonight, then,' Clare said. 'Come on. Let's get back to the station and call the prison.'

It was almost eight o'clock when Clare finally got through to the assistant governor.

'Complete surprise,' he said in response to her questions. 'He's been no bother, Paul. We've searched his cell and there's nothing. Had his cellmate in for questioning too. Either he's been well drilled or he knew nothing about it.'

'Any Covert Human Intelligence Sources in the prison?' she asked.

'Probably. We've an officer who acts as CHIS handler. I'm not sure who his contacts are, but I can speak to him in the morning.'

'Quicker if we speak to the CHIS himself.'

'Sorry, Clare. No can do. We go through the handler – to protect the CHIS.'

'Surely in a case like this.'

'Nope. Any direct contact with a CHIS could endanger his life. It's through the handler or not at all.'

Clare sighed. 'What about visitors?'

'I'll get you a list of Paul's visitors ASAP. It might be tomorrow, though. We've had a flu bug going round the office so we're a bit short-handed.'

'You couldn't manage it tonight?'

'I'll do my best. We don't want him at large any longer than you do. But I can't promise.'

'Fair enough.' She paused for a moment, running through a checklist in her head. 'Can you get me a list of your releases as well, please? Last two months.'

'Yep. No problem. Anything else?'

'Just the usual – Paul Devine's family, known associates, phone calls, letters. Oh, and the funeral – whose was it?'

'I'll check that too. And you'll be wanting next of kin for the two officers. If you can hold on.'

A minute later Clare had phone numbers for Debbie Gates and Kim Carter. She thanked the assistant governor and ended the call. The number he'd given her for Kim matched the one Chris had tried earlier. He called it again but it rang out.

'Try the other one,' Clare said.

Chris dialled the number for Debbie Gates but it went straight to voicemail. 'What now?'

'We'd better start digging.' She drummed absently on the desk with her pen. 'A missing prisoner is one thing but the two prison officers, well that's something else. If they've not turned up by morning we'll need to set up the incident room. I'll request mobile phone data for the officers and their wives. I'd also like the background on Paul Devine's trial. If you could ask Jim to look into that. As soon as we get the list of Devine's known associates I want a watch put on them. And Chris, I'm sorry, but not a word to your family.'

He met her gaze and she thought she detected a hint of defiance.

'I mean it. Not until we know what's going on.'

He shrugged and went out of the room, letting the door slam behind him.

Tuesday

Chapter 2

Jim had left a note on Clare's desk confirming he'd requested a transcript of Paul Devine's trial.

You might be quicker speaking to Robbie, though,

he'd written.

He attended the robbery and gave evidence.

I've warned him you might want a word.

She pushed the note to one side, tucking it under her unwashed coffee mug. Then she turned to her computer and clicked to open the inbox. The emails began to load and she saw there was one from Perth prison. 'That's something at least,' and she sent it to the printer. As she rose to collect the printout, the door opened and Chris appeared. She regarded him and saw the dark circles beneath his eyes. 'You okay?'

He nodded. 'Yeah. Didn't sleep so well. You know.'

'I can imagine. You didn't—'

'No, I didn't.' His tone was testy and she noticed he was avoiding her eye.

'Don't suppose you had a look on social media.'

'Yeah, I checked. But that's all. I didn't message anyone. But God knows what they'll say when they find out I knew.'

'And?'

'Offline. No updates. Not been active on Messenger for a couple of days.' He shook his head. 'Clare, I'm worried.'

She clapped him on the back. 'Come on. I've a load of info from the prison. We'll get a coffee and work out a plan.'

They took their coffees into the incident room and sat at one of the desks. The email printout ran to two pages and she laid these out to read. 'Okay, Paul Devine's visitors first.' There were only two names on the list.

'Anthony Devine,' Chris said. 'Prisoner's brother. Last visited four weeks ago.'

'Definitely a person of interest,' Clare said. 'And this must be the girlfriend.'

Chris peered at it. 'Laurie Keegan. Not so sure about her. She's only visited once, just after he was sentenced. That's months ago.'

'Still need to check her out, though.'

'Yeah, I know.' Chris yawned. 'Might be worth checking on the cellmate's visitors too. They could have been visiting to pass a message to Paul.'

'Good point.' Clare scribbled this on the printout, then she studied it again. 'Prison releases – looks like six in the last month.' She scanned the list. 'But none with a direct connection to Paul Devine. Not even the same hall.'

'Want them checked?'

Clare thought for a moment. 'It wouldn't do any harm. See where they're living, if they're working, who they hang about with.' She returned to the printout. 'No letters. The only phone calls were to the brother. That seems to be it.'

'Anything on the funeral?'

Clare read on. 'Seems it was an uncle. Conducted by a retired minister – the Reverend Iain Jacobs.' She drew a line under his name. 'We'll speak to him today if we can. See if there was anything unusual at the cemetery.'

'What about the CHIS?' Chris asked.

'Says he'll get back to us on that.'

Chris leaned across and scanned the email. 'It's not much, is it?'

'Nope.' Clare checked her watch. 'I'm going to send a quick reply and chase up the phone data for the officers and their wives.' She rose from her seat. 'Then you and I are going to pay some calls. See if the wives have turned up for work.'

—

'We'll do the clothes shop first,' Clare said, turning into Market Street. The car rumbled over the cobbles, Clare's eyes trained on the parking spaces.

'Here,' Chris said, pointing to an empty space outside a phone shop.

They emerged from the car into the cool autumn air, stepping back as a couple of red-gowned students ran past, arms full of books.

'Somebody's late,' Chris observed.

'At least they hurry when they're late.'

'Ouch. So, where's this clothes shop?'

'Further up. Just past Luvians.'

'Suppose it's too early for an ice cream?'

'Definitely.' Clare quickened her pace, stopping short of Eccentricity's window to take it in. It was decorated with autumn colours, a cream painted stand holding an array of jumpers in red and orange. As they stood, a young man moved into the window and began arranging a dark red military jacket on a headless mannequin. 'You been inside?'

Chris shook his head. 'Not Sara's kind of thing.'

'They have men's clothes as well.' Clare studied her DS. 'Second thoughts.'

Chris made for the door. 'Come on. It's too early for this. Let's see if Debbie Gates has turned up.' He pushed open the door and a faint bell sounded towards the back of the shop, just audible above the music.

'I know this,' Clare said, her voice low.

'Cranberries.'

She nodded, recognising the song now. A woman in a Rab puffer jacket was browsing through a stand of winter coats. Clare moved to the checkout where an assistant was unpacking a large cardboard box filled with cellophane-wrapped clothes. She looked up as they approached.

'Help you?'

Clare flashed her warrant card and introduced herself and Chris. 'Is Debbie Gates here today?'

'I was wondering that myself,' the woman said. 'She's late. Should have been here half an hour ago.'

Clare sensed Chris was about to speak and she went on quickly. 'Was she in yesterday?'

The woman shook her head. 'Day off.' She glanced at her watch again.

'Is she often late?' Clare asked. 'Or off sick?'

'Not Debbie. Very reliable. Always phones if she's not well.' Her brow furrowed. 'I hope there's nothing wrong.'

Clare smiled. 'We just need to speak to her. Could you give us the number you have for her please?'

The woman hesitated then reached under the counter for her phone. She tapped and swiped, holding the phone out for Clare to see. Clare checked the number against the one she had for Debbie and nodded to the woman. She fished a card out of her pocket. 'If Debbie does get in touch would you ask her to call me, please?'

The woman said she would, and they left her to her cardboard box.

They emerged into the street, dodging past a party of tourists ambling along, cameras slung round their necks. The sun had come out from behind a cloud thanks to a stiff breeze that had blown up and Chris began unbuttoning his coat. He made to head for the car but Clare indicated the other direction.

'We'll be just as quick walking down Church Street.'

He trailed after her, catching up as she turned into Church Square. The L-shaped street skirted round the back of Holy

Trinity Church and Clare raised her eyes to take in the historic tower. 'It's a pretty significant building,' she said, gazing up at it. 'John Knox preached here.'

'I know,' he said. 'Cradle of the Reformation and all that.'

Clare gaped at him. 'You knew that?'

'Don't sound so surprised. You're not the only one who knows stuff. And anyway.'

'Anyway, what?'

He shrugged. 'Name of a band I was in. At school.'

Clare stopped in her footsteps, her hand on his arm. 'Hold on, you were in a band?'

'Yeah. So?'

'And it was called Cradle of the Reformation? Are you serious?'

'It's a cool name.'

'It's a poncy name, Chris. Tell me it wasn't your idea.'

'Nah. The drummer's dad was a history teacher. He got it into his head it would be a good name. And nobody liked my suggestion.'

Clare began walking again. 'Go on, then. What did you want to call it?'

'You'll only laugh.'

'Probably. But we could do with a laugh. Go on. Hit me.'

He hesitated. 'The Actinides.'

'The what?'

'Actinides. Chemical elements. I was into science at the time.' He glanced at her. 'Go on. We're almost at the bank. Get it out of your system.'

She slapped him on the back. 'For what it's worth, I think it's a lot better than Cradle of the Reformation.'

'Me too!' He looked so pleased Clare almost felt sorry for him. They were at the bank now.

'Come on. Let's hope Kim Carter's arrived for work.'

The heat hit them when they entered the bank and Clare pulled her scarf away from her neck. They were met by a young woman with long blonde hair, wearing a navy and red uniform. Clare showed her badge and asked for Kim. The woman's brow creased.

'I'm not sure if she's in today.'

'Perhaps we could see the manager?' Clare asked.

The woman picked up a telephone on the desk and spoke into it. A few minutes later a man in a light grey suit approached and introduced himself. Clare asked if there was somewhere private they could talk, and he led them into a small room with a desk and three chairs. He closed the door behind them and indicated they should sit.

'I understand you're looking for Kim Carter.'

'That's right. Is she in today?'

'I'm afraid not. I think she's off sick.'

Clare was suddenly alert. 'Did she phone in?'

'Actually, I'm not sure. If you'd like to wait, I'll check.'

A few minutes later he returned. 'It's not like Kim,' he said. 'There must be some family problem. No one's heard from her this morning and she was off yesterday too. One of the staff called and left a message but I gather she didn't reply.' He looked from Clare to Chris. 'I'm guessing you're here because there's a problem.'

Clare gave him a smile. 'Nothing to worry about. But we are keen to speak to her.' Again she took a card from her pocket. 'If Kim does get in touch would you ask her to call me?'

The man took the card, his brow creased. 'Erm, of course.'

They rose and Clare thanked him. Outside she began walking quickly. 'Come on,' she said. 'We've wasted enough time. There's five people missing. It's time to put a team together.'

They cut back through Church Square and, as they reached the car, Clare said, 'What did you play?'

'Eh?'

'In the band. Did you play something? Tell me you weren't the lead singer? Oh wait, I bet it was the tambourine.' She laughed. 'It was, wasn't it?'

'You don't deserve to know, Inspector, and you will *never* know!'

–

Robbie was typing up notes from the accident he'd attended when they arrived back at the station. 'I can fill you in on that trial now,' he said.

Clare considered this. 'I think we'll gather in the incident room in five minutes. Spread the word, would you?'

Minutes later she entered the room and looked round at them. A mix of uniformed and plain-clothes officers but, either way, it wasn't enough. She'd have to beg favours from other stations. But how to use them? That's what she had to decide.

She moved to the front and all eyes turned to face her. 'Thanks, everyone,' she began. 'You've probably heard we have a bit of a situation. A convicted armed robber, Paul Devine, escaped from a prison van yesterday, somewhere around Dunino. What's more, the two officers who accompanied him have also disappeared and their wives haven't turned up for work.' She saw Chris and Sara, his fiancée, exchange glances but she pressed on. 'Let's put someone on both houses in case they do appear. I've already requested mobile phone data for both couples and a warrant to access the houses. I want their bank records as well, and ANPR for any vehicles. See what they were up to in the days before they disappeared. I'll sort the warrants out but let's do as much as we can in the meantime.' She waited a moment while the officers made notes, then she went on.

'I've had some information from Perth prison, and we need to follow that up. More to come, hopefully. But let's focus on the prisoner first.' She scanned the room and caught Robbie's eye. 'Maybe you could fill us in on the trial, Rob?'

Robbie eased himself off the desk and moved to the front. 'Jardine's Jewellers,' he began. 'Far end of South Street, towards the cathedral. Held up last year by an armed gang.'

'How many?' Gillian, one of his uniformed colleagues, asked.

'We don't actually know,' Robbie said. 'Paul Devine was the only one convicted. He entered the shop, toting a gun. We know there were another two outside, posing as security guards, turning away any potential customers. There was a car waiting as well, so there must have been at least four of them.'

'Any of the others brought in for questioning?' Clare asked.

'Nope. Just Devine. We still don't know who the rest of the gang were.'

'How did they identify him?'

'The jeweller's assistant. Devine had previous and she'd seen his face. She went through photos and picked him out.'

'He wasn't masked?'

'He was, actually. But he only pulled the mask on as he approached the shop door. She just happened to be putting a tray of rings in the window when she saw the car stop outside. She saw the three men get out. The other two were already wearing the fake security guard helmets but Devine was unmasked for a few seconds. She saw them approach the shop, realised what was happening but didn't have time to warn the jeweller.'

'Didn't they have one of those fog devices?' Clare asked. 'They're pretty good for that kind of robbery.'

'They did but there wasn't enough time to deploy it. Devine was waving the gun about, threatening to shoot. I'm guessing they were pretty terrified.'

Clare raised an eyebrow. 'But she identified him from a quick glance through the window?'

'He'd a tattoo as well. On his wrist. She saw it as he pointed the gun.'

'What about the jeweller?'

Robbie shook his head. 'He hadn't seen the man's face and he was in a bit of a state. He didn't remember the tattoo.'

Clare considered this. 'We'll have to alert the jeweller and his assistant. They need to know Devine's out.' She looked round for Jim. 'Could you look up their addresses please and give them to Robbie and Gillian?' She turned back to the pair. 'As soon as you have the addresses get round there to advise them.'

'Should we station someone on their houses?' Robbie asked.

'Possibly,' Clare said. 'They should be okay in daylight but I'll review it as the day goes on. Meantime, you know the drill. If they live alone, try to get a friend to stay with them. Better still, get them to stay with someone else, away from their homes. Doors and windows locked, make sure someone knows where they'll be at all times.'

'Is it worth monitoring their mobile phones?' Robbie asked.

Clare frowned. 'It's unlikely we'd get authority for that. It'd take too long anyway, and I doubt they'll be targets. My money's on Devine trying to recover his share of the robbery. But we need to warn them, just in case. He wouldn't be the first absconder with revenge on his mind.'

Jim indicated he would find the addresses, and Clare went on.

'It'll help if we can find out why Paul Devine escaped. According to the prison he's behaved himself so far. No trouble. And nothing to indicate he was planning anything. There is a CHIS handler at the prison who might be able to shed some light on it, but we can't afford to wait for that. We have four innocent people missing and,' she glanced across at Chris, 'we can't ignore the possibility they may have come to some harm. So we look into his known associates. Any family, friends, anyone involved in his previous offences. I'll request a warrant for that too. Hopefully it'll come through quickly.'

'Do you want them interviewed?' Jim asked.

'Definitely not, apart from his brother and ex-girlfriend. They need speaking to. But I don't want any of his other associates contacted. If they are assisting him, we don't want them warned off. Let's have covert surveillance on their houses and their workplaces. I want ANPR sightings of any vehicles and info from their bank accounts. Devine's unlikely to have much cash on him and bank cards leave a trail. If any of them are withdrawing large sums from ATMs I want to know about it.' She saw their expressions and she nodded. 'I know, guys. It's a huge job. But we'll get Tech Support on board and as many extra officers as I can lay my hands on. Okay?'

This seemed to placate them, and she went on. 'Have I missed anything?'

'Were the jewels recovered?' Sara asked.

Clare looked at Robbie again and he shook his head.

'Nope. Devine exercised his right to silence. The thinking at the time was the rest of the gang had stashed his share somewhere until he was released.'

'Or they've cashed his share in,' Sara said.

Clare considered this. 'It's a good point and it could be motivation enough for him to attempt an escape – get out while there's still a chance they have some of his share.'

'Could be Devine heard they were planning to leave the country,' Robbie added.

Clare frowned. 'To be honest I'd have expected them to do that after the robbery. But it's a fair point. We'd better alert ports and airports. Do we know how much the haul was?'

Robbie looked blank. 'Sorry, boss. Can't remember offhand. It was a lot, though.'

'It's enough of a motive,' Gillian said. 'But why have the prison officers not turned up? And why are the wives missing too?'

'Could be whoever helped spring Devine knocked them on the head,' Robbie said.

Chris winced at this and Clare's heart went out to him. Maybe it would be better to deploy him elsewhere for a few days.

'Don't forget the wives,' Gillian went on. 'Is it possible they're all in it together?'

Clare shrugged. 'I can't see it, to be honest. It would have to be a pretty big haul for two officers and their wives to risk everything for a share.'

'I agree,' Chris said, his voice tight. 'We need to find them. God knows what's happened.'

Clare threw him what she hoped was a reassuring smile. 'Okay, folks. Back to basics. Jim, could you chase up the mobile phone data for the two couples and beg some cops from neighbouring stations, please? I'd like a couple of plain-clothes officers to call on Devine's brother and his former girlfriend. They were his only visitors in prison so we need them spoken to.'

Jim nodded and Clare went on. 'The rest of you get out there. Make sure you have Devine's photo. Check farm buildings, barns, outhouses – anywhere he could be hiding. And keep an eye out for the vehicle too. Jim will give you the description and reg. And,' she glanced at Chris, 'I think we need to go public on the prison officers and their wives. Names and photos, please, Jim, and something about being concerned for their safety. Nothing else.' She smiled at them. 'Thanks, guys. Keep in touch and we'll reconvene later on this afternoon.'

'What now?' Chris asked when the others had drifted off.

'Now DS West, we are going to visit the minister who conducted that funeral.'

—

The Reverend Iain Jacobs lived in a small, whitewashed cottage on the edge of Pittenweem.

'I thought ministers lived in huge manses,' Chris said as they climbed out of the car.

'I think he's retired.'

As they approached, the front door opened and an elderly man greeted them with a smile. He was dressed in dark grey trousers and a ribbed sweater and Clare thought he might be in his seventies; but his expression was alert, his eyes intelligent.

'Detective Inspector Mackay?' he said, his accent bearing a faint Hebridean lilt.

Clare introduced Chris and the minister led them indoors. The short hallway gave onto a bright sitting room with an ill-assorted collection of furniture. A fire burned in the grate, the walls either side of the fireplace lined with bookshelves. A longcase clock hung on a wall next to the window, its pendulum swaying gently back and forth with a sonorous tick. A battered armchair was next to the fire, a leather-bound book and a pair of reading glasses discarded on a mahogany side table. It was a homely, cheerful room but it felt to Clare as if she'd stepped back in time – to another era.

He indicated a small sofa and offered them tea or coffee, but Clare waved this away.

'We won't keep you long,' she assured him.

He waited for them to sit, then he eased himself down into the armchair. 'I gather you are enquiring about Monday's funeral?'

Clare was grateful to him for coming to the point. 'You'll be aware one of the mourners attended from custody.'

He nodded. 'Indeed. I have to say the two officers were most discreet but it was difficult not to notice the handcuffs.'

'Was the funeral well attended?'

He shook his head. 'Just a couple of relatives, and the pall-bearers, of course. Sad, really.'

'Who were they?'

'It was organised by a nephew – Anthony Devine. A very simple affair. Just a few words, a prayer then the committal.'

'And did you speak to the handcuffed man?'

'Oh yes. I always make a point of speaking to mourners, particularly when it's such a small funeral. I said how sorry I was and I was glad he was able to attend.'

'And did he reply?'

'He did.' The minister smiled. 'He said it had been a very nice service and he thanked me. I said I'd pray for him and I moved away.'

'Can you think, please,' Clare went on, 'whether he spoke to Anthony Devine at all? I believe they're brothers.'

The minister smiled. 'Oh yes. They had quite a conversation. Even shared a joke, from what I saw. I was glad about that. Whatever he'd done, it's not an easy life for prisoners.'

'Did they chat for a while?' Clare asked.

He considered this then he said, 'Three or four minutes I think. Maybe a little longer. I did notice the officers seemed to be a bit impatient, while the brothers were chatting, you know? Perhaps their time was limited.'

Chris shifted forward in his seat. 'Did you notice anything else about the officers?'

'Oh, I'm not sure. Perhaps a little detached from the proceedings. I imagine it's difficult to feel part of a funeral when the deceased is not known to you.'

'Were they uncomfortable at all? Nervous?' Chris persisted.

Clare tapped his ankle gently with her foot but he ignored this.

'Nothing at all you can tell us about them?' he went on.

The minister's brow creased, and Clare rose before he could answer. 'I'm very grateful to you, Reverend Jacobs. Thank you so much for your time.'

Chris sat on, his eyes trained on the man.

Clare put a hand on his shoulder. 'Time we were heading back to the station. Thank you again.'

Chris rose slowly. 'You will let us know if you remember anything?'

The minister studied Chris as though trying to understand his persistence; then said of course he would and showed them to the door.

Clare started the car engine and pulled away. Instead of heading back towards St Andrews she drove through the narrow streets until she came to the shore road. She swung the car round into one of the spaces facing the harbour and killed the engine. She looked out towards the sea, past the boats bobbing up and down with the sway of the tide, scanning it for dolphins but there was no sign of them. A cormorant sat on a rock, its wings spread in the distinctive crucifix pose.

'Apparently they do that to dry their wings,' she said with a glance at Chris.

He stared at her. 'You think we've time to sit and look at the sea?'

She met his gaze. 'I'll pretend I didn't hear that. But I can't pretend you're handling this professionally.'

He looked away. 'What do you expect?'

'Chris…' she began.

'Don't even think of taking me off this case,' he said.

She was silent for a moment. 'I've no choice. I have a duty of care towards you, never mind five missing people to find.'

'One of whom's my cousin, don't forget.'

'And that's why you have to step back.' She softened her tone. 'Chris, I'm sorry. But it has to be this way. You can't be objective, and I need someone who's capable of assessing things dispassionately. I can't focus on this case if I'm worrying about you.'

'I'll go over your head.'

She saw him swallow and she gave him a moment to compose himself before she spoke again.

'Let's get back to the station. There's plenty to do and you can definitely be involved. But I do want you behind a desk for the next few days.'

He didn't speak.

'Okay?'

He turned to face her and she saw his face was flushed, his jaw tight. Then he turned back without a word, staring straight ahead at the waves as they lapped over the foreshore rocks.

'Oh Chris.' She reached over to give him a hug but he sat, unmoving, his frame as stiff as a board. She drew back and watched him for a moment then threw the car into reverse and backed out of the space.

Chapter 3

'You want me to investigate a stolen tractor?' He stopped just inside the station door which slid closed behind him.

Clare regarded him. 'Problem?'

The door slid open again as the sensor detected an elderly man making his way up the ramp towards the entrance. Clare drew Chris over to the side but he shrugged off her hand.

'You want to send an experienced DS to find a tractor?'

'You don't think the farmer deserves our best efforts?'

Chris sighed. 'What I'm saying is you could easily send a couple of uniforms to check it out.'

'Yes I could. If I *had* a couple of uniforms to spare. But we've five missing people, one of whom is a convicted armed robber, so they're all out looking for him.'

'You're just trying to get me out of the way.'

'Frankly, Chris, it's an idea that appeals more by the minute. So stop being a baby and go and do some real police work. And leave the attitude at the station door.'

He turned without a word and stomped off. Clare watched him, then headed back towards her office. Jim forestalled her. 'He's just worried.'

Clare smiled at the desk sergeant. 'I know, Jim. And that's why he's better off out of it. At least until we know a bit more.' She carried on towards her office and, as she opened the door, her phone began to ring. 'DI Mackay,' she said, lifting it to her ear.

'Dave Manning,' a voice said.

Clare searched her memory and then she remembered. The assistant governor at Perth prison.

'Following up on Paul Devine,' he went on.

'You have something?'

'Not really. I spoke to the CHIS handler this morning. There was no prior warning of Devine absconding.'

'Nothing at all?'

'Sorry. Whoever planned this did a cracking job of keeping it quiet.'

'How good's the CHIS?'

'We class him as reliable. He's provided good intel in the past. My instinct is very few, if any, knew about it.'

Clare sighed. 'Does that tell us anything?'

'Only that it's likely a professional job. Devine might even be out of the country by now.' He hesitated. 'Don't suppose there's any sign of our lads?'

'Not yet,' Clare said. 'But we've every available officer out looking for them. Any intel from their colleagues?'

He shook his head. 'Not a peep.'

'Any trouble with the officers in the past?'

'Nope. Both good records. Get on well with the prisoners. They strike a good balance, you know? Keeping control without pissing anyone off.'

Clare thanked him for the information and ended the call. She sat thinking for a minute then dialled the DCI's number. He answered on the first ring.

'Hi Clare. Everything okay?'

'I need a favour, Al. But I don't want a fuss about it.'

'Go on.'

'I need a DS for a few days. Ideally one who's not been in the station before.'

'You've taken Chris off the case?'

'Had to. He's not thinking clearly. I'm tempted to move Sara sideways as well. They do live together.'

'That needs care,' Al said. 'You don't want to be accused of not trusting her.'

Clare sighed heavily. 'I know. Ach, she'll be fine. She's sensible enough. Anyway, if you do know someone...'

'I hear Dundee are sending you a couple of detectives. Would one of them not do?'

'Bill and Janey? They're good guys. But I'd rather not have one of them as Chris's stand-in. They've worked with him before. It'd be awkward for them.'

'Leave it with me. Good detectives are pretty thin on the ground just now but I'll see what I can do.'

—

Bill and Janey arrived just after lunchtime, followed closely by Nita from the Cupar station.

'There's a few more folk on the way,' Bill said, and Clare smiled her thanks. She brought them quickly up to date with the enquiry.

'Still no sign of the POs?' Janey asked.

'Afraid not. Or the wives.' She sat back for a moment, thinking. 'We need to get eyes on Paul Devine's known associates.'

Janey turned to Bill. 'You've had dealings with him, haven't you?'

He nodded. 'I jailed him a few years ago.'

'So you'd know who he hangs around with?' Clare said.

He shrugged. 'Some.'

'Could you do me a list please, Bill? We'll set up a watch and get intel on their phones and bank accounts.'

Jim tapped on the door and Clare looked up. 'One of the Cupar lads called in on Laurie Keegan – Paul Devine's girlfriend, or rather, ex-girlfriend.'

'And?'

'Doesn't sound like they're in touch. She visited him not long after he was sentenced and said it was over. According to her he accepted it and she's not heard from him since.'

'No visit requests? Letters?'

'Nope.'

Clare sat mulling this over. 'I'd like to keep her under observation. Can you sort it out please?'

'Aye. No bother. Visible?'

'No. Covert. I doubt his escape is anything to do with Laurie. But, if he is looking for assistance, he may try and contact her. She knows we're aware of her so let's pay particular attention to her movements. Even the smallest thing might be significant. Erm, what about the brother?'

'Anthony? No luck there. But I do have an address for his workplace.' Jim flicked over a page on his notebook.

Clare held out her hand. 'I'll take it. He was at the funeral Paul attended so I'd like to speak to him myself.'

–

Anthony Devine worked at Hardman & Son, funeral directors on the outskirts of town. Clare eased her car into the tightly packed car park next to a dark green van and walked round to the front door. She pushed it open and was struck by a heaviness in the air. The walls were painted off-white, hung with a set of watercolours depicting Scottish mountain scenes. The windows were screened by vertical blinds in the same shade as the walls, the only light coming from soft downlighters. A mahogany desk stood to one side, a dark-suited woman standing behind. She smiled as Clare approached and wished her good afternoon. Clare took out her warrant card and asked for Anthony Devine. The woman frowned and excused herself. She disappeared through a door marked *Staff Only*, returning a few minutes later.

'Mr Devine is dealing with something at the moment but, if you'd care to wait, he'll be with you as soon as possible.'

Clare took one of the seats opposite the desk and sat taking in her surroundings. She'd attended one or two funerals but, so far, hadn't experienced the grim task of arranging one. She wondered idly about her parents. Both were still in good health but one day perhaps she'd be sitting in an office like this being told the price of coffins. As if on cue, a door at the end of the office opened and an elderly woman emerged supported by a young man who Clare thought might be her son. The woman's face was puffy, her eyes red-rimmed and Clare guessed she'd just lost her husband.

She avoided their eyes as they walked slowly past, the woman clutching a crumpled tissue. They were followed a few minutes later by a slim man in dark trousers and a pale blue shirt.

'Detective Inspector Mackay?'

Clare rose from her seat. 'Mr Devine?' She became aware the receptionist was pretending to busy herself behind the desk, and she indicated the door. 'It's a lovely afternoon. Maybe we could step outside for a few minutes?'

She led him to the back of the car park and they perched on a low wall. It was a sheltered spot, warm in the autumn sun, the only sound the cries of gulls from the East Sands, carried on the wind.

'This'll be about Paul,' Anthony Devine said.

'Have you seen him?'

He shook his head. 'Not since Monday. The funeral,' he added.

Clare watched him carefully. He didn't seem uneasy but sometimes it was hard to tell. Maybe he'd had practice over the years, covering for his brother. 'Have you any idea why he absconded from custody on Monday?'

'Not a clue. I thought he'd resigned himself to his sentence. Ready to bide his time. He'd have been out in three years if he'd behaved himself.'

'You spoke to him at the funeral?'

'Aye.'

'Can I ask what you talked about?'

'The usual. Our uncle, mainly. I said how it'd been sudden. Heart attack. Paul said it was good he hadn't suffered. I asked how he was getting on and he said he was managing.'

'Nothing to indicate he planned to escape?'

'Nope.'

'A witness at the funeral thought the two of you shared a joke,' Clare said, watching him carefully. 'Can you recall what it was about?'

He shook his head. 'Didn't have much time, really. The prison lads seemed keen to get away.'

'How did you leave things with Paul?'

He shrugged. 'I said I'd visit in a few weeks. Then one of the officers said it was time to get back.' He shifted his position on the wall and glanced at the building. 'We are kinda busy today.'

Clare smiled. 'One more thing – if Paul does get in touch, you must contact us. We will catch up with him and the longer he's on the run the more serious the consequences.' She fished out a card and handed it to him. 'I'm sure you realise perverting the course of justice is a serious charge – one that usually carries a custodial sentence.'

He regarded her for a moment then took the card, turning it in his hands. Then he rose from the wall and dusted off the back of his trousers. 'I wonder what you'd do,' he said, 'if it was a member of your family?'

And, with that, he walked back towards the front of the building leaving Clare to wonder how she would react.

Chapter 4

'We've identified three of Devine's known associates,' Jim said as Clare headed for her office.

'And?'

'We've managed to find concealed surveillance points for two. They should be set up pretty soon. Still working on the third.'

Clare nodded. 'I'd like someone on the brother, too. Work and home. I'm not convinced about him. Also, let's put in a request for his phone and bank details.'

'Will do. Janey, Bill and Nita are following up Devine's cell-mate's visitors; and I gather there's a lad on his way from Dundee.' He lowered his voice. 'A replacement for Chris.'

'Thanks, Jim. Hopefully not for long.' She rubbed her temple, trying to think if there was anything else. 'Oh, could you try and keep Sara busy? I'd like her as far away from this as possible.'

'Already done,' he said. 'She's looking back through farm machinery thefts. Might be something that helps with Chris's missing tractor.'

Clare smiled. 'Thanks, Jim. Any progress on mobile phone data for the two couples?'

'I'll chase it up.'

She thanked him and pulled her notepad across the desk. Time to make a list. There was a tap at the door and a young man in a navy checked suit appeared. He was tall and slim, his blonde hair slicked back on top, cut short at the sides. He came forward into the room, his hand extended.

'DS Max Evans.'

Clare realised this must be Chris's replacement and she rose to shake his hand.

'Thanks for joining us, Max. I take it you met Jim on your way in?'

'I did.' He looked round, beaming. 'It's a lovely station. I must say I'm looking forward to working here. And with you, obviously,' he added.

Clare studied him. He was certainly different from Chris, and from most of the world-weary detectives she'd come across, and she wondered how long he'd been a DS. She was about to ask him where he'd worked previously when the door opened and Robbie put his head round. Clare waved him in and introduced Max. The two men nodded, then Robbie turned back to Clare.

'Spoke to the jeweller.'

'How was he?'

'Pretty worried,' Robbie said. 'Asking for police protection.'

'You didn't promise that?'

He shook his head. 'Gave him the usual advice and I said we'd have someone on patrol near his house overnight.'

'Thanks, Robbie. What about the assistant?'

'Not caught up with her yet. The jeweller said she's taken annual leave for a couple of weeks.'

'Has she gone away?'

'He wasn't sure but he thought she might have. Said it was a last-minute thing. She'd asked the previous week if she could take some time off. He'd asked why and she said she could do with a break.'

Clare frowned. 'He didn't press her on it?'

He shook his head. 'Apparently she'd not taken leave for months. Shop wasn't particularly busy so he agreed.'

'Checked the house?'

'Yeah. No one at home.'

'Any neighbours around?' Clare asked.

'No. She lives in a cottage on the Toll Road.'

Clare's brow creased. 'Where?'

'It runs between Guardbridge and Balmullo.'

'Family?'

'According to the jeweller she's a bit of a loner. He's not aware of any family members and he doesn't think she's on social media.'

Clare wondered about that. There was any number of reasons this woman might not be at home. She could have an appointment or even be away for a few days. All the same... 'Give me the address, Robbie. I think we'll call round.'

—

As they drove towards Guardbridge, Clare updated Max on the case.

'So they've been gone, what, twenty-four hours?'

She checked the car clock. 'A bit more. Since lunchtime yesterday.'

He sat silent for a minute then he said, 'Funny the wives going missing too. Reckon they're involved somehow?'

Clare glanced at the satnav and signalled to turn left onto the Toll Road. 'It's possible.'

'Or could be Devine has something on them. Maybe he's blackmailing the officers,' he suggested. 'They might all be in it together. We should check their bank accounts.'

Clare sighed inwardly. 'Thanks, Max. I'll bear it in mind.'

'You're welcome! I mean, you never know, do you? Who to trust. You can't tell, these days.'

She was beginning to think a little of Max would go a very long way when he said, 'Should be just after this farm. If you drive on slowly I'll look out for it.'

Clare rolled her eyes. It was going to be a long afternoon. He was right, of course. As they rounded a bend the cottage came into view.

'I think this is it,' he said, and Clare drew the car into the side, bumping it up on the verge. Max climbed out ahead of Clare, and they stood taking it in. It was a small single-storey dwelling, whitewashed with a grey slate roof. Two tubs of polyanthus stood either side of the front door. To the right of the cottage was an old wooden garage, a bolt securing the door.

'Check that, would you?' she said, and Max strode off, pulling a pair of forensic gloves from his pocket as he went.

Clare rapped on the front door and listened for any sound within. When none came she moved to a window and, shading her eyes from the daylight, peered into what seemed to be a sitting room. There were easy chairs arranged round an open fire, a rug in front of it. A gateleg table stood against the wall, two dining chairs at either end. There was a door beyond the table, possibly through to a kitchen but she couldn't tell. She stepped back and walked round the house to find Max pulling back one of the garage doors, lifting it to avoid it dragging on the gravel.

'Car's still here,' he said. 'She must be inside. Unless she's gone for a walk.' He marched round to the back of the house. Clare found him standing on an upturned plant pot peering in a window.

'See anything?'

'No. Just a normal kitchen. Tidy enough. No evidence of anyone leaving in a hurry.' He stepped down, brushing off his hands. 'Maybe she's gone out with a friend. We could ask at the farm down the hill. See if anyone saw her this morning. Or check if she's ordered a taxi.'

The sound of a vehicle climbing the hill cut across the cool afternoon air and Max walked quickly back round to the front of the cottage. Glad of a minute to herself Clare turned from the house to study the garden. It wasn't large, with farmland visible beyond a hedge. In the distance a large green tractor with a seed drill attached was making steady progress across a gently sloping field. *Sowing winter wheat*, Clare thought, *before the weather turns*. It crested a rise, disappearing from view, and Clare's gaze dropped again to the garden. An old shed stood against a fence, not large but big enough for a garden of this size. It looked to be in the same wood as the garage with a grimy window to the right of the door. The glass had slipped down in the frame, leaving a small gap at the top. As Clare studied it she noticed a fly buzz around the glass then disappear through the gap into the shed. She squinted against the afternoon sun, low enough at this time of year to be in her eyeline and she saw the fly buzzing inside the shed. She began walking down the garden and, as she neared it, she realised there was more than one fly. Her heart rate quickened and she reached in her pocket for a pair of forensic gloves.

'Driver hasn't seen anything,' Max called as he walked towards her. 'Said he'd keep an eye out, though. Nice man. He—'

'Max?'

'Yes?'

'I think we may need SOCO out.' She stepped forward and eased the bolt across with a gloved hand. The door swung open on its hinges and Clare stepped back as the cool afternoon air disturbed the flies.

'Oh God!' Max's hand went to his mouth and he stepped back.

Clare glanced at him. 'Give Jim a call and tell him to get someone round to the jeweller's house immediately. The shop, too. I want to know he's okay. Tell whoever he sends not to say anything – just a courtesy visit, that sort of thing. Then tell him to get onto the press office. I want an update out as soon as possible. Paul Devine wanted on suspicion of murder.'

She pushed the door gently back, placing a plant pot against it to avoid handling the bolt again. With one eye on the white-faced DS, she took out her phone to call SOCO.

Chapter 5

Raymond Curtice, the SOCO officer, arrived an hour later and his team began erecting a tent over the entrance to the shed. He pulled the hood of his white suit over his head and adjusted his mask. Then he bent to scrutinise the body. After a minute or two he stood up and approached Clare and Max.

'Well, the body's fully rigid. Rigor hasn't started to wear off so I wouldn't say she's been dead too long. Somewhere around twenty-four to forty-eight hours. But you'll need the post-mortem to confirm that.'

'I'm guessing death's due to that contusion on the head,' Max said.

Clare threw him a glance. *Contusion?*

Raymond must have noticed this. His lip twitched as though suppressing a smile. 'The bash on the head – yes, I'd agree. I'd guess she's been struck more than once but it's the doc's job to pronounce on that.'

'Any sign of a weapon?' Clare asked.

Raymond surveyed the shed. The back wall had a row of hooks on which hung an array of hand tools. 'Hard to say. Could be any of these. But if your killer has half a brain, he or she won't have left the weapon lying around for us to find.' He looked down at the grass and round the garden. 'I can't be sure yet but, looking at the blood loss, she probably wasn't moved far.'

'Killed in the shed, then?' Clare asked.

'Shed or just outside.' He indicated the floor. 'See how there's blood near the door but none on the step? Grass looks relatively blood-free as well, although we'll check that. My guess is she's been on her way to the shed and the killer's surprised her from behind. There's a couple of nets of logs and some kindling. She could have been out here to fetch wood for the fire.'

Clare stood visualising it. Then she glanced towards the house. 'I'll need a team in there too. In case the killer's been inside.' She hesitated. 'Don't suppose...'

Raymond followed her glance. 'Just let us do the door and the handle. Then you can have a brief look. Fully suited, mind. You know the drill. Touch nothing, take nothing, leave nothing.' He looked across at Max and lowered his voice. 'Just you, though. Not the boy wonder.'

'Thanks, Raymond.' Clare turned to Max. 'I'm going to get a suit from the car. Could you get back onto Jim, please? I want a search of the fields bordering the property. You're looking for anything that might indicate someone was concealed there. Weapon, too. Anything heavy enough to have caused that head wound. He or she might have thrown it over the fence in a panic. And let the farmer know it's off limits for now, then get the field gate taped over.'

She left Max with this string of instructions and went round to the front of the house. It would take SOCO some time to finish with the back door so there was no immediate rush. Walking past the car she headed down the road until she came to the bend. She turned back and saw the cottage was still visible so she carried on until it was out of sight. Then she stood on the verge, trying to put herself in the killer's shoes. He – or she – would probably have come up this road. He might even have parked further down and walked up. Stick a backpack on, carry a couple of walking poles and no one would bat an eyelid. She began walking back up the road, her eyes left and right, until the cottage came into view. Then she stood considering what the killer might have done. The cottage was screened by a mix of fence and hedges but they weren't high. Mounting the verge she saw there was actually a break in the fence. She hadn't noticed it before, probably because there was a blue-green conifer in front of it. Maybe Maggie had planted it to screen the garden from the gap. The field had recently been ploughed and the soil was rutted in furrows but there was an unploughed margin round the edges. Easy enough for someone to go through the field gate further down the road and walk up the edge towards the cottage. It would have taken seconds for the killer to slip through the gap and sneak up on Maggie. Better tell Max to hold off on the search of the field. Maybe Raymond's team would find something there.

The back door was propped open, a SOCO examining it closely when Clare returned to the garden. She pulled on her forensic suit and waited patiently until the officer stood back to allow her to enter. 'If you could avoid brushing past the door,' the officer said, and Clare nodded.

The kitchen was small, the units old but it was clean and tidy. A fluorescent strip light flickered intermittently, and Clare longed to turn it off.

'Driving me mad,' the SOCO said, indicating the light, and Clare gave a sympathetic smile.

A wooden chopping board stood propped up against the tiles, a four-slice toaster next to it. There was a whistling kettle on a free-standing gas cooker but otherwise the kitchen was free of clutter. There was certainly no evidence Maggie had been entertaining a visitor.

She moved through to a small sitting room. Recognising the furniture, she realised this was the room she had peered at through the window. A stack of newspapers and a box of matches sat next to an almost empty log basket. Perhaps Raymond's guess was correct. Maggie had been about to light the fire and she'd gone out to the shed for logs. The killer, lying in wait, would have seen the light from the kitchen as the door was opened and watched Maggie make her way down the garden. Once she was in the shed it would have taken seconds to slip past the conifer and sneak up behind. One bash with a hammer, or whatever it was, would have propelled her forward, leaving her helpless as the killer rained down the fatal blows. All guesswork of course. They'd have to wait for the pathologist's report.

Clare studied the rest of the room. There was a comfortable-looking armchair next to the fire, a small table beside it. A magazine lay discarded on another chair but otherwise it was tidy enough. A further door revealed a short hallway with two other doors off. Bathroom and bedroom, she guessed. But the doors were closed and she didn't want to touch them before SOCO had finished so she retraced her steps to the kitchen. As the SOCO stood back to let her leave she noticed a pair of slippers at the door. Maggie must have put on outdoor shoes to go to the shed.

Emerging into the garden, she heard the sound of a vehicle coming to a halt and she walked round to find Neil Grant the pathologist stepping out of his car.

'We have to stop meeting like this,' he said, and Clare laughed politely.

'Good to see you, Neil.'

'So?'

'Woman found in her garden shed. Raymond thinks dead for around twenty-four hours. Head wound.'

He reached into the back of the car and withdrew a large briefcase. 'Okay, let's have a look at her.'

It was late afternoon by the time Clare and Max had finished at the cottage. After discussing it with Raymond she'd put the search of the field margin on hold to allow his team to examine it.

'What now?' Max asked.

Clare rubbed her head. What indeed. She looked at Max's face. He was terribly keen and that was great but she felt he had the potential to be exhausting. She and Chris hadn't always seen eye to eye but they were used to each other now. Max reminded her of a dog she'd seen when she'd taken Benjy to dog training. One of the better behaved ones that trotted at its owner's heels, face upturned for the next instruction. Benjy, on the other hand, had been so delighted by the presence of so many other dogs he'd rarely, if ever, glanced at Clare. The training had not proved a success and she had given up the Sunday morning sessions with considerable relief.

And now she had Max dogging her footsteps, like a faithful puppy. It was certainly refreshing after Chris but how long could she stand it? She dragged her mind back to the case, forcing herself to concentrate. 'Now,' she said, 'I think we'd better call in on our jeweller. Let him know his assistant won't be coming back to work.'

Chapter 6

Finlay Jardine lived in an Edwardian house in Donaldson Gardens, a quiet leafy street a short distance from the town centre. Clare nosed the car in behind one of the pool cars and, as she killed the engine, a plain-clothes officer she recognised but couldn't name stepped out.

'Anything happening?'

He shook his head. 'The wife's at home. Mr Jardine's still at the shop.'

'There's someone keeping an eye on it?'

The officer nodded. 'Parked opposite. Popped in a couple of times to reassure him. Last call he thought Mr Jardine was getting ready to close for the night.'

Clare thanked the officer and turned towards the house, taking it in. A sandstone wall bordered the garden with a wooden gate to the left and an open drive to the right. A substantial front door with a fanlight above was painted in a soft blue, flanked by two immaculately trimmed bay trees in galvanised steel tubs. Either side of the door were bay windows with broad wooden-framed panes. Looking up, she saw a further two storeys, the top level built into the eaves of a cross gabled roof.

'Attractive house,' Clare said, clicking to lock the car.

'It is,' Max enthused. He squinted up towards the roof and pointed. 'See the terracotta ridge tiles? They're quite elaborate. That dates the house.'

Clare stared at him, wondering if this was what she sounded like to Chris when she pointed out architectural features.

'Sorry,' he said, the colour rising to his cheeks. 'I like this stuff.'

Clare smiled. 'Me too. They're interesting, houses.'

He positively glowed at this. 'I get these magazines every month. All about house styles and so on. I could bring in some of the back copies if you like.'

Clare was starting to think she should watch what she said to Max. He seemed to pounce on everything with an eagerness that could become wearying. 'Maybe when this investigation is over,' she said.

'Oh of course! So, shall we?'

They walked up the drive which curved round to the front door past a double garage with dark red roller doors. A lamp burned in one of the front room windows, giving it a welcoming glow. Clare pressed a bell on the front door and a distant ring sounded somewhere inside. Moments later the hall lit up behind the door and they heard the sound of footsteps tapping across a wooden floor. The door was opened, flooding the entrance with light. A woman stood, her face fixed in a polite smile. Her hair, a neat bob, was tending to grey, silver hairs threaded through the blonde and, from her skin tone – the presence of the odd liver spot – Clare thought she might be in her sixties. She was slim, dressed simply in dark red skinny jeans and a long black top. Her ears were studded with tiny pearls and her hand bore a simple gold wedding band, a fine bangle at her wrist. This, Clare thought, must be Finlay Jardine's wife.

'Mrs Jardine?'

'Yes?'

Clare held out her warrant card, introducing herself and Max. 'I gather Mr Jardine's not at home.'

The woman checked her watch. 'No, he's still at the shop. But he should be back any time, now.' Her brow creased. 'Is this about the prisoner who's escaped?'

Before Clare could answer, a dark-coloured car swept into the drive, bathing the garden in its headlights. Max made to approach it but Clare held out a hand. Glancing down the drive she saw the officer who'd been watching the house giving the thumbs up. Finlay Jardine was home.

Sylvia Jardine led them into a sitting room with the single lamp burning on a table near the window. She flicked a switch on the wall and three more lamps came to life around the room. Suddenly, Clare was aware it was growing dark outside. Sylvia moved to the window and pulled a cord, allowing a trio of cream blinds to fall. She indicated two teal-coloured sofas. 'Please, take a seat.'

They sat down, Clare studying the room. The walls were hung with paintings by Scottish colourists, the chairs scattered with brightly coloured cushions. A few late roses were arranged in a tin jug, lending their fragrance to the room.

Finlay Jardine had followed them in and he waited for them to sit, then perched on the arm of an old club chair, the fingers on one hand worrying a crease in the leather. Clare thought he was a little younger than his wife. Mid-fifties, perhaps. He was dressed in a plain grey suit, a dark blue tie knotted tightly at the neck. He wore thick-rimmed tortoiseshell glasses which Clare thought made his eyes look smaller than they were. There was a small badge on his lapel. She strained to see what it was but couldn't make it out. His hair was receding at the temples and seemed unnaturally dark. He was clean shaven, the skin on his face beginning to sag and she thought a beard might give his face more character.

'Hasn't it become cold now,' Sylvia said, rubbing her hands, one eye on her husband. She knelt to click on a gas fire which Clare had mistaken for a wood burning stove.

She regarded this with interest. Maybe that would be a practical solution to her increasingly ineffective open fire. Then she dragged her mind back to the matter in hand. 'I'm afraid I have some bad news, Mr Jardine. Regarding your assistant, Margaret White.'

Finlay blinked a couple of times and the colour drained from his face.

'Maggie?' His voice was barely above a whisper. 'Something's happened to Maggie?'

Clare nodded. 'Earlier today the body of a woman was discovered at Miss White's house.' She paused for a moment to let this sink in then went on. 'I must stress she has still to be formally identified. But evidence gathered so far suggests it will turn out to be that of your assistant.'

They stared at her, and she thought she would never get used to breaking this kind of news. Admittedly Maggie White was only an employee but the pair seemed genuinely shocked.

Finlay was the first to find his voice. 'Maggie is dead?'

'I'm so sorry, Mr Jardine.'

'But what happened?' Sylvia asked. 'Surely Maggie was too young?' She moved to stand behind her husband and put a hand on his shoulder. 'It doesn't seem possible.'

'Was it her heart?' Finlay asked. 'I suppose it must have been for it to be so sudden.'

Clare shook her head. 'I'm sorry to have to tell you we believe Maggie was killed.'

Sylvia's eyes widened. 'Killed? You mean someone…'

'I'm afraid so.'

'But who?' Finlay began. He broke off for a moment, as though processing this, then the words came tumbling out. 'Oh my God,' he said, 'it's that prisoner, isn't it? The one who held us up at gunpoint.' He turned to his wife, his eyes moist. 'It's him,' he breathed.

She was bent over him now, rubbing his upper arm. She glanced at Clare. 'Is it? Is it the same man who robbed our shop?'

'I always said Maggie shouldn't give evidence against him,' Finlay went on, his voice rising. 'I told her. Don't do it, I said. And I was right, wasn't I? This proves it.' He broke off and Clare took her chance.

'We're waiting for a post-mortem examination to be carried out and I have every available officer working on it. But I'm hoping you can help us.'

He stared at her. 'Help? How?'

Clare glanced at Sylvia. She had drawn a small chair up next to her husband and was sitting very still now, as though lost in thought. 'I wonder,' Clare said with a glance at Max, 'if a cup of tea might be an idea.'

Sylvia seemed to recall herself and she moved towards the door. 'Yes of course. Or coffee?'

Clare smiled. 'Tea is fine.'

Max took his cue and rose from his seat. 'I'll help you,' he said, following her out of the room.

Clare waited until he'd closed the door then she turned back to Finlay who seemed to be recovering his composure. 'We need to know as much as possible about Maggie,' she said, her voice gentle. 'What she did in her spare time, who she knew, any problems she might have mentioned – anything at all.' She paused, and when he didn't respond she went on. 'Did she live alone?'

Finlay nodded. 'As far as I know. She never spoke about anyone else.'

'Boyfriend? Girlfriend? Anyone particular she spent time with?'

He shook his head. 'She never mentioned anyone to me.'

'How did she spend her days off?'

He thought for a moment then said, 'I'm not sure, really. She did like walking, though.' He nodded at this. 'She lives in the country – or lived, I suppose.' He frowned at this. 'Where was she? When you found her, I mean?'

'At home.'

'Someone broke in?'

Clare avoided the question. 'How long had Maggie worked for you?'

'About two years.'

'And before that?'

He sat back, thinking, his fingers steepled. 'I believe she worked for a theatre company in England. Something to do with organising the props.' He seemed to be relaxing now and Clare pressed on.

'Why did she leave?'

'The company shut down. Ran out of money, she said.'

Clare hesitated, taking her time to frame the next question. 'Mr Jardine, I'm sorry to ask but your relationship with Maggie – did it ever stray beyond employer–employee?'

His brow creased. 'I'm not sure what you're suggesting, Inspector.'

'I'm sorry but we need to ask these questions. So, was there ever anything between the two of you? Anything romantic or sexual?'

He looked at Clare for a moment before replying. 'Of course not,' he said. 'Maggie – I mean she was nice enough but, as you see,' he waved his hand around the room, 'I'm very happily married.'

Clare thought a tastefully furnished room didn't necessarily equate to a happy marriage but she decided not to press the point. 'Have you been to her cottage?' she went on.

'Once or twice,' he said. 'Only to drop her off, though – when her car broke down, you know?'

The sitting room door opened, and Sylvia held it for Max who entered behind her bearing a tray of cups and saucers. She lifted a small table across and indicated he should set the tray down. Then she handed out the teacups. Clare added milk to hers, waiting until they were all seated again before going on. 'Did Maggie own her cottage?'

'No,' Finlay said. 'She rented it.'

'What about family?'

The couple exchanged glances and Finlay shook his head. 'I got the impression her mother lives abroad. I don't think they saw much of each other.'

'No one else?'

'Not that I know of,' Finlay said.

'Maybe we could go back to the robbery,' Clare went on. 'Can you tell me as much as you remember about it, please?'

Sylvia put down her cup and saucer. 'Is that really necessary? It was dreadfully upsetting for Finlay.'

He waved this away. 'It's fine,' he said. 'I know you have your job to do. And I've been over it in my head a few times.' He put down his cup and saucer then folded his hands. 'It was early morning. Just after nine. I'd been setting out a tray of rings when Maggie arrived and I asked her to put them in the window. She was doing this when she started to say something then the door opened and a man burst in.' He shivered involuntarily. 'He had a gun, as you probably know. He handed me a bag and told me to fill it. I took the rings from the counter and a few more trays. Then he told Maggie to unlock one of the display cases. Watches, you know?'

'How long did it take?'

'No more than a minute. Two at most. Long enough, though. He took most of my stock.'

'And you didn't see his face?'

He shook his head. 'No. But Maggie had seen him get out of the car. So she was able to give a description. She even picked him out of a line-up.' His face creased. 'Maybe if she hadn't...' He sat silent for a moment then his eyes widened. 'Oh God,' he said, 'do you think he'll come after me next?' He looked round, panicked, as though expecting someone to come through the window at any moment.

'I doubt it,' Clare said. 'After all, you weren't able to identify him. And we'll post an officer outside for the next day or two. Just until we pick Mr Devine up.'

'What about the shop?' he said. 'Anyone could come in. And I'll be alone in there.'

Sylvia took hold of his hand. 'Finlay, stop,' she said. 'You can close the shop for a day or two. No one will mind. I'll go into town and put a notice on the door.'

'No!' he said, his voice rising. 'I don't want you anywhere near that shop.'

'We can put something on the shop door for you,' Clare said. 'And I can assure you we'll be watching your house, day and night.'

'You see?' Sylvia said. 'You'll be perfectly safe here. The police will find him, and we can all go back to normal.'

He eyed her. 'Maggie can't. Can she?'

They finished their tea then Clare said, 'There is one other thing I have to ask.'

Finlay and Sylvia exchanged glances and Clare went on.

'We would be grateful if you were able to identify Maggie. We've not been able to contact any family so far and we do need to have it confirmed.'

Finlay's mouth opened as if to speak but he seemed to be struggling for the words. He turned to his wife, his eyes wide, the panic evident. 'I couldn't,' he said, at last.

Sylvia's eyes rested on him and she shook her head. 'I really don't think it would be good for Finlay. He was anxious enough when we heard about the prisoner escaping. But this news about Maggie, well, you can see how he is.'

She had a point. Finlay was becoming more agitated by the minute. There was no guarantee he'd be capable of identifying Maggie, the state he was in; and it could easily make him worse. She smiled at Sylvia. 'What about you, Mrs Jardine? Would you be able to identify Maggie for us?'

Sylvia looked at her husband. She seemed to be hesitating.

'You can't Sylv,' he said. 'You can't.'

'It's okay, Finlay. It's fine.' She held his gaze for a moment then she turned back to Clare. 'I'll do it,' she said. 'I'll identify Maggie.'

–

It was quiet at the mortuary by the time Clare and Max led Sylvia to the viewing room, most of the staff having gone home.

'Take your time,' Clare said. 'There's absolutely no rush.'

Sylvia glanced at her and moved forward, standing for a few moments. Then she turned back to Clare and nodded. 'That's Maggie,' she said.

'Just to be clear,' Clare said, 'you are confirming the deceased person in front of you is Margaret White, your husband's employee?'

'Yes, that's Margaret White.'

They walked to the car in silence, Sylvia electing to sit in the back. She was quiet on the return journey and Clare was concerned enough to offer to go into the house with her but she shook her head.

'I shall have a large whisky and an early night,' she said.

They watched as she walked up the path, triggering the outdoor light which cast eerie shadows across the garden. Finlay must have been watching from the window because he opened the door as she reached it. Then the door was closed and the security light went out, leaving the garden in darkness once more. Clare waved to the police officer stationed outside the house and pulled out into the road.

Chapter 7

'Positive ID on Maggie White,' Clare said to Jim as she shrugged off her coat.

'Oh aye?'

'The jeweller's wife agreed to do it. He's the nervous type. Didn't feel up to it so the wife stepped in.'

'You'll need someone else, though,' Jim said. 'Given she's not a relative.'

'Yeah, I know. Suppose we could try the farmer down the road from her. But ideally I'd like her next of kin. Any luck with that?'

'Maybe,' Jim said. 'Her mother's been travelling for the past few years but we think she's in Ireland just now. Somewhere south-west. The Garda are on it so hopefully we'll hear soon.'

'What about Devine's associates?'

'Nothing of note so far. But the warrant's been granted for their phone and bank records so we should hear something soon.'

'And the brother?'

'Anthony? Last I heard he'd gone straight home from work. Still there.'

'Okay, Jim. I want eyes on him all night please.' She looked up, expecting him to leave but he seemed keen to linger. 'Something on your mind?'

'I was just thinking, you've Chris working on the stolen tractors and now there's a murder on top of the missing prisoner.'

'You think I should bring in another team?'

'Worth considering.' He seemed to be choosing his words. 'It's not that I don't think you're capable...'

'But you think it's too much for one DI?'

'Something like that.'

Clare bristled. She knew it wasn't meant as a criticism, that he only had her best interests at heart. All the same. 'There's a connection, Jim. I'm sure of it. There's every chance Paul Devine escaped custody to take revenge on Maggie White. As far as I'm concerned it's a straight murder hunt.'

Jim looked as if he was going to speak again, then he gave a slight nod. 'I'm sure you're right. I'll drum you up some more troops for the morning.'

Clare softened. 'I'd appreciate it. I'll brief them at eight tomorrow.'

After Jim had left she sat at her desk running through the day's events. Had she covered everything? Everyone available was out looking for Paul Devine and the prison officers. SOCO were still working at Maggie's cottage and Neil Grant had promised he'd try to fit the post-mortem in the following day. The registration of the van and descriptions of the five missing people had been circulated across the whole of Scotland and there seemed nothing else to do. She sent Max home and headed out to the car park, climbing wearily into her beloved Mercedes. She drove home along the Craigtoun Road, blinking away tiredness.

The DCI was returning from Benjy's evening walk when she drew up in front of Daisy Cottage. He waited for her to climb out of the car. 'You're late,' he said, kissing her on the forehead. 'Tough day?'

'Just a bit.' She bent to rub Benjy's neck and he jumped up, leaving muddy paw prints on her trousers. 'I'm too tired to scold you,' she said, and Benjy responded by licking her hand.

'Come on,' the DCI said, 'I'll get you some supper.'

'Oh don't worry. I'll be fine with tea and toast.'

'Shame. I was going to do lamb chops and crusty bread. Never mind. I'll give it to Benjy instead.'

'Suppose I could force it down.'

As Clare ate, Benjy sitting hopefully under the table, she told the DCI about her day.

'Sounds like you need another team to share the load,' he said, tearing off another hunk of bread.

'Oh not you as well,' Clare groaned. 'Jim's already had a go at me.'

He stretched across the table and took her hand. 'He may have a point, Clare. You've an escaped prisoner, two missing prison officers plus their wives and now a murder.'

She looked down at his hand, his long fingers wrapped round hers. It was a comforting sensation – reassuring, even – and she let her hand rest there, enjoying the moment. Then she met his eye. 'I know,' she said, 'I know. But I do think it's all connected. It's too much of a coincidence, Devine going missing and Maggie ending up dead.'

'I'm sure you're right. But the missing prison officers changes things. It's more than a straight man hunt. It could be a double abduction or the officers could be involved. Or worse.'

'Don't! I'm trying not to think that.'

His expression softened. 'Just see you don't overdo it.'

She squeezed his hand then withdrew hers. 'I won't. Oh, let's change the subject. Talk about something else. Anything!'

'How about a wood burning stove to replace your open fire?'

She stared at him. 'That's a coincidence. I was in a house today and they had a gas fire disguised as a stove. It set me thinking.'

'Yeah, I've seen those. But I'm talking about the real thing. The chimney's already there. Okay, you'd probably need a flue liner. But it's pretty much a straight swap. And, if we get a move on, it could be in for Christmas.'

'And it would be warmer than the fire?'

'No comparison. You'll be sitting out in the hall to escape the heat.'

She laughed. 'I doubt that, given how draughty this place is. So what do we do? How do we find out about it?'

He leaned back and took a large white envelope from the kitchen work surface. 'I just happen to have some brochures. I could ask a couple of suppliers to come out to do a survey – give us a quote.'

Clare picked up the envelope and withdrew the glossy brochures. Flicking through she was suddenly overwhelmed with tiredness. 'Can I look at them another time?'

He smiled. 'Of course. It's only an idea.' He rose and began clearing away plates. 'Put your feet up. I'll sort the kitchen out.'

She pushed back her chair and wandered over to the sofa, sinking down on it. She kicked off her shoes and lifted up her feet. Benjy jumped up to join her, resting his head on her chest. As she stroked him behind the ears she felt the beat of his tail against the back of the sofa and the cares of the day began to melt away.

Wednesday

Chapter 8

The station was buzzing when Clare arrived the next morning. She looked round for Chris but there was no sign of him.

'He's got a lead on those tractors,' Jim said when she asked. 'He's set up a surveillance team and they'll do a night shift tonight.'

She thanked Jim and went to her office to check emails. As she waited for the computer to come to life there was a tap at the door and Sara put her head in. Clare was immediately on alert. Sara and Chris had been a couple for a few years now and she guessed what was coming.

'I want to work on this case,' Sara said. 'You need as many bodies as you can get and if I have to look at one more missing tractor report I'll go mad.'

'Sara…' Clare began.

'I know what you're thinking,' she said, her face flushed. 'You think I'll take everything straight back to Chris. But you're wrong.'

Clare hesitated but Sara went on.

'For a start we're hardly going to see each other with him starting nights. And for another thing, I take this job very seriously. I don't gossip to my family or my friends so I can do the same with Chris; and,' she went on, her voice bordering on shrill, 'if you find out I've said a single thing to him, well you can sack me on the spot.'

Clare looked at Sara's face, bright pink now, and her heart softened. She indicated a seat and Sara lowered herself down, perching on the edge, her back ramrod straight. Clare gave her a smile.

'How's he holding up?'

Sara shrugged. 'About how you'd expect. He's worried sick. Doesn't know what to think. He keeps going on Alan's Facebook page to see if there's anything.'

Clare sat back and thought for a moment. 'Okay, Sara. You can join us for the briefing and we'll take it from there. But remember this: if you do relay any information to Chris you'll be facing a misconduct hearing. All right?'

Sara nodded and Clare smiled again. 'Pass the word round. Briefing in ten minutes.'

–

An air of stuffiness hit Clare as she entered the incident room. The blinds were closed against prying eyes and every available space had been given over to spare desks, chairs and laptops. Following the discovery of Maggie White's body, the Dundee and Cupar stations had sent as many officers as they could spare. She moved to the front, beside the whiteboard, and studied it. Jim had pinned up photos of the two officers and their wives. The prison had supplied Paul Devine's photo and there was one of Maggie, taken from the jewellery shop's website. It was a formal photo, the pose professional, but Clare sensed there had been a fun side to Maggie too. Something about the expression in her eyes. Then she forced herself to detach. Five missing and one dead. It was a hell of a lot to deal with. There was no time for sentiment. She turned back to face the room and took a deep breath.

'Thanks so much, everyone,' she said, nodding to the new faces. 'We've a lot going on here so I appreciate your help.'

There was a murmur acknowledging this and she went on. 'Maggie White.' She tapped the photo. 'Jeweller's assistant. Found dead yesterday with a severe head injury. We don't know yet when she died but it was probably some time on Monday. The post-mortem's set for this morning, all being well.'

Max raised his hand. 'I can attend if you like?'

Clare shook her head. 'Can't spare you, Max. And I'm sure Neil Grant will fill us in when it's done.' She looked round the room. 'I'll be surprised if the head wound wasn't the cause of death but we won't know the type of weapon for a few hours yet.'

'Where did she live?' Robbie asked.

'A cottage on the Toll Road, between Guardbridge and Balmullo. The nearest neighbour is a farm further down the road. Otherwise it's pretty isolated.'

Bill raised his hand. 'I spoke to the farmer last night. He wasn't much help, though. He hasn't been past the cottage for a few days so he couldn't say if there were any cars parked nearby. He did say Maggie was a keen walker and he'd often see her striding up the road or heading over the fields. Apart from that, he couldn't tell us much.'

Cheryl, a plain-clothes officer from Dundee, caught Clare's eye. 'Anyone in the frame for it, boss?'

Clare tapped Paul Devine's photo. 'Possibly this man. Paul Devine, a prisoner at Perth. Serving six years for armed robbery on the shop where Maggie worked. Maggie's evidence helped convict him and, on Monday, he escaped custody, somewhere in Fife.'

'What about the other shop staff?' Cheryl asked.

'There's just the owner, Finlay Jardine. I think the wife helps out occasionally but it seems Mr Jardine and Maggie were the only staff. We spoke to him yesterday. He didn't identify Devine in court but he's convinced Devine killed Maggie out of revenge. Terrified he'll be next.'

'Would he have had time to kill her?' Bill asked.

Clare exhaled. 'It's hard to be sure. The PM will give us an indication of when she died but it will only be an indication. We can be pretty sure about Devine, though. He was seen and spoken to at a funeral in Pittenweem about midday and he should have arrived back at the prison around two.' She moved to indicate the photos of the two prison officers. 'For anyone who wasn't here yesterday, these men are the prison officers who escorted Devine to the funeral on Monday – Gavin Gates and Alan Carter. They went missing with Devine and there's been no trace of them since. It seems they reported problems with the van tracker then it stopped working. The prison phoned to check they were okay and they confirmed they were fine. And that's the last anyone heard of them.' She looked back at the board and indicated the photos of Debbie Gates and Kim Carter. 'To complicate matters, both officers' wives are also missing.'

She glanced across at Jim. 'I take it there's been nothing overnight?'

He moved to the front of the room. 'Not much. Surveillance is in place now at Paul Devine's known associates.'

'Anything suspicious?' Clare asked.

Jim shook his head. 'No visitors. Two of them came home from work last night and didn't go out again. The other's been home since yesterday afternoon. Still there this morning.'

'What about the ex-girlfriend?'

'Aye. Laurie Keegan. Again, nothing suspicious. She works in a call centre. Finished last night at ten and went home via Tesco. She's still there this morning.'

Clare nodded her thanks and turned back to the room. 'Paul Devine has a brother, Anthony. Works at an undertaker's in the town. We spoke to him yesterday and he hadn't much to say, but I'm concerned he might be assisting his brother so we've had someone on him since last night.' She glanced at Jim. 'Who's there just now?'

'Liv and Erin.'

Clare had worked with the two officers before and she knew they could be relied on. 'Thanks, Jim.'

'What about phone records?' one of the Cupar officers asked.

'In hand. The Fiscal's granted a warrant for phone and bank records for the two officers and their wives, plus Devine's brother, the ex-girlfriend and a handful of known associates. We're also seeking access to the officers' houses. I'm hopeful, given the seriousness of the case, we'll have that today. Tomorrow at worst; and we're checking ANPR for the officers' vehicles.'

Clare glanced round and caught Max's eye. 'We'll need a fair few bodies on the phone records but could you take the bank accounts please? Shouldn't be a big job.'

Max indicated he would do this, and Clare went on.

'Who's watching the jeweller's house?'

'A couple of Dundee lads,' Jim said. 'All quiet. Mr Jardine agreed not to open the shop today and the wife's staying at home, too, so it's easy enough to keep an eye on them.'

'Thanks, Jim. Make sure we have someone there round the clock please; and let's get the CCTV from the shop for the week leading up to Maggie White's death, including the day she died. I want it checked for any suspicious customers, any known faces. Anything at all, I want to see it.' She stood for a moment trying to gather her thoughts, then she continued. 'The hijacked vehicle was a standard white prison van driven to the funeral by the two officers. There's been no trace of it, no ANPR hits, nothing. Where is it? Could be it has false plates now and it's long gone. Or it might be hidden somewhere. So eyes open for that, please.' She hesitated. 'There is one other thing. It seems likely Paul Devine is Maggie White's killer. He has motive and he certainly had the opportunity. But it could just be a coincidence. So I want a couple of you on Maggie, please. Her employer didn't think she was on social media but that doesn't mean she wasn't. Let's check that. Find out what she did when she wasn't at work. Did she have a partner? Friends? Where did she have her car serviced? And once SOCO clear us to search the house I want any computers, laptops, paperwork – you all know the drill. We need to be absolutely sure we're not missing something.'

Robbie and Gillian, two of the uniformed officers, indicated they would do this, and Clare smiled round at them. 'Okay, folks. That's it. Keep in touch.'

As she headed for her office her phone began to ring.

'It's Liv, boss. Just letting you know Anthony Devine's on the move. He's stopped at Tesco. Erin's gone in after him. I'm keeping an eye on the car.'

'Thanks, Liv. Might just be doing his shopping but it's worth checking.'

Clare put down her phone but it began to ring again. An unfamiliar number.

'Inspector,' a female voice said, 'this is Sylvia Jardine. After you left yesterday I remembered something.'

—

'What exactly did she say?' Max asked as they approached the forty miles an hour sign at Guardbridge.

'Apparently Maggie told Finlay the farmer wanted her cottage for one of his workers.'

Max put a hand on the car door as Clare negotiated the roundabout. 'The farmer was her landlord?'

'He was. But he definitely didn't mention it when Bill spoke to him last night.'

'And Maggie didn't want to leave?'

'Nope. She refused. Said she'd done lots to improve the cottage and that it was home so she was staying.'

'And he didn't like that?'

Clare signalled left to turn up the Toll Road. 'He did not. According to Sylvia Jardine he began making threats.'

'Like what?'

'Said he was coming round to inspect the cottage; and, if he didn't like the decor she'd have to put it back the way it was.'

'Doesn't sound unreasonable,' Max said.

'No,' Clare admitted. 'I suppose not. But he also said it would be a pity if he accidentally dropped a trailer load of slurry outside her door. Said his trailer was a bit wobbly these days and you never could tell when it might slip.'

'So she told the Jardines?'

'She did. And Sylvia quoted the 2016 Tenancy Act, saying it was illegal for the landlord to coerce her into leaving. She told Maggie to send him a solicitor's letter.'

'Do we know if Maggie did that?'

'Not yet. But if she has a solicitor, we'll find him or her and check it.' Clare glanced in the mirror and signalled to turn at the sign for Motray Farm. 'The sooner we get full access to that cottage the better.' She killed the engine. 'In the meantime, let's go and rattle the farmer's cage.'

Eric McGovern was standing by a tractor fitted with manure forks, talking to a younger man in overalls. He didn't see them at first and Clare took the opportunity to study him. He was older than she'd expected – mid-sixties, maybe. He was dressed in a dark brown fleece jacket, jeans and stout boots, his hands driven deep into his pockets. His hair was grey and wiry and, as he became aware of them and turned, she saw his face was bronzed and weather-beaten, suggesting a life spent largely outdoors. She smiled but the smile wasn't returned. He spoke a few more words to the younger man then ambled over to greet them.

'Polis, I'm guessing?' He nodded at the tractor. 'Lad's away to spread shit on the fields. Good stuff, cow shit.' He looked down at their shoes and a smirk formed on his lips. 'But you lot won't know much about that, with your fancy clothes.'

Clare wondered if he'd deliberately said *shit* in a misjudged attempt to offend them. 'Oh we're pretty used to folk shovelling all sorts when we talk to them.'

He had the grace to laugh, then he indicated the farmhouse. 'You'd better come inside. Easier to talk in there.'

They followed him across the yard towards a solid block of a house built in local sandstone. He led them past the wooden front porch round the side and opened a cottage-type door, the pale blue paint peeling here and there. They stepped into a small lobby with boot and coat racks on one side and a door to a toilet on the other. Another door lay ahead and he kicked this open with his boot and led them into a large kitchen. It was a bright room, thanks mainly to rows of downlighters set into the ceiling. There was a single casement window with a sink below, and a row of rather dated kitchen units to the left and right. A wooden table stood in the centre of the room with bench seats either side. On one of those a girl of about sixteen in red tartan pyjamas sat painting her toenails a vivid green.

'Time you were dressed,' Eric McGovern barked.

The girl made no reply other than to roll her eyes. She carried on painting a nail then put the brush back in the bottle, twisting it closed. Then she picked it up and, spreading her toes, she walked carefully on her heels towards another door.

'Nice colour,' Clare said, and the girl flashed her a smile.

'Electric Emerald.'

He waited until she had left and indicated the bench seat. 'Best check for that green stuff.'

Clare gave the bench a cursory sweep with her hand then sat, sliding along to make room for Max. 'Your daughter?'

'Aye. Should be in school the day but she claims she's no' well. She's well enough to put that muck on her toes.'

Clare laughed. 'Kids, eh?'

He made no reply to this but picked up an old aluminium kettle and filled it at the tap. He put it down on a cream-coloured Aga and turned back to face them. 'Tea?'

'No thanks,' Clare said. 'We won't keep you.'

He stood, arms folded, his back against the Aga. 'This'll be about the tractor GPS.' It was more of a statement than a question.

Clare frowned. 'You've had a theft?'

'Christ! Do you guys no' talk to each other?'

She sighed inwardly. 'When was this?'

'Just Monday, there. I'd only had it a couple of months. But I'm guessing from your expressions you've no' found it.'

'I've an officer working on farm equipment thefts,' Clare said. 'I'll chase it up with him when I'm back in the office.'

He rolled his eyes. 'Aye right. So, if it's no' the GPS it'll be about Maggie. You found whoever did it?'

Clare didn't answer this directly. 'Can I ask when you last saw her?'

'Couldn't say, really. Used to see her car going up and down but I never saw her that much.'

'She must pay you rent, though.'

There was a flicker of something in his eyes and Clare wondered if he'd hoped the ownership of Maggie's cottage wouldn't come up. 'You didn't mention you owned the cottage when my officer spoke to you yesterday,' she added.

He shrugged. 'Didn't think it mattered.'

Clare watched him but his expression bordered on the defiant. 'And the rent?'

He eyed her for a moment. 'Direct debit, arranged through the agency. Straight into my bank every month. Poor woman,' he added, his sudden air of solicitude unconvincing. Then he spoke again, brisk this time. 'I'll need to get into the cottage. What'll happen to her stuff?'

Clare regarded him. He was a little too eager to have the cottage cleared out. 'It's a crime scene at the moment,' she said. 'So it's out of the question.'

He frowned. 'She was killed in the house? I hope there's no mess.'

Clare wondered about that. Was he fishing? Or did he know she'd been killed outside? 'We'll release a statement in due course. Just a few more questions for now.'

'Go on, then.'

The noise from the kettle grew louder as it came to the boil and he moved sideways, away from the steam.

'How did you get on with Maggie?'

'Okay, I suppose.'

'You had a good relationship?'

'Aye.'

'Did you recently ask her to vacate the cottage?'

Steam began to pour from the kettle, the lid rattling as the water boiled. He picked up a cloth and lifted the kettle off the

Aga. The cloud of steam lessened and the lid settled back down. He dropped a teabag in a mug and poured water on top.

'I only asked if she'd any plans to move on,' he said, his back to them.

'What made you think she planned to move?'

He took a teaspoon from a drawer and fished out the teabag, dropping it in the sink. 'I only asked. Handy to know. We're always needing accommodation. For the workers, like. I thought, you know – woman of Maggie's age – maybe she'd want to buy her own place. So I mentioned it.' He dug the teaspoon into a bag of sugar and added two spoonfuls to his mug, stirring it noisily.

'You didn't, for example, threaten to drop a lorry load of slurry at her front door if she didn't move out?'

He finished stirring the tea and threw the spoon in the sink. It clattered against the white ceramic. Then he picked up his mug and turned back to face them, the ghost of a smile on his lips. 'Now why would I do something like that?'

'Perhaps you thought it might encourage her to leave.'

He laughed. 'Course not. That would be against the law, wouldn't it?'

Clare regarded him levelly. 'It would indeed.' She watched him sipping his tea. 'Where were you on Monday?'

'Depends what time.'

'Let's go from first thing.'

He shrugged. 'Here, mostly. Nipped over to Cupar to pick up a part for the tractor.'

'What time was that?'

'About two. Three, maybe.'

'How did you pay?'

'Eh?'

'The part for the tractor. I presume you paid for it?'

'Aye. Cash.'

'You have the receipt?'

His eyes narrowed. 'I'm not sure. Is it a problem?'

'I'd have thought a businessman like yourself, Mr McGovern, would keep careful records of all your expenses. Helps cut the tax bill, doesn't it?'

'Given what I spend on farm equipment in a year, I'm no' too worried about a six quid oil filter.'

'Where did you buy it?'

'Slavens,' he said. 'They've a unit on the trading estate. Near the old sugar beet factory silo.'

Clare nodded. She knew it. A vast concrete tower that dominated the skyline. 'Remember who served you?'

'Nope.'

'Did you see anyone at the cottage?' Max asked.

He turned to regard Max with some amusement. 'He speaks No, son. I didn't pass the cottage. I went down the road and through Guardbridge. More direct, isn't it?'

'You didn't think it worth avoiding the roadworks at Clayton? Quite a hold-up. Local radio have been all over it this week.'

He smiled. 'Yeah. It was quite a hold-up. I'll know next time.'

Clare caught Max's eye. They were learning nothing here. 'Just one more thing, Mr McGovern.'

'Aye?'

'We're keen to confirm the identity of the body. Would you be prepared to come to the mortuary and help us with that?'

His hand went to his chin. 'I'm no' keen, to be honest with you. It's no' so long… my mother, ye know?' He broke off, shaking his head. 'And besides, I didn't know the lassie that well. I was her landlord but it was all done through the agency.'

'It really would help us,' Clare persisted. 'It could even be done by video link if that would be easier.'

He shook his head. 'No. Sorry.'

Clare watched him for a moment, then she rose from the bench and Max followed suit. 'I'll leave a card here,' she said. 'Call me if you remember anything, please.'

'Aye, whatever. And you'll let me know when I can get in the cottage? I'll need to book a skip.'

As they walked back to the car Clare said, 'It'll be a cold day in hell before I tell that man anything. He can damn well wait. Good call on the roadworks, by the way.'

Max's face lit up. 'I was caught in them the other day. Took ages to get through. I could be wrong but I reckon he'd have remembered the hold-up – mentioned it to prove where he was.'

'So he must have gone up past the cottage,' Clare said, clicking to unlock the car.

'Must have. The question is, did he even go to Cupar and, if so, did he stop at Maggie's cottage on the way?'

They climbed in and Clare started the engine. 'He seemed surprised, though. When I said the house was a crime scene.'

'As if he knew the body wasn't in the house?'

'Yeah,' Clare said. 'And I bet Bill didn't mention that when he spoke to him last night.'

'Suspicious?'

'I dunno. I can't see him killing Maggie just to get her out of the house. He'd have found another way to make her life a misery.'

'He wasn't keen to ID the body,' Max said.

Clare nodded slowly. 'No, he was not. And yet he must have spoken to her when he threatened to drop a load of slurry at her door. That's not the kind of thing you put in an email or a letter.'

'Could have been by phone,' Max said.

Clare considered this. 'Yes, it could. But somehow I don't think it was. I think he probably made these threats to Maggie's face, with no witnesses around. And I'd very much like to know why he refused to identify the body.'

Chapter 9

Liv called again as Clare was drawing into the car park. 'Anthony Devine, boss.'

Clare jumped out of the car, phone clamped to her ear. 'Go on.'

'It's maybe nothing but he went into Tesco, like I said. Erin kept an eye and she followed him back out again. I was on the car and I saw him put four bags in the boot. But when he arrived back home he only took three of them into the house.'

'Could you see what was in any of the bags, Liv?'

'Sorry, no. Erin said it was just the usual stuff. Tins of soup, bread, breakfast stuff, milk. Nothing out of the ordinary.'

'Just normal food,' Clare said slowly.

'Yeah, I think so.'

'Okay. Is he back in the house now?'

'Yeah.'

'Thanks, Liv. Stick on his tail; and let me know if he heads out again.'

'Could be things for the car,' Max said when Clare relayed the conversation. 'Windscreen wash and the like.'

'It could,' Clare conceded. 'But how likely is it he'd put something like that in a carrier bag? Most folk buy those jerry cans.'

'You're thinking he's bought extra food for someone else? Like his brother?'

'I am. And if he heads out tonight we'll be ready for him.'

–

It was late afternoon when Raymond called to let Clare know they'd finished in Maggie's cottage.

'We're still working on the shed, though,' he said. 'And the field margin. But we've taken fingerprints from around the house doors and so on; and we found a partial footprint in the bedroom so we'll compare it with the victim's shoes. No sign of blood spatter in the house, though. It all points to her having been attacked just outside the shed.'

'Anything else?'

'Yeah. There was a set of keys hidden under a plant pot. So anyone could have been in the house.'

Clare thanked Raymond and went to find Max. 'Come on. I want a proper look round that cottage.'

The SOCO team were carrying out a fingertip search of the field margin when Clare drew into the verge behind their van. She handed Max a bundle of evidence bags and walked round to the garden, waving to Raymond as she entered the kitchen for the second time.

'Gloves,' she said to Max, 'in case we find something,' and he fished a pair of gloves out of his pocket.

The fluorescent tube light had given up and Clare went round the units, feeling under the cupboards for concealed lights, but there were none. SOCO had left a free-standing lamp in a corner and Clare bent to plug this into a socket on the skirting board. The room was flooded with light and she moved round, checking drawers and cupboards. But she found nothing unusual.

The sitting room was as she remembered it and she moved to a small desk under the window. The top drawer held a sheaf of bills and letters secured by a bulldog clip and she handed these to Max to drop in one of the bags. She scanned the room, checking the sockets for chargers, but there was no sign of a mobile phone.

They moved on to the bathroom which revealed nothing other than the usual toiletries and over-the-counter medicines. Entering the bedroom, Clare's eye was drawn to some mud on the light grey linoleum. It didn't look clear enough for the partial footprint Raymond had taken. She looked back towards the bedroom door and saw another clearer mark. The partial print. There was something nagging at her but she couldn't put her finger on it.

'Check for jewellery,' she said to Max, and he began opening and closing bedroom drawers.

As he busied himself, Clare studied the room, trying to get a sense of Maggie White. Who she had been, what she'd been like. The bed was neatly spread with an old-fashioned candlewick cover in a soft pink colour. Clare hadn't seen one of these for years, not since she'd helped clear out her grandparents' house. Perhaps it had been a family heirloom, kept for sentimental value. A small table sat to the side of the bed, home to a lamp and a framed photo. Clare picked the photo up and immediately recognised the backdrop as Inveraray Castle, near Loch Fyne. Two women stood in front of it, happy and smiling, but rain-soaked in their see-through plastic ponchos and colourful wellies. From the difference in their ages, she thought it must be Maggie and her mother. The younger one had dark curly hair and was recognisable as a younger version of the woman in the jeweller's shop photo. The resemblance to the older woman was unmistakable, although her curls tended to grey.

And then Clare remembered a music festival she'd been to at Inveraray. Years ago. She'd forgotten all about it but now, looking at the photo of the two women, she remembered. Probably the wettest she'd ever been in her life. Suddenly it dawned on Clare that she might have been at the very same festival. It had only run for two years so there was every chance she'd seen the pair, maybe stood behind them in the queue for the bar – or the toilets!

It was hard to connect the smiling young woman in the photo with the body they'd found in the garden shed, a sad end for this happier younger Maggie. She put the photo down and turned to the wardrobe.

Max had stopped searching and seemed lost in thought.

'Max?'

'Odd thing,' he said. 'There's lots of jewellery in this top drawer here. Some of it's hallmarked. But the drawer itself's in a bit of a mess.'

Clare glanced across. 'Maybe she lost something. Looking for it in a hurry.'

'I'd say someone was. Look at the rest of the place. It's pretty tidy, yeah?'

Clare looked round the room. He was right. There were cushions on the bedspread, neatly arranged against the headboard, and the dressing table was almost free of clutter. She moved to the wardrobe and opened it. Maggie's clothes were draped on identical wooden hangers, the order methodical: trousers and skirts to one side, tops and blouses at the other. She leafed through them. 'Some nice stuff, here,' she said. 'Not designer but not Primark either.' She closed the wardrobe doors and turned back to survey the room again. 'It is tidy,' she said, thinking of her bedroom at Daisy Cottage. Or her side of the bed at least.

'Now come and see these drawers,' Max said. He indicated the top drawer and Clare peered in. There was a large jewellery box and several smaller ones which she presumed held earrings or rings. The large box stood open revealing necklaces and bangles while the smaller ones were in disarray.

'And this,' Max pulled open another drawer of tops and T-shirts, the mess of clothes quite unlike the orderliness of the wardrobe. 'See what I mean? Someone's been looking through these.'

Clare nodded. 'I agree. Good spot, Max.' She realised suddenly what was bothering her. 'That mud,' she said, studying the floor. 'Follow me.' She led him back through to the kitchen and indicated Maggie's slippers standing by the door. Then she pointed to a shoe rack against the opposite wall. It held an assortment of trainers, walking boots and a pair of smart brown brogues. 'She doesn't wear her shoes in the house, does she? There were none in the bedroom. So who's left the muddy footprint? And what were they looking for?'

As they headed for the car Raymond called them over. He held out a clear evidence bag. 'Just picked this up on the field margin, near that gap in the fence.'

Clare peered at the object in the bag. It seemed to be a round piece of plastic. She'd seen something like it before but she couldn't remember where. 'What is it?'

'It's called a basket. Fits on the bottom of a walking pole to stop the pole sinking into soft ground.'

'The farmer down the hill said Maggie was a walker. Could it be from one of her poles?'

'It's possible,' Raymond said. 'We're still going through the contents of the shed looking for a likely weapon so we may yet find her poles.'

Clare thanked him and they walked back to the car. 'Come on,' she said to Max. 'My turn to make you a coffee.'

—

'Liv's been back on the phone,' Jim said as Clare made for her office.

'And?'

'Couple of things. Anthony Devine came out again and drove to work. He's been at the funeral home since then. Must be doing a late shift.'

Clare stopped in her tracks. 'Did he take anything out of the car boot?'

'Liv says not.'

'Okay. And the other thing?'

'Might be something or nothing,' Jim said. 'But he had a delivery. Package put through the door. Young lad, dark clothing.'

'After he'd left for work?'

'No. That's the odd thing. Devine was at home but the lad didn't ring the bell.'

'Was he driving – the lad?'

'On foot.'

Alarm bells were ringing in Clare's head. 'Does Anthony have any previous?'

'Aye. He was cautioned a while back for possession of Class C. There were rumours he was dealing other stuff as well, but it was never proved.'

'They're a delightful pair, aren't they?'

'No argument there,' Jim said. 'Do you want it checked out?'

She shook her head. 'We'd never get a warrant on the strength of a lad delivering a package. He might have been a neighbour. Something delivered to the wrong house.'

'Odd he didn't ring the bell, though.'

'Not really,' Clare said. 'Some folk are shy. Young lads don't always have the social skills to chat to their neighbours.'

'Suppose you're right.'

'That it?'

'For the moment. The phone and bank records came through so a couple of the lads are going through them now. Nothing so far, I gather.'

'Thanks, Jim. Keep me posted.'

Clare's phone began to ring and she clicked to take the call. Neil Grant.

'Just finished your post-mortem.'

'And?'

'No surprises. She was the victim of a violent attack with a blunt instrument. Death was due to a brain haemorrhage caused by at least six blows to the head. Otherwise she was fit and healthy.'

'Blunt instrument – can you be any more specific?'

'It's hard to say but could be a hammer with a fairly big head.'

'Like a club hammer?'

'Aye, that sort of thing. From the direction of the blows I'd say the assailant was right-handed. That's certainly consistent with the way she fell.'

'Anything else?'

'Only that he or she was probably a bit taller than your victim. She was about one metre sixty-five, or five foot five if you want it in old money. So you're looking for someone at least a couple of inches taller. I've still to write up my report and I can run tox tests if you like but that'll take much longer. I thought you'd want the basics for now.'

Clare ended the call and sat weighing this up. Then she went in search of Max who was in the kitchen.

'Just boiled the kettle,' he said.

'Forget that. Come on. We've a call to pay.'

Chapter 10

Anthony Devine made no effort to conceal his irritation at another visit from Clare and Max.

'I don't know what you expect me to say,' he snapped. 'I don't know where Paul is and there's nothing else I can tell you.'

'I'd like you to show us what's in the boot of your car,' Clare said.

He stared at her. 'You what?'

'If you don't mind.'

'Got a warrant?'

She met his gaze. 'Nope.'

'So I'm within my rights to refuse.'

'You are. But your refusal would be noted and a jury – if it came to it – would be entitled to draw their own conclusions.'

He exhaled audibly. 'Fucksake.' Then he turned on his heel. 'C'mon then, if you're coming. But don't blame me if you get oil on your posh suits.'

It had grown dull and Clare felt the first spits of rain carried on the wind. She pulled her coat round her as he led them out to the car park behind the building. He clicked the remote control and the car's interior lights came on. He fumbled around at the back and the boot rose up. They peered inside and Clare's eyes ran across the contents: a grey plastic petrol can, foot pump, can of oil and the Tesco carrier bag.

'I'd like to see what's in the bag please.'

'Help yourself.'

'I'd prefer if you emptied it.'

He rolled his eyes and reached for the carrier bag, removing the items one at a time. 'Coffee, teabags, Custard Creams, sugar, Hobnobs and a box of Quality Street for the girl on Reception 'cause it's her birthday tomorrow.' He upended the carrier bag to prove it was empty. 'It was my turn to buy the tea and coffee stuff. Satisfied?'

'That's fine,' Clare said. 'But why leave it in the boot?'

He shrugged. 'Forgot about it. I was running late. Needed to get in.' He began repacking the carrier bag. 'So, if that's all?'

'Not quite,' Clare said. 'I understand a package was dropped off at your house this morning.'

His eyes narrowed. 'You been spying on me?'

'One of my officers was out on patrol. Obviously, with Paul going missing, it makes sense to take a turn past your house. So, was there a package?'

He began repacking the Tesco bag then he shut the boot again. 'Oh yeah,' he said, not meeting Clare's eye. 'It was a DVD. Lent it to a mate months back. That was him just getting it back to me now.'

Clare watched him for a moment. 'Name?'

'*Reservoir Dogs*.'

'The mate!'

'To be honest, I can't remember. I've lots of mates, lots of DVDs. We all borrow from each other.'

'You can't remember who borrowed it.'

'Sorry. So, if there's nothing else?'

'Believe him?' Max said as they watched him walk back towards the building.

'Not a single word. Question is, what was in that package?'

—

'Call for you while you were out,' Jim said. 'Raymond from SOCO.'

Clare thanked Jim and went to hang up her coat, shaking off the rain. She switched the light on in her office and moved to warm her hands on the radiator. Then she took out her phone and called Raymond.

'Okay, the first thing is I think your killer has disposed of the weapon. I've had a word with Neil Grant and there's nothing in the garden shed that matches the pattern of injuries. Nothing in the garden or the field margin either. Sorry about that.'

'No problem, Raymond. I didn't really think you'd find it. Worth a shot, though. You said *the first thing* – is there something else?'

'There certainly is. A stash of money.'

'Where?'

'Buried in a bag of compost. It was young Molly, my assistant, who spotted it. She's a keen gardener and she noticed there was a bag of ericaceous compost.'

'Eri... what?'

'Ericaceous. It increases the acidity of the soil. Some plants need a more acidic soil but round here it tends to be alkaline. Gardeners use ericaceous compost for certain types of plants. The hydrangea's an interesting one because you can use the compost to change the flowers making them more pink, or blue. Now Molly spotted a couple of hydrangeas in pots but the flowers were pink. If Maggie had used the ericaceous compost the flowers would have been blue, or less pink at least. So she wondered why Maggie had the compost. She investigated the bag and found the money wrapped up in plastic near the bottom.'

'Any idea how much?'

'Not yet. We'll need to check it for prints, although money's usually hopeless. Been through too many hands. But there are bundles of fifty-pound notes. At a rough guess I'd say it's well over ten thousand pounds.'

Clare thanked Raymond and went in search of Max. 'I think we know why Maggie's drawers were in a mess. SOCO found a stash of money in the garden shed.'

'So it was a burglary gone wrong?'

'Could be. The question is where did the money come from and who knew she had it?'

By eight o'clock Clare decided to send the team home. 'Cupar and Dundee will cover the surveillance between them. Back in for eight tomorrow.' She was about to shut down her computer when an email marked *urgent* pinged into her inbox. She saw it was from the Chief Superintendent. The message was brief and to the point.

> DCI Ben Ratcliffe will join you tomorrow morning. Ben will take over the search for Paul Devine, the prison officers and their wives, freeing you up to lead the hunt for Maggie White's killer. Please give him access to all evidence and afford him the usual co-operation and courtesies.

'To hell with that,' she said out loud, switching off her computer. She had hoped that Al Gibson might have been appointed to oversee the case. But since their relationship had become common knowledge, his bosses seemed to be keeping him busy at the Bell Street station across in Dundee. 'Like we can't be trusted,' she muttered, grabbing her coat and turning out the light. As she reached the front entrance Chris entered dressed in black waterproof trousers and a long anorak.

'It would have to be raining, wouldn't it,' he muttered.

'Always the same when you're on surveillance. What's the plan?'

'Got a lead on a possible target vehicle. Good intel from a reliable source. We've got all routes in and out of the farm covered so fingers crossed.'

'Good luck with it,' Clare said. 'Hope it works out.'

'Clare...'

She smiled. 'Sorry, Chris. Nothing yet. But we are watching Paul Devine's brother. Mind you, he knows we're watching him now so he'll be careful. But he'll slip up sooner or later. They usually do.'

'Soon enough for Alan?' Chris walked off, leaving the question hanging in the air.

–

Daisy Cottage was in darkness when she arrived home. Benjy's head appeared at the window, his paws on the sill and he began to bark loudly. Then he disappeared and she heard him breathing hard behind the front door. She opened it and he launched himself at her. Peeling him off, she stepped inside, glad to feel the warmth from the heating. Clare shrugged off her coat, hanging it on a hook to dry, and kicked off her shoes. In the kitchen a portion of the DCI's home-made lasagne sat defrosting on a chopping board with a note next to it.

> *Forgot I had a dinner thing tonight.*
>
> *Might be late so don't wait up.*
>
> *Benjy fed and walked.*
>
> *Hope things went ok today.*
>
> *Love you,*
>
> *A x*

'Not exactly okay,' she said, in response to the note. 'Not exactly.' She turned on the oven and put the lasagne in to heat. Then she took a bottle of red from the wine rack and set about removing the cork. A package addressed to her lay on the kitchen table beside a couple of circulars. She poured herself a glass of wine and picked the package up, wondering what it contained. And then she remembered. Her sister's Jude's favourite bath oil. She'd seen it discounted in a catalogue and, in a rare moment of organisation, she'd ordered it for Jude's Christmas present. She weighed it in her hand and her mind went back to Anthony Devine. What had been in his package – the one he claimed was a DVD? Was it drugs? Or money perhaps – like the stash they'd found in Maggie White's garden shed?

Thursday

Chapter 11

'You come across a DCI called Ben Ratcliffe?' Clare asked, as she poured Benjy's food into his bowl. The dog fell on it, eating noisily.

'You have no authority over that dog,' the DCI observed. 'I always make him wait for his food.'

'Yeah, I know. I'm good cop, you're bad cop. Anyway, do you know him?'

'Ben Ratcliffe? Not sure.'

She regarded him. 'I thought you knew everyone.'

He shrugged. 'There's so many new folk. Why are you asking?'

'Because I've been told to hand over the missing prisoner case to him. Email from the Super last night. I've to concentrate on the murder.'

'Did you tell him you thought they were connected?'

'Hah. It wasn't that kind of email.'

'Ah, I see.'

'So you don't know him?'

He rose and picked up his breakfast dishes. 'That's what I said.'

Clare watched him. He was loading the dishwasher, his back to her and she wondered if he was being completely honest. Did he have some history with Ben Ratcliffe? If there was something, he certainly wasn't keen to share it. 'I'd better get away,' she said. 'Early briefing and I want to be in before he arrives. Maybe I can persuade him there's a connection.'

He turned from the dishwasher, closing the lid. 'Do bear in mind there might not be.'

She didn't reply but stooped to ruffle Benjy behind the ears. Then she forced a smile. 'See you tonight.'

–

The car park was busy when Clare pulled in. She looked round for evidence that Ben Ratcliffe had arrived but there were too many new cars to work out which might be his.

'He might not even be here yet,' she said to herself, checking her watch. She climbed out of the car and saw Chris emerge from the station door. He noticed her and ambled over.

'You look tired,' she said.

He yawned. 'I'd forgotten how long a night is.'

'Any luck?'

'Not last night. But I went back and spoke to the farmer whose tractor was nicked last week. Sounds like it might have been stolen to order. He had three tractors all in the same shed. But this one had been retrofitted with an autonomous kit.'

'Which is?'

'Basically it turns an ordinary tractor into a self-driving one.'

'Crikey. How much does that cost?'

'Farmer says thirty grand, on top of the cost of the tractor. And he'd only had it a month. His insurers are not happy.'

'I'm not surprised. I presume you've checked cameras around the farm?'

'Yeah. But the farmer reckons they'll have stuck to the back roads. Probably rented shed space somewhere. They'll store it until the fuss has died down then move it on.'

'You need to check anyone who rents shed space then. Maybe speak to transport companies too – the kind that hire out low loaders.'

Chris rolled his eyes. 'I have done a bit of detective work before, you know.'

'Just checking.' She gave him a smile and made to leave.

'You'll keep me updated?' he said. 'About Alan.'

'I will, Chris. When I can. Now get yourself home to bed.' She stood and watched him walk across to his car as though the weight of the world was on his shoulders, and her heart went out to him. She could only hope the officers and their wives would turn up soon. Lost in thought, she crossed the car park and went in the front door. Her eye was immediately caught by a tall man standing with his back to the public enquiry counter. He had an air of authority and she realised this must be DCI Ben Ratcliffe. As she approached he gave her a nod.

'DI Mackay?'

Clare smiled and held out her hand. 'DCI Ratcliffe?'

'Ben's fine.'

'Clare.' She saw several pairs of eyes were watching the exchange. 'Let's grab a coffee. We can chat in my office.'

Sara was in the kitchen when Clare and Ben entered. Clare introduced them and Sara volunteered to make the coffees.

'You must come here more often,' Clare joked. 'I can't remember the last time anyone made me a coffee.' That wasn't quite true, of course. Since his arrival, Max had been offering to make coffees at every opportunity. But she felt faintly nervous of this man and found herself chattering on, perhaps to avoid an awkward silence. He seemed pleasant enough but there was an intensity about his gaze that made her suspect he missed nothing. His suit was expensive, too, the cloth fine, the cut tailored. *No,* Clare decided. *Ben Ratcliffe would not miss a thing.*

She kept up a string of small talk until they were in her office. 'I suppose you'll want to use my desk,' she said.

He looked surprised. 'Why would I do that?'

It was Clare's turn to look surprised. 'DCI's privilege? Every time I've had one base himself here they've used my office.'

He raised an eyebrow. 'Pretty rude.' He nodded at his laptop bag. 'All I need is a network point and a decent desk. If there's a room I can use, so much the better.'

'That we can do.'

Ben's phone began to ring and he fished it out of his jacket pocket. He sighed and swiped to take the call. 'Sophie?'

Clare busied herself, switching on her computer and pretending to look for something in her drawer.

'There is literally nothing I can do about that. I'm at work. You'll just have to—'

There was a tap on the door. Ben was still on the phone so Clare opened it to find Jim waiting.

'Didn't like to disturb you,' he said, but Clare waved this away.

'The Jardines,' he went on. 'They want to open the shop. Mr Jardine says he's losing too much money keeping it shut.'

'I can understand that,' Clare said. 'Can we spare an officer to sit outside the shop? I do want to keep someone on the house.'

'Leave it with me. I'm sure we can borrow someone from another station.'

Clare thanked him and opened her office door wide enough to see Ben had finished his call.

'Sorry about that,' he said. 'You got any kids?'

'No.'

'Take my advice: don't!'

She laughed. 'I'm sure it's worth it.'

He shrugged. 'Yeah, it is. But sometimes… don't ask me what I'm meant to do about a fourteen-year-old who's left her PE kit at home.'

'At my school they made us do it in our pants.'

He shook his head. 'I'm not sure there's a suitable reply to that.'

'Probably not. So, shall I bring you up to speed?'

Ben Ratcliffe listened while Clare explained the two cases.

'I'm convinced there's a link,' she said. 'It's too much of a coincidence, Devine escaping then the woman who testified against him killed the same day.'

'They may be linked but, if you assume that, you might miss things. Either way, we've been told how to manage this so let's get on with it. I'll deal with the prison issue. You stick to the murder.'

Despite his initial friendliness Clare detected an air of authority in that last statement. Most DCIs, with a couple of exceptions, managed to convey the sense that they were a team of equals, working towards a common goal. But it looked like Ben Ratcliffe was the other kind. Ah well. She rose from her chair. 'I'll speak to Jim, the desk sergeant. He'll sort you out a temporary office. Then maybe we could do the briefing together?'

—

News of Ben's arrival had spread round the station and the hum died down as they entered the incident room. Standing a little way off from Clare, he cut a striking figure. He wasn't directly in her eyeline but she couldn't help being aware of his presence. She made an effort to gather her thoughts, then looked round the room.

'Morning everyone. First of all, let me introduce DCI Ben Ratcliffe. Ben is taking over the investigation into Paul Devine and the two missing couples, and I'll concentrate on finding Maggie White's killer.' She paused to let this sink in, then went on. 'Obviously we have a connection between Paul and Maggie so it makes sense to have joint briefings, for now, at least. But the investigations will be led separately.' She glanced at Ben. 'If information relevant to both cases does come to light it will of course be shared.'

Ben gave a brief nod and Clare went on. 'Okay, anything come in overnight?'

Max raised his hand. 'Anthony Devine went straight home from work and didn't leave.'

Ben said, 'I'll need to speak to the surveillance teams,' and Max indicated he would arrange this.

'A package was put through Anthony Devine's letterbox yesterday morning,' Clare said. 'The caller didn't ring or knock. We spoke to Devine later that day and he claims it was a friend returning a borrowed DVD. But he couldn't tell us the name of the friend. Claimed he and his friends lend each other DVDs all the time. Frankly, I doubt it. He has a caution for possession of Class C so it's possible the package was either drugs or money.'

'Has his house been searched?' Ben asked.

Clare shook her head. 'At present we don't have evidence connecting him to Paul's disappearance. I think we'd struggle to get a warrant.'

Ben raised an eyebrow but said nothing and Clare went on. 'What about Paul Devine's known associates?'

Max raised his hand again. 'Nothing suspicious.'

'Bank and phone records?' Ben asked.

'Nothing to indicate they're assisting Devine,' Clare said. 'But we're monitoring them.'

She looked round the room. 'Prison officers and wives – where are we with that?'

Nita raised a hand. 'No ANPR sightings of their cars but I'm planning to look further into their movements on the days before they went missing. Start from when they were last seen, at work, maybe.'

'Good thinking, Nita.' She scanned the room. 'If you and—'

Ben cut across her. 'My team will take that.' He nodded at Nita. 'You can leave it with us.' He turned back to Clare. 'We'll handle the search of the officers' houses as well.'

Clare was conscious that the eyes of the room were on her and she forced her lips into a smile. 'Of course,' she said, acknowledging this. 'Thanks for flagging it up, Nita. Was there anything else on the two couples?'

Heads shook and Clare went on. 'Right, let's move on to the murder. Who was chasing up Maggie White's mother?'

Jim raised a hand. 'I had a call from the Garda this morning. They're pretty sure she's travelling in Galway but nothing yet.'

'Thanks, Jim. Now, we know Maggie died from repeated blows to the head, probably from a club hammer, or similar. SOCO haven't found a likely weapon so those of you out on enquiries bear that in mind. They did, however, find a small piece of plastic they believe came from a walking pole – the kind hillwalkers use. And there's a partial footprint and traces of mud in Maggie's bedroom which we think came from someone other than Maggie. Her bedroom drawers were untidy, too, which doesn't fit with the rest of the house. It could be an intruder was searching for something and it's possible that person also killed Maggie.'

'Any idea what they'd be looking for?' Bill asked.

'It might be money,' Clare said. 'SOCO found a stash of notes hidden in the shed. Who would have known Maggie had hidden money? Where did she get it and why was she hiding it? Why wasn't she keeping it in the bank?'

'Avoiding tax?' Gillian suggested.

'More likely proceeds of crime,' Robbie said.

'So, was Maggie White involved in something?' Clare went on. 'Drugs — or some other racket? Let's look more closely into her.'

'Could there be a link between Maggie's money and Anthony Devine's mysterious package?' Sara said.

Clare cast a glance at Ben. 'It's possible. Perhaps Maggie and the Devine brothers have some other connection. Something we've not uncovered. If DCI Ratcliffe agrees, let's dig into their pasts. See if they knew each other before the robbery.'

Ben nodded again and Clare caught Janey's eye. 'I'd like you and Bill to take that please?'

Robbie raised his hand. 'What about the Jardines?'

'For anyone who wasn't here yesterday,' Clare said, 'Finlay Jardine is the jeweller whose shop Paul Devine robbed. Maggie White, our murder victim, worked for him. We've had a cop on the Jardines' house since Maggie's body was found and we'll have someone on the shop today.' She turned back to Robbie. 'We'll keep a watch on them for the next twenty-four hours and review it after that.' She scanned the room. 'Anything else?'

There were murmurs of *No, boss*, and she smiled round at them. 'Okay, folks, I think that's it, unless?' She looked across at Ben, but he shook his head.

As the officers drifted off he waited for Clare. 'You said you might have a room I can use.'

Clare led him to a spare interview room. 'Is there anything else you need?'

'No, I'll be fine, thanks. I presume it's all up on the network?'

'It is. So, what are your thoughts?'

He didn't answer this directly. 'I'll just get myself sorted out and make a start.'

'You'll be needing some officers.'

'I'll let you know.' He indicated the door. 'Mustn't keep you.'

Clare left him to it, closing the door behind her. She walked back to her office, unable to shake off the feeling there was something she wasn't being told.

Chapter 12

Clare found Max in a corner of the incident room, poring over the prison officers' bank records.

'I'd forgotten I asked you to look at these,' she said sitting down beside him. 'Strictly speaking we should hand them over to Ben.'

'Yeah, I know. But I started it yesterday so thought I might as well finish. Then I can let him know if there's anything. Only...'

'Yes?'

'There's this.'

Clare pulled the bank statement over to see what he meant. It was Alan and Kim Carter's account.

'There's a few small transactions in the days before the van disappeared. But this one caught my eye. See the date?'

She squinted at it. 'Last Saturday.'

'Yes. Six thirty in the evening. A card payment of thirty-four pounds to Jasmine Palace.'

'I know it,' Clare said. 'Chinese takeaway. Pretty good. It's down one of the lanes off South Street.'

'Quite a lot, isn't it?' Max said. 'Two people wouldn't eat thirty-odd pounds worth of takeaway food, would they?'

'See what you mean. They must have had company.'

'Could it be significant?'

Clare glanced towards the interview room Ben was using. The door was firmly shut. She should take this to him, really. But she could always tell him later. Say she'd forgotten about it. She scraped back her chair. 'Come on,' she said. 'Let's pay them a visit.'

Jasmine Palace was closed but to the side of the door was a buzzer for the flat above.

'Chen,' Clare read. 'Might be the owners.' She pressed the buzzer and after a minute they heard a voice.

'Yes?'

Clare introduced herself and Max and asked if they could speak to the owner of the takeaway.

'Just a moment.'

She waited for the buzzer but instead the outer door was opened by a woman in her forties. She introduced herself as Mei Chen and said she and her husband owned the takeaway.

'We'd like to ask about an order on Saturday night.'

Mei laughed. 'We must have had forty orders on Saturday night. I'm not sure I'd remember.'

'The name was Carter,' Clare said, 'and it was for thirty-four pounds.'

'Alan Carter?'

'Yes, that's him. Do you remember?'

Mei nodded. 'He's a regular. Orders every couple of weeks. Always a big order. He tips, as well.'

'Can you remember the time?'

She shook her head. 'Sorry. I don't do the deliveries. That's my son.'

'It was a home delivery?'

'Yes. We deliver free in the St Andrews area.'

'Might your son remember?'

'He would. But he's at school just now.'

'At school?' Clare couldn't keep the surprise out of her voice.

'He's eighteen. Passed his test. He only helps out at the weekends. He'll be home about four if you want to speak to him.'

'Actually,' Clare said, 'we could do with speaking to him now. Is he at school in the town?'

'Albany High,' Mei said. 'But I'm not sure he'd like—'

Clare smiled. 'Don't worry. We'll be discreet.'

Albany High lay on the outskirts of town on a flat sprawling site. They were buzzed in by the receptionist who asked them to wait while they located Simon Chen. A few minutes later a young man with a school tie loosely knotted came walking along the corridor. He knocked at the reception window and the receptionist indicated Clare and Max.

Clare rose and went to greet him. 'Hello Simon. I'm Detective Inspector Clare Mackay and this is Detective Sergeant Max Evans.'

Simon looked from one to the other. 'What's this about?'

'Just a couple of questions. Maybe we could sit.' She indicated the chairs outside reception, and he followed them across. When they had sat down Clare went on. 'I understand you do home deliveries for your parents' business?'

'Yeah. Friday and Saturday nights.'

'Last Saturday, you delivered to a regular customer, Alan Carter.'

He nodded. 'Yeah. They're regulars.'

'Can you tell us what time you delivered?'

His brow furrowed as he thought back. 'Somewhere between seven and eight, probably. It's hard to be exact but around then.'

'Who did you see?'

'Alan. He answered the door, took the food and gave me a fiver.' He smiled. 'Nice guy. Always tips.'

'How did he seem?'

Simon shrugged. 'Pretty normal, I suppose. I dunno. Seemed okay.'

'You didn't notice anything unusual?'

He stared at them, his brow creased. 'Is Alan okay?'

'We're trying to contact him,' Clare said, noncommittally. 'So if there was anything...'

He considered this. 'It sounded like he had friends in – when he opened the door, I mean. I could hear laughing and music.'

'Did you notice anyone hanging about in the street?'

'Sorry. I had another delivery waiting for me back at the shop. I wasn't really paying attention. It's a quiet street, though,' he added. 'Not usually many folk out and about at night.'

Clare glanced at Max to see if he had any questions but he shook his head. 'Thanks so much, Simon. We'll let you get back.'

He laughed. 'Double chemistry. I'm in no rush.'

As they walked back to the car Clare's phone began to ring. She fished it out of her pocket. 'Hold on,' she said to Max, and he waited while she clicked the screen. 'Jim?'

'Clare, I think you'd better get back here. Quick as you can.'

–

'Where are they?' she asked as they rushed into the front office.

Jim indicated one of the interview rooms. 'Doc's speaking to them now.'

'How did they seem?'

He sighed. 'Traumatised, exhausted, couldn't get much sense out of them.'

'Nothing about the husbands?'

'Nope. To be honest I didn't want to push it. One look at them and I knew we'd need the doc. I reckon he'll say hospital.'

'Where were they found?'

'Seems they were walking near the crossroads at Pitscottie.'

'Out towards Cupar?' Clare said.

'Aye. A passing motorist stopped to ask if they needed help but they legged it. Must have been terrified. He dialled 999 and we sent a car. Didn't take the lads long to realise who they were.'

'And they didn't say where they'd been since Saturday?'

Bill shook his head. 'Seems they said very little. The cops who attended thought they were in shock and radioed ahead for a doctor.'

Clare frowned. 'I have to speak to them.'

'You can only ask.'

'Does the DCI know?'

'Aye. He's asked me to let him know when the doc's finished.'

'I'd better see him.'

Ben was tapping away at his laptop when Clare looked in the door. His sleeves were rolled up and his tie loosened. A Moleskine notebook lay open on the desk, a Sheaffer pen beside it. He shut the laptop down and motioned to her to come in. As he did so a mobile phone next to the notebook buzzed with an incoming message and he picked this up, putting in his trouser pocket.

Clare glanced at the notebook, trying to read his writing upside down but he snapped it shut and met her eyes.

'You heard about the wives, then?'

She nodded. 'Ben...'

'It's my interview, Clare.'

'Yes, I know. You've made that clear. But Jim seems to think they're a bit shaken up. It might be an idea to have a female in there with you.'

He raised an eyebrow. 'Meaning you?'

'Meaning me.'

He regarded her for a moment. 'Okay. As long as we're clear I'll be leading it.'

'Of course.'

She left him to his laptop, closing the door softly. As she wandered back out to the front office to wait for the doctor the front door flew open, swinging back on its hinges and Chris came running in. He was dressed in grey sweat pants and a faded sweatshirt and his hair was rumpled. 'Is it true?' he said. 'You've found Kim and Debbie?'

Clare put a hand on his arm and steered him towards an empty interview room. 'In here.'

He shook her off and turned to Jim. 'Are they here? Where are they?'

Jim put a firmer hand on Chris's arm and drew him into the room. Clare followed, motioning to Max to wait in the front office. She closed the door and turned to face Chris, indicating a chair. He followed her look but stood his ground. 'I want to talk to them.'

Clare opened her mouth to speak but she was forestalled by Jim who gently but firmly pressed Chris down into the chair. Then he sat opposite, placing himself between Chris and the door. 'Just you listen to me, son.' He nodded towards the front office. 'We don't know what we're dealing with here and you've been an officer long enough to know a poorly handled interview can go badly wrong for us in court. You go storming in there, demanding to know what's gone on, and you'll cause all sorts of problems. So, I might be twenty years older than you and a few inches shorter, but I can promise you this: if you make any attempt to speak to those women, I will march you bodily out of this station myself. And you won't bloody well be back.'

Clare gaped at Jim. In all the years she'd worked in St Andrews not once had she heard a cross word from him, let alone heard him swear. His eyes were fixed on Chris and the younger man dropped his gaze. The moment had passed.

'Erm, thanks, Jim,' Clare said. 'I can take it from here.'

Jim rose and Chris looked up. 'Sorry, Jim.'

He shrugged. 'Ah well. Sometimes we all need a wee reminder.'

Clare was relieved to see Chris forcing a smile. 'Like you could march me out of here,' he said.

Jim raised an eyebrow. 'We'll never know now, will we?'

Clare waited until Jim had left the room then she sat down opposite her DS. 'You okay?'

'Dunno. I mean, how are they? Kim and Debbie?'

'I've no idea. I only arrived a couple of minutes before you.'

'Is there no way I can see them?'

Clare shook her head. 'You know the answer to that, Chris. Jim's right. We don't know if they're victims or even offenders. So we play it strictly by the book.' She rose from her seat. 'You stay here and I'll get you a coffee. As soon as the doctor's finished with them, if they're fit to be interviewed, I'll see them.'

'You and the boy wonder,' Chris said, shaking his head.

Clare ignored this. 'And, unless there's a good reason, I can promise you I'll come back and tell you what I can. But for now – you stay put.'

She found Max in the kitchen, making coffees. 'Thought you could do with one,' he said.

Clare smiled. He was so eager to please. 'That's really kind, Max, but you don't have to bother. I can make my own coffee.'

'I know. But I was doing it anyway.'

'Tell you what, give mine to Chris please. He takes it the same as me and he could do with one. And, when you've done that, could you do me a favour? Nip across to the shop and see if they have any Wagon Wheels.'

He stared. 'The biscuits?'

'Well I don't mean the wheels off a wagon.'

As he turned to leave, Clare saw the doctor emerge from the room he'd been using and she approached him.

'Thanks for attending so quickly, doctor. How are they?'

'I want them off to hospital. They've both had a serious shock. Sorry but, in my opinion, they are not fit to be questioned.'

Clare's face fell. 'Can we just ask about their husbands, please? Both are still missing and we haven't a clue where to start looking.'

'If I can sit in and providing the questioning isn't oppressive. But I would advise you not to seek any information that could prove evidential. If I was called to testify I'd have to say it was potentially unsound.'

'Thanks, doc. I'll wait for my DCI. Meantime, I'll ask Jim to call an ambulance.'

Five minutes later Clare, Ben and the doctor entered the inter-view room and she had her first sight of Debbie Gates and Kim Carter. She realised straight away the doctor was right. The pair were white-faced, their eyes hollow. Their clothes were grubby and they obviously hadn't been able to wash for a few days. They huddled close to one another and eyed Clare but said nothing, and her heart went out to them. If these women *were* involved with Paul Devine's escape they'd clearly had no idea what they were getting into.

From their photos, she worked out that Kim was the blonde, Debbie darker-haired. Ben introduced himself and Clare and told the women they would shortly be off to hospital for a check-up. 'I'll send two female officers along to make sure you're safe at all times,' he said. 'Won't be long now.'

The women exchanged glances then nodded.

Ben went on. 'We're very anxious to find your husbands. Is there anything you can tell us that might help?'

Debbie dabbed at her eyes with a tissue but Kim seemed more composed. 'We don't know. We were taken from my house. Put in a van. But we don't know what happened after that.'

'When was this?'

Kim's eyes flicked back and forward, as if she was trying to remember. Then she gave herself a little shake. 'Sorry, it was Saturday. Saturday night. It seems so long ago now.'

'What time?'

Kim looked at Debbie.

'Eight,' Debbie said. 'We'd just had a takeaway delivered.'

Jasmine Palace, Clare thought. It made sense. 'Can you remember anything about the van?'

Kim shook her head. 'They blindfolded us before they took us out.'

'It wasn't a car?'

'Definitely not,' Kim said. 'It had a sliding door. I remember the noise. And we didn't have seats. They just threw us in. I rolled over and hit my head on the side of the van.' She put a hand up and touched her head lightly.

Ben noted this down. 'Have you any idea why you were taken?'

Kim took a few breaths in and out and licked her lips. Clare indicated the plastic cup of water on the table and Kim lifted it to her lips, her hand shaking. She sipped at it, spilling a little, then set it down again. 'All I know is,' she said, 'they told us if the boys didn't do as they wanted...' she broke off.

'They threatened your husbands?' Clare said, her voice as gentle as she could make it.

Ben threw her a glance but said nothing.

'They said they would – they'd *damage* us.' Kim's eyes filled with tears and she began to sob, gulping in air. The doctor looked at Ben, and he nodded.

'I think we'll leave it there, ladies. Thank you for what you've told us.' He rose, scraping back his chair. 'Once you've had proper medical treatment I would like to speak to you both again. But I think we should get you to hospital as soon as possible.'

–

Clare sent Nita and Janey after the ambulance. 'Stick with them,' she said. 'If they're likely to be kept in overnight see if Dundee can send a couple of officers to relieve you.' Then, as promised, she went to update Chris with brief details.

'Were they badly hurt?' he asked, his face creased with worry.

'I don't think so,' Clare said. 'More shaken than anything.'

'What about Alan and Gav?'

'Sorry, Chris. They don't seem to know. But as soon as they're cleared for interview we'll try again. They may know more than they realise.' She put a hand on his arm. 'You'd better get back to bed. You've another night watching tractors ahead of you.'

He shook his head. 'Like I'll sleep now.'

Clare rose from her seat. 'It's good news, though. We know the wives are okay. There's every reason to believe the men are too.' She smiled. 'We'll find them, Chris. I promise.'

Chapter 13

Ben agreed to a press release going out and Clare offered to phone Suzi.

'You've just caught me,' she said when she heard Clare's voice. 'I'm late for a meeting.'

'I'll make it quick then. Our two prison officers' wives have turned up. They're off to hospital so I've only had a brief conversation with them. But there's no sign of the husbands.'

'I can get it on the teatime news,' Suzi said. 'Tell me what you want.'

'Doesn't have to be much. Erm, the wives of two prison officers who have been missing since, second thoughts, don't mention how long they've been gone. Just that they are safe and well but we're still seeking the officers.'

'No problem.'

'Thanks, Suze.' Clare ended the call and wandered into the incident room. Bill was tapping away at a computer. 'Any luck finding a connection between Maggie and the Devines?'

'Nothing yet,' he said. 'The Devines are both Fife lads but Maggie grew up in England. Only came up here a few years ago. I checked to see if she had previous but not so much as speeding ticket.'

Clare thought back. 'There wasn't anything on the PM about drug use, was there? No track marks?'

Bill shook his head. 'Nope. We could request tox tests but there's nothing to suggest we need them.'

'So where did the money come from?'

'Could be she was dealing, or maybe some other scheme.' He sat back thinking. Then he said, 'All that jewellery.'

'What about it?'

'There must be hundreds of rings and necklaces in that shop. I wonder if our Maggie was on the fiddle?'

'Good point, Bill. I might look in on the Jardines again. Ask them how easy it would be to steal a ring or two.'

—

Sylvia Jardine hadn't sounded particularly welcoming on the phone. 'I hope you won't say anything to upset Finlay. It was hard enough for him to come back into the shop today. He's worried sick about Devine.'

'Nothing like that,' Clare said, keeping her voice light. 'But I would like to find out a bit more about Maggie – the kind of work she did.'

Twenty minutes later Clare and Max drew up outside the shop. She was pleased to see a uniformed officer from the Cupar station on duty at the door.

'All okay so far,' he said, and Clare thanked him.

'Grab yourself a coffee,' she said. 'We'll be here for a bit.'

He escaped thankfully and Clare stood back to take in the shop. It was painted in a soft green with windows either side of a central door, above which the name Jardine Jewellers was picked out in navy blue. The windows were bright with discreet lighting making the displays of rings and necklaces sparkle. It was that rare thing, an arrangement which looked simple but was so hard to achieve. Having seen the Jardines' home Clare suspected Sylvia had a hand setting out the shop.

She pushed opened the door and they went inside. A dark blue carpet felt soft beneath Clare's feet and there was an air of calm after the busyness of South Street. To the left and right, glass cases held necklaces, watches and an assortment of other pieces. In the centre of the shop a long glass counter displayed rows of sparkling rings in individual boxes. A pair of occasional chairs stood to the side, for customers presumably. Sylvia Jardine was standing behind the counter, smiling as the door opened. She was more formally dressed than at their last meeting, in a dark grey shift dress, a pewter brooch the only adornment. Clare smiled back but when Sylvia recognised them her lips thinned.

'Finlay's in the back,' she said.

'I wonder if we could speak to you both?'

Sylvia hesitated, her hands on the counter. 'Just a moment.' She opened a stout door behind her and Clare heard a murmur of conversation. She reappeared a moment later, Finlay at her back. He made an attempt to smile but his eyes couldn't mask the anxiety he clearly felt.

'How are you, Mr Jardine?' Clare began.

'Oh, you know. Up and down.'

'Is there any news of Devine?' Sylvia asked.

'Not yet. But we are making progress,' Clare said. 'It's Maggie I'd like to speak about.'

Sylvia glanced at her husband. 'That's more your department, Fin.' She turned back to Clare. 'I didn't see Maggie that often, you see? I'm only here when she's on holiday.' She touched her husband lightly on the shoulder. 'You speak to the officers. I'll do us some coffee.'

He watched her as she moved to the door. Then he looked back at Clare and Max, peering through his glasses. 'What is it you wish to know?'

'A bit of background, really. What her responsibilities were – that sort of thing.'

Finlay's brow creased and he seemed genuinely puzzled by the question. 'Well, she was my assistant. She helped me here in the shop. I'm not sure what else I can tell you.'

'Did she ever open up and close the shop for you?'

His face cleared. 'I see what you mean. Yes, sometimes. I was usually here before her but she had a set of keys in case I was delayed.'

'So she would know the code for the alarm?'

'She would, yes. We change it every so often but I always told Maggie. You're surely not suggesting...'

Clare shook her head. 'Nothing like that. We're just trying to get a picture of what Maggie did. Even the smallest detail might help us find the person responsible for her death.'

The door behind Finlay opened again and Sylvia appeared bearing a tray of china mugs. She set this down on the counter and handed the mugs out. 'Biscuits?'

Clare waved this away. 'Just the coffee is fine.'

Max sipped his coffee. 'Lovely,' he said, and Sylvia smiled.

'I buy it ready-ground from a little shop across the road. We grind the beans ourselves at home but this is perfect for the shop.'

'The stuff we have at the station,' Max went on, pulling a face. 'Especially the way Clare here makes it.'

Clare watched them as Max chatted. Finlay was relaxing but Sylvia seemed less susceptible to his charms. She clasped her mug in both hands but she didn't drink from it. All her attention was on Finlay and what he was saying.

'Sometimes she would help with the orders and checking the stock,' he said. 'But I think she preferred to be out front. She was very good with the customers, you know. Good at persuading them to spend a little bit more for a really special piece.'

'Was Maggie well paid?'

Finlay's eyes widened. 'I'm not sure that's—'

'It would be useful to know if she had any money worries,' Clare added quickly.

'Not as far as I knew. And we did pay her well, you know. More than other shops, I'd imagine.' He looked from Clare to Max. 'Why are you asking?'

Clare didn't answer this directly. Instead she said, 'Did you ever have any suspicions Maggie might not have been entirely honest?'

Sylvia put down her mug. 'In what way?'

Clare decided to tell them about the cash. 'A large sum of money was found at Maggie's house,' she said, watching them carefully for a reaction.

Finlay blinked a couple of times and he opened his mouth to speak but Sylvia beat him to it.

'Money?' she said. 'As in cash?'

'Indeed.'

'How much was it?'

Clare studied Sylvia. It seemed an odd question. 'We've not counted it as yet but it is a substantial sum.'

Finlay looked at his wife. 'I can't see how she could have done anything dishonest while she was here. I check the stock very carefully.'

'Would it be possible for her to overcharge a customer?'

He rubbed the back of his neck. 'In theory, I suppose. But the till receipts wouldn't square with the takings.'

'Did you ever see anyone hanging about outside the shop?' Max asked. 'Anyone waiting for Maggie, say, at lunchtimes? Or the end of the day?'

Again, Finlay seemed at a loss. 'I honestly didn't notice. I mean, there could have been.'

Clare took a moment before posing her next question. Then she said, 'Did either of you ever suspect Maggie might be involved with anything else not strictly legal?'

They exchanged glances. Sylvia was the first to find her voice. 'Do you mean fraud?'

'Possibly,' Clare said. 'Or drugs.'

Finlay shook his head. 'Oh no,' he said. 'Nothing like that.'

'Mrs Jardine?' Clare said when she didn't reply.

Sylvia glanced at her husband. 'You know, Fin, it would explain a lot.'

He frowned. 'Such as?'

'Her moods,' Sylvia said. 'Think how often you came home saying Maggie had been in a mood that day. She was forever up one minute, down the next. What if she wasn't just selling drugs but taking them as well? That would definitely account for the moods. And I know we paid her well for shop work but she did have nice things. Always well dressed. Maybe that's where the money came from.'

Finlay stood considering this then he nodded slowly. 'I never thought of that. But you could be right.'

Clare regarded them. Were they correct? Was Maggie a drug dealer? It would certainly explain the money in the shed. It might even explain why she was killed. But there were no drugs found in the cottage, unless she had hiding place they didn't know about. A lock-up or something like that. 'You were aware Maggie had a car?' she said.

Finlay's brow creased. 'A red Nissan, I think.'

Clare looked towards the street outside. 'Parking's quite difficult round here,' she said. 'Where did Maggie leave her car when she was working?'

His brow creased. 'I'm not sure. Possibly the North Haugh.'

'Closer than that, Fin,' Sylvia said. 'I usually park at the harbour. Balfour Place is free if you can get in. I'd guess Maggie parked there.'

'She didn't have a lock-up in town, or anything like that?'

Sylvia raised an eyebrow. 'I really wouldn't know.'

Clare stood thinking for a minute. If Maggie had been involved with drugs surely they would have found some evidence at her cottage. She wondered if SOCO had been over the car and made a mental note to check this with Raymond. Perhaps Maggie was simply one of those people who didn't trust banks. But why hide the money in the shed?

'How did you pay Maggie?'

'Standing order, each month,' Finlay said.

'Straight into her bank account?'

'That's right.'

Clare considered this. There were only two reasons a person hid money: to keep it from being discovered or to keep it from being stolen. She had to know if it had come from the shop. She looked from Finlay to Sylvia and came to a decision. 'I'd like to ask you both to give us a sample of your fingerprints.'

Sylvia stiffened. 'For what reason?'

'The money,' Clare said. 'It would help us to know if it came from the shop. If Maggie had been dipping into the till it's possible your fingerprints might be on some of the notes.'

'Along with many other people's I imagine,' Sylvia said. 'Honestly, Inspector, the poor woman has just been murdered.'

'And we're trying to find the person responsible.'

'I think we all know who's responsible,' Sylvia snapped. 'Surely your efforts would be better directed towards locating Devine.'

Clare bit back the irritation she felt at this. 'We have a large team working on that,' she said, keeping her voice level. 'It's only a matter of time until we find him. And let me assure you if we don't find a match on the bank notes your prints will be destroyed.'

'It would help us enormously,' Max said, smiling at Sylvia.

The smile did the trick and she unbent a little. 'When would we have to do it? We can't possibly shut the shop. We've lost enough business as it is.'

Clare smiled. 'Closing time would be fine. If you could pop into the station and ask for Sergeant Jim Douglas.'

Sylvia glanced at her husband. 'It seems we have no choice.'

Finlay forced a smile. 'If it helps find Devine.'

The officer outside the shop was finishing his takeaway coffee when Clare and Max emerged and they went straight to the car.

'About those prints,' Max said.

'Yeah?' Clare started the engine and pulled out into South Street, heading east towards the ruined cathedral. The sun was low in the sky at this time of year and she pulled down the sunshade.

'Are those polymer bank notes not a problem for fingerprints?'

Clare signalled right and turned into Greenside Place, slowing for the twenty miles an hour sign. 'So I believe.'

'Why bother taking their prints then?'

'We might get lucky,' she said. 'But it was interesting to see their reaction. I'd say Mrs Jardine wasn't at all keen to have her prints taken.'

Chapter 14

The SOCO report confirmed Maggie's car had been searched and nothing significant found. Reading on, she saw another set of keys had been unearthed in the cottage but that all keys on the ring had been accounted for, including those for the Jardines' shop. It didn't look as if Maggie did have a lock-up. Maybe she wasn't involved in drugs after all. But, if she wasn't, where had the money come from? Clare returned to the report and saw the cash amounted to a little over twenty thousand pounds. She finished reading it and sent a quick email to Raymond to let him know she would be sending two sets of fingerprints to compare with the bank notes. Then she sat back in her chair to think. She was pretty sure Paul Devine was responsible for Maggie White's death. The question was why? Had he escaped with that in mind, or had he simply taken the chance to settle a score? The whole thing seemed so risky. The escape could have gone wrong. Someone could have seen him heading for the cottage. Maggie could have fought back. Why not just forget about her and keep his head down? It didn't make any sense.

And had the officers been complicit in his escape? With their wives taken hostage, Clare wouldn't blame them if they had. But where were they now?

As she sat mulling this over an email popped up. She clicked on it, hoping it was from Raymond. But it was an automatically generated message from Human Resources headed *Personal Development Conversation*. Her heart sank. She loathed these annual reviews, finding them a complete waste of time. This was the second reminder and she knew she'd have to arrange a date.

She scanned the email and saw her *Conversation* was with Super-intendent Penny Meakin. Clare hadn't met her. She'd recently moved up from the Borders and her name had appeared on a few emails and circulars. She clicked on Penny's name and was taken to her contact details. The photo showed a blonde woman of around forty, hair scraped back, expression severe. Clare thought longingly of Superintendent Campbell, now retired and spending his time on the golf course. He'd been a friend as much as a boss and she missed having him at the end of a phone. She pulled her keyboard across the desk. There was no point in getting off on the wrong foot with Penny Meakin. She scrolled down the email and clicked to accept the appointment.

She was about begin filling out the online form for the *Personal Development Conversation* when the door burst open and Max came in.

'Boss, it's Anthony Devine.'

'What about him?'

'He's been lifted off the street. He was leaving work when a van roared up, two men jumped out and huckled him into the back.'

Clare was out of her seat, grabbing her coat. 'Tell me?'

'White van, sliding doors. We've got the reg. Sara's running it through the database now.'

'Probably false plates,' Clare said. 'Or stolen. Who was keeping an eye on the funeral home?'

'Robbie. Nothing he could do. The van was gone in seconds. He went after it but he lost them.'

'Any other witnesses?' Clare asked, heading for the incident room.

'Yes, the owner – Anthony Devine's boss. He'd just come back from collecting a body so he was still outside. Robbie's bringing him in now.'

'False plates, boss,' Sara called.

'No surprise there. Get onto traffic, though. Get a description of the van circulated. Heading...' She glanced back at Max.

'South out of town,' he said.

'Got it,' Sara said.

Clare suddenly remembered DCI Ratcliffe. 'I'd better let Ben know.' She turned towards his office but Sara stopped her.

'He's gone out,' she said. 'Back late afternoon.'

Despite the seriousness of the situation Clare allowed herself a little smile. It was vital they spoke to the witness without delay. She decided she'd send a message to Ben letting him know but only once the witness had arrived.

A few minutes later Robbie entered the station with a white-faced man. He was soberly dressed in a dark suit and introduced himself as Donald Keys. For a split second Clare half expected to hear Chris whispering a joke about donkeys; and then she remembered why he wasn't there – why he couldn't be anywhere near this investigation.

Suddenly she was filled with a burning desire to catch Paul Devine at all costs – to catch him *and* whoever had helped him escape. Possibly the same men who'd abducted the two women. She wanted them all in custody, heading for long sentences. But more than that, more than anything else, she wanted to sit Chris down and tell him his nightmare was over.

She led Donald Keys to an interview room and called Ben Ratcliffe's number. It went to voicemail and she left a brief message. Then she signalled to Max and they went to speak to their witness.

'I'd just opened the back door of the hearse,' Donald Keys told them. 'I saw Anthony heading away for his lunch – he usually went out for some air. So I waved to him and he said something about only being half an hour. I turned back to the hearse then I heard tyres screeching. I thought there was going to be an accident so I looked round. Next thing I saw a van had stopped. The door was drawn back and two men were on the pavement. They grabbed Anthony and dragged him into the van. Then the door slid shut and it was gone.' He shook his head. 'It was over in seconds.'

'Could you describe the men?'

He shrugged. 'Not really. Dark clothing, I think. Hats – or maybe balaclavas.'

'Can you remember if anything was said – or shouted?' Clare asked.

He sat thinking for a moment, his head bowed. Then he raised his gaze. 'I don't think so. There was probably some shouting but nothing I could make out; and it really was over in seconds. By the time I realised what was happening the van had gone.'

'Can you describe it?' Clare said.

He frowned. 'White. Bit like a Transit.'

Clare nodded. That matched Robbie's description. 'Anything written on the side? Any markings? Scrapes or bumps?'

'Not that I could see. I wasn't really close enough.'

'If you could think back to the moment you realised Anthony was being forced into the van,' Clare said. 'Was it your impression he knew the men?'

Donald shook his head. 'I'm sorry. I really couldn't see.'

Clare smiled. 'Not to worry. Maybe you could tell us a bit about Anthony.'

'Of course. What would you like to know?'

'How long has he worked for you?'

Donald sat back and thought for a moment. 'About three years, I think.'

'Good employee?'

'Very.'

'What exactly does he do?'

'A bit of everything, mostly behind the scenes. He helps transport the deceased, prepares them for loved ones to view – that sort of thing. He does the odd funeral now and then but I think he prefers being in the back shop.'

Clare racked her brains trying to think what else to ask. Surely there was something he could tell them. 'Were there ever any callers for Anthony? At work, I mean?'

He ran a hand through his hair. 'I really couldn't say. Maybe the lady on reception would know but I don't recall anyone.'

'The funerals he helped with – was there a special reason for him being there?'

'Staff holidays, mostly,' Donald said. 'When we were short-handed.' He frowned. 'I can't remember much about them but it'll be in the records. If you want.'

Clare couldn't see how it would help but it was worth checking. 'If you could call us with the details once you're back in the office. And if you wouldn't mind asking the receptionist about callers – phone or in person.'

They learned little else and Clare ended the interview. She asked Donald Keys to hold on for a few minutes and she left the room to try Ben's number again. This time he answered. 'I went ahead and interviewed him,' she said. 'I didn't think it could wait.'

To her surprise, Ben seemed quite laid-back about it. 'I'm sure you'll have covered everything.'

'You don't want him to wait so you can see him yourself?'

'No need. I'll read the statement when I get back. On my way now.'

Donald Keys left, promising to call with the information Clare had requested.

Ben arrived a few minutes later and Clare gave him a copy of the undertaker's statement. 'I realise this is your investigation but I think we should get it on the news ASAP.'

He nodded. 'I agree. I'll get onto the press office now. What about the women? Any word from the hospital?'

'Not yet but I'll give the officers up there a call.'

'Thanks.' Ben sat down and opened his laptop. Then he looked up at Clare. 'Anything else?'

She regarded him. There was a lack of urgency in his manner and that worried her. She'd never dealt with anyone like him before. Mindful he was one rank senior to her, she chose her words carefully. 'Should we look into why Anthony Devine has been snatched off the street?'

'Does it matter? Surely what's important is finding him.'

'But, if we know why he was taken it might help us track him down? I'm concerned his life's in danger.'

'There's any number of reasons someone like Anthony Devine could have been picked up. He could be dealing drugs and encroached on someone's patch. Or it could be Paul wants to contact him but he knows we'll be watching. If Paul has the clout to arrange his own escape, picking his brother up wouldn't be hard. Unmarked van, false plates, choose the right moment and he's gone.'

Clare nodded. 'Yes, I suppose.'

'There is, of course, another possibility,' Ben went on.

'Which is?'

'We're assuming Paul Devine's behind the whole thing. But what if he isn't?'

'You mean,' Clare began slowly, 'that Paul Devine didn't escape custody. You're suggesting he was ambushed?'

He shrugged. 'It's possible. And if that's what happened, it doesn't look good for either of the Devines.'

'And the prison officers?'

Ben shrugged off his jacket and let it fall back on his chair. 'Clare, look, I know your sergeant's worried sick and there's no point in adding to that, but you have to consider we may not find those officers alive.'

A knot began to form in Clare's stomach. She'd been hoping every day, every hour, there would be some news of the two men. But it had taken Ben to give voice to her fears for her to realise this case might not have a happy ending. Her mouth was dry and she swallowed. 'But the wives,' she said.

'What about them?'

'They let them go.'

'So? Look, Clare, until we speak to them properly we won't know anything for sure. But, from the little they've told us, I'd say they were taken as bargaining chips – to make sure the men did what they wanted. These women were terrified. Scared out of their wits. It's unlikely they'll be able to tell us anything that'll identify their abductors. But their husbands? Well, they're trained prison officers. Experienced in dealing with protests, fights, all sorts. It would only take one of them to spot something – to be *seen* spotting something – for them to become a liability.'

Clare felt as if her legs could no longer support her and she sank down into a chair. 'Oh God,' she said.

'You'd better prepare yourself in case you have to give your young sergeant some very bad news.'

Chapter 15

The Jardines arrived to have their fingerprints taken a little after five. With Ben's words still ringing in her ears, Clare decided she couldn't face them and she asked Max and Sara to take the prints.

'Make sure they're escorted home,' she added. 'Go into the house with them, check it's secure and I want two cops outside all night, please.'

When they had gone Clare sought out Jim. 'Anything from the hospital?'

'Not, yet. Nita and Janey are with them, though. Last I heard, they were waiting on a doctor.'

She glanced at the clock. They were running out of day. 'It's going to be tomorrow, isn't it?'

Jim nodded. 'Probably.'

'Oh well. Can't be helped. Thanks, Jim.' She wandered through to the incident room and Max appeared at her back, a plate of buttered toast in his hand.

'I was getting hungry,' he said, setting the plate down on the desk. 'Help yourself, boss.'

'Call me Clare, Max,' she said, taking a triangle of toast. 'And thank you. This is just the job.'

'I can nip out for some proper food if you like.'

Clare looked round the room. There was only Max and Bill there. The rest must be out on surveillance. 'Let's pool what we know first. See where that gets us.'

Bill drew his chair across. 'Okay. The two women were abducted on Saturday night.'

'So they say,' Max put in.

'Yes,' Clare said, 'we have to consider they may not be telling the truth. Hopefully it won't be too long before Ben interviews them. But, for now, let's assume they were abducted on Saturday. That's four days ago.'

'Where were they found?' Max asked.

'Pitscottie,' Clare said, and Max nodded.

'I know it. So where have they been since then?' he asked.

'From the looks of them,' Bill said, 'somewhere they weren't able to wash or change their clothes.'

'Okay,' Clare said. 'Let's assume they were kept somewhere near Pitscottie. In a cottage, say. Somehow they got away – either they were let go or they escaped. They made their way to the road and we picked them up.'

'But we still don't know why they were abducted,' Max said.

Bill shrugged. 'Seems obvious to me. To put pressure on the husbands so they'd co-operate with the escape. Mind you, that doesn't explain why it took four days for the wives to reappear.'

Clare sighed. 'No, it doesn't; nor does it explain why the officers are still missing.' She thought for a minute then said, 'Let's look at the report from the prison again.' She pulled a laptop across the table and began to tap at the keyboard. Bill and Max shifted their chairs round so they too could read the screen. 'Says here the tracker on the prison van was playing up. Could the officers themselves have interfered with it?'

'It's possible,' Max said. 'I'm not sure how it's done but I don't think it would be difficult.'

Clare read on. 'Then the tracker stopped working altogether. The prison called one of the officers who confirmed everything was fine and they'd be back within the hour. And that was the last they heard.' She sat back, considering this.

'They could have been under duress when they took the phone call,' Max said, and Clare nodded.

'Okay. Let's assume the tracker stopped working, somewhere after leaving Pittenweem. Shortly after that the van stops. Could be the officers were following instructions or maybe it's hijacked – another vehicle blocking the road, that kind of thing.

'What was the last known location?' Bill asked.

'Dunino. A tiny hamlet south of here. About five miles away, I think.'

'How far is it from Dunino to Pitscottie?' Max asked.

Bill exhaled. 'Now, you're asking! It would be across narrow B-roads. I'd guess around ten miles. But it is a guess.'

'Close enough,' Clare checked her watch. 'Think I'll call Janey. See if there's any chance of the wives getting out tonight.' She swiped to find Janey's number and waited for an answer, clicking her tongue in irritation when it went to voicemail.

'Maybe in a dead spot,' Bill suggested.

'Yeah, could be. I'll try Nita.' Again, Clare waited. She was about to end the call when Nita answered.

'Sorry, boss. Janey's talking to the doc now.'

'Any chance?'

'I doubt it. They've both had a drip put up. The nurse I spoke to said they'd probably want to observe them overnight. Dundee are standing by to relieve us in a couple of hours, if they are kept in.'

Clare ended the call. 'Looking doubtful for tonight,' she said, putting her phone down. 'Can't be helped. Let's get back to Monday morning.'

'Okay,' Bill said, 'the tracker on the van develops a fault, last known location Dunino. No trace of the van since Monday afternoon.'

Clare nodded. 'Why would that be? If they'd torched it someone would have seen the smoke.'

'Could be Paul Devine used it to get away.'

'It's a bit of a risk,' Max said. 'Surely he'd ping a camera somewhere?'

Clare shook her head. 'Not if you know where to go. Plenty of roads without cameras, especially in Fife. Or they could be using false plates.'

'So the officers are either being held with Paul Devine, or they're hurt.'

'Or worse,' Clare added.

'There is another possibility,' Max said.

Clare turned to look at him. 'Go on.'

'The officers could be in on it. They could be willing participants.'

Clare frowned. 'I'm not sure, Max. Why would two officers risk everything? Their jobs, pensions, let alone see their wives taken off into the night.'

'If they're not willing,' Max persisted, 'why are they still missing?'

It was a good question. It fell to Bill to give voice to their thoughts.

'Unless they're dead.'

They were silent for a moment, then Clare said, 'Anything from the officers' phones?'

Bill shook his head. 'Not a peep. According to Ben's team they're both out of action. Either they've been destroyed or the SIM cards have been taken out.'

'And bank accounts?'

Bill hesitated.

'Yeah, I know,' Clare said. 'We've been told to leave it to Ben's lot. But he did agree information relevant to both crimes would be shared. I'm making a judgement call here. Those bank details could be relevant to Maggie's murder.'

Bill looked at Clare for a moment. Then he rose and left the room. A minute later he returned with a sheaf of papers. 'Got copies from Jim,' he said, putting the printouts down on the desk. 'There's the takeaway on Saturday night. We knew about that. And there's some small stuff on the Sunday too, but nothing since.'

Clare ran a finger down the transactions. 'Looks like Gavin Gates paid for petrol on Sunday morning and spent £25 in Tesco. Then he used the machine to take out £50 cash.'

'What about Alan Carter?' Max said, stretching across to read the statement.

'Contactless payments to Subway, Costa Coffee and he withdrew fifty quid as well.' Clare sat back, rubbing her chin. 'It doesn't sound like they were planning anything. Unless… Gavin paying for petrol – anything come in on their cars, Bill?'

'Not that I've been told.' He picked up his phone. 'Soon find out, though.'

They waited while Bill had a brief conversation with the prison. Then he put his phone down on the desk. 'They're going to check and get back to me.'

'Bit odd,' Max said, brushing toast crumbs off his trousers. 'All those transactions; and the petrol too. Imagine you've watched your wife being taken away at gunpoint. Would you be doing something as normal as putting petrol in the car?'

'Maybe he was running low,' Clare said. 'How much was it for, Bill?'

Bill scanned the bank printout again. 'Just shy of thirty pounds.' He looked up. 'That's not a full tank, is it?'

'No,' Clare agreed. 'He's topped it up.'

'Bit suspicious,' Max said.

Clare shrugged. 'Maybe. Maybe not. My dad refuses to let his car go down below half full. He says he doesn't want the fuel pump sucking up all the crap from the bottom of the tank.'

Bill ran his finger down the list of transactions. 'Doesn't fit,' he said. 'The last two petrol bills were close to sixty quid.' His phone began to ring and he snatched it up.

'Dave Manning,' the voice said. The assistant governor at the prison. Bill switched the speaker on for Clare and Max to hear. 'Regarding the officers' cars,' he began, 'Alan Carter's vehicle's still in the staff car park. But Gavin Gates didn't bring his car in on Monday.'

'It's Clare here, Dave,' she said, leaning towards the phone. 'Is it possible they lift-shared?'

'Oh hi, Clare. No, we don't think so. I've had a look at the car park CCTV and it looks like Alan arrived alone.'

'But Gavin was at work?'

'Oh yes. He arrived for his shift okay – just before eight in the morning.'

'Could someone else have given him a lift?' Clare asked.

'It's possible. But they were the only two officers from Fife on duty that day. He could have caught a lift from a friend, though. Maybe someone else who works in the town.'

Clare thanked Dave Manning and Bill ended the call. She sat thinking for a moment then said, 'Max, go and ask Jim to send someone round to Gavin Gates's house. See if there's any sign of his car.'

As Max rose the incident room door opened and Chris came in. He was dressed in jeans and a dark jacket.

'Just heading out on surveillance,' he said. 'There's a couple of farms with new kit, similar to the tractors that are being nicked. I've set up a watch.'

Clare smiled. 'Sounds like a good plan, Chris.'

He seemed keen to linger. 'Don't suppose there's any news?'

'Nothing yet.'

'I could help out with the murder.'

'Maybe — if we definitely rule out a connection. Stick with the tractors for now, though, and we'll review it in the morning.'

As Chris turned to leave, Jim appeared and handed Clare a note.

'Donald Keys,' he said. 'Funeral guy? You were asking about funerals Anthony attended.'

Clare glanced at the note. 'Not many at all,' and Jim agreed.

'Two were holiday cover over at Cupar and the other was a private family cemetery.'

'Brunton,' Clare said. She shook her head. 'Where is it?'

'I know it,' Chris said. 'Remember that bit of trouble at Hazelton Walls? The cottage?'

Clare remembered it well. A previous case when they'd been faced with one man holding another at knife point. 'How could I forget.'

'It's a mile or so along the road from there.'

'Christieson family,' Clare read.

'Think they own a bit of land,' Chris said. 'Probably why they have their own graveyard.'

Clare smiled. 'Thanks, Chris. Good luck with your tractors.'

'Gee, thanks.'

–

By 9 p.m. Janey confirmed the two women were being kept in hospital overnight. Max reported there was no sign of Gavin Gates's car at his house.

'Make sure the registration is noted as a vehicle of interest,' Clare said. 'If Gavin – or someone – is driving around they may just slip up and pass a camera.' Leaving Max to this task she emerged from the station into the cool evening air. She stood on the step gazing up at the sky. As she looked, a carpet of stars began to appear; and the longer she stood the more she saw. For a moment, she forgot about Paul and Anthony Devine, about the two prison officers and poor Maggie White, lying in a mortuary fridge. A toot from a nearby van brought her back to reality and she walked down the steps and clicked to unlock her car.

Friday

Chapter 16

Chris had gone home to bed before Clare arrived at the station. She found a note on her desk telling her they'd had no luck but would try again tonight. She sank down in her chair, holding the note. They weren't having much luck with the farm thefts and it wasn't the best use of resources when they were so stretched. But it was keeping Chris clear of the hunt for his cousin so it was worth another night or two. It might throw up something.

There was a tap on the door and Max pushed it open with his foot, He entered, bearing a mug in one hand and a piece of cake in the other.

'From Zoe,' he said

Clare eyed the cake. 'She's been baking again.' And then a thought struck her. 'It's not even eight o'clock, Max. She's surely not in already?'

He flushed and avoided her eye. 'Actually, she gave me the cake last night.'

'Last night, eh?' Clare said, trying not to smile. 'So, you and Zoe…'

He shrugged, his face still red. 'We had a meal together. That's all. She'd made a cake and said I could take a couple of slices for today.'

'Uh-huh.'

'Anyway, she's good fun.'

'I'm sure she is. Just watch she doesn't take advantage of you!'

'Very funny. So, boss, should I bring my coffee in or are you about to do a briefing?'

'Bring it in for a minute. And Max?'

'Yes?'

'Call me Clare.'

Ten minutes later Clare entered the incident room and called the briefing to order. Jim confirmed Ben was delayed and that he'd authorised Clare to brief both teams.

'For anyone who doesn't know,' she began, 'Paul Devine's brother, Anthony, was snatched off the street around lunchtime yesterday. Two men in dark clothing bundled him into a white van, similar to a Transit. We believe it headed south out of town but we've had no sightings since.'

'Any idea why?' someone asked.

'No, but it's hard to think it's not connected to Paul's escape,' Clare said.

'Did the brothers get on?' Max asked. 'Any conflict between them?'

Clare shook her head. 'Not that I'm aware of. Having spoken to Anthony, I didn't get that impression. But we can't rule it out. We do know Anthony had a caution for Class C possession. Can we look back to see if there's anything else? Any domestics involving the brothers? Maybe something that didn't get as far as a caution. Could be we attended and it fizzled out. Let's check, please.'

Heads nodded and Clare went on. 'As you all know a package was delivered to Anthony's house a couple of days ago. He claimed it was a DVD. But now he's disappeared, I'm even more convinced that was a lie. So what was in that package?'

'If he is dealing,' Bill said, 'it could have been money or drugs; and if he's upset someone — moved in on their patch — maybe they've lifted him to give him a slap.'

'Let's check the hospitals.' She scanned the room. 'Sara, could you look into that, please? Speak to the ambulance service too in case they picked him up.'

'What about pharmacies?' Sara said. 'He might not have wanted to go to hospital in case they asked awkward questions. If he bought stuff to patch himself up he'd be on their CCTV.'

'It's a good idea,' Clare said, 'but we don't have the manpower just now.' She smiled at the young PC. 'I'll bear it in mind, though, if he doesn't turn up soon.' She looked round the room. 'Any other thoughts on the package?'

'Burner phone,' Bill said.

Clare nodded. 'Makes sense. Maybe Paul's hiding out somewhere and needs help: money, food, a car even. Could be whoever sprung him on Monday arranged for a phone to be delivered to Anthony.'

'And if Anthony wasn't willing,' Bill went on, 'if he was ignoring Paul's calls, maybe that's why they snatched him.'

'Hold on, though,' Jim said, 'if Paul has men working for him – men who have access to a van and kids to drop off phones – what does he need Anthony for?'

It was a good point. 'Well?' Clare said. 'Any ideas?'

'That jewellery shop,' Max said. 'How much did they get away with?'

Clare frowned. 'I'm not sure what the final figure was.'

'I heard close on half a million,' Sara said.

'That much?'

'They've a lot of high-end stuff. Rolex and other designers.'

'And it wasn't recovered?'

Sara shook her head. 'I remember someone at the time saying they'd likely hang onto it for a bit. Wait for the heat to die down. The insurers had offered a big reward so every dealer would have been on the lookout.'

'Could be the others gave Paul's share to Anthony,' Bill said. 'To keep safe until he got out. That might explain why they grabbed him.'

Clare's head was spinning with it all. There were so many possibilities. 'Okay, let's talk it through.' She paused, trying to order her thoughts, then went on. 'Let's say the gang spring Paul on Monday. He's hiding out somewhere but he knows we'll be watching Anthony so he has to keep away. He – or whoever helped him escape – arranges for a lad to drop off a phone. Then he tries calling, but Anthony doesn't pick up. Eventually Paul loses patience and sends the gang to lift him.'

Bill nodded. 'Yeah, I'd say that works.'

She frowned. 'But why would Anthony ignore the calls? And, if he was keeping Paul's share of the robbery safe, where is it?'

There was no response to this. 'Beats me too,' Clare said. 'But let's keep it in mind.' She glanced down at her notebook and went on. 'Our two prison officers' wives are still in Ninewells Hospital. I'm hoping they'll be released for interview today. From what they said, it looks like they were abducted on Saturday night, maybe to force the husbands to co-operate with Paul's escape.' She scanned the room for Ben's team. A couple of them nodded to indicate this was their understanding. 'Anything from the search of the officers' houses?' she asked.

'Nothing that helps,' one of them said.

Clare let her glance rest on him for a moment. He could scarcely have said less. Was there something he wasn't telling her? Keeping it all back for Ben's ears only? The officer's face was a mask and she decided to take it up with Ben later.

'One more thing, before we leave Paul Devine,' she went on. 'Gavin Gates's car. It's not at the house and not at the prison. He didn't lift-share with Alan Carter on Monday morning. Maybe he parked at Tesco, further up the road. Or one of the other car parks nearby. Either way, the CCTV suggests he arrived at the prison on foot. So why didn't he travel with Alan and where's his car?'

'Lift-share with someone else?' an officer suggested. 'Maybe he drove to a friend's house and left the car there.'

'Could be. But so far we've not been able to find anyone. Jim has details of Gavin's car. Make sure you know what you're looking for.'

She glanced at her notes again. 'Okay. On to Maggie White. Obviously Paul Devine is our chief suspect. But we can't ignore the stash of money found in Maggie's shed. It's a little over twenty thousand pounds. Could that be anything to do with Paul Devine's share of the robbery? It seems unlikely. I'm also looking into the possibility Maggie was dipping into the till.'

'Surely they'd have noticed twenty grand going missing,' Robbie said.

'Depends how long she's been doing it. She's worked at the shop for two years. She could have salted a fair bit away in that time. But I agree it sounds unlikely. And most of the shop transactions would be card payments anyway.'

'Has to be drugs,' someone said. 'That amount of cash.'

'Normally I'd agree,' Clare said. 'But there's not so much as a cannabis plant at Maggie's cottage and no evidence she had a lock-up or anything like that.'

'Remember the prints,' Jim said.

Clare nodded her thanks. 'As Jim says, we took fingerprints from the Jardines, owners of the jewellery shop. It is hard getting decent prints from polymer notes. But, if we found even a single print matching one of them, at least we'd know the money came from the shop.'

She looked round the room. 'Anything else?'

Heads shook and she smiled. 'Okay, that's it. Keep in touch.'

Back in her office Clare checked a few news websites and was pleased to see the missing officers still featured prominently. She clicked on the photos of the two men. 'Where are you?' she said softly.

There was a tap on the door and Max came in. 'Janey and Nita are on their way up to Ninewells to relieve the night shift. They'll speak to the medical staff when they arrive.'

Clare frowned. 'We need to interview these women urgently, Max. Let me know as soon as there's any news. Anything else?'

'Just checked the phone and bank records for the prison officers. Nothing new. No calls, no cards used.'

Jim's head appeared round the door. 'That's the DCI arrived.'

Clare thanked him and rose from her seat. She looked longingly at Zoe's cake and decided it would taste better once she'd updated Ben.

Chapter 17

It was just after midday when Clare heard the two women had been released from hospital.

'We're on our way back now,' Jancy said. 'With you by one.'

Clare went to break the news to Ben.

'That's fine,' he said. 'I'll see them.'

She hesitated. 'I'd really like to be in the room. Max – my sergeant – too. I still think the two cases are linked. Plus, they know me from yesterday.'

He regarded her for a moment then he gave a slight nod. 'Okay. But I'll lead the questioning.'

She turned to leave then stopped, remembering how little Ben's officer had disclosed at the briefing. 'The search of Alan and Gavin's houses – did it turn up anything useful?'

'Not according to my team.'

'And they're clear to go back home again? Kim and Debbie?'

'Yeah. All good.' He smiled politely. 'If you could let me know when the women arrive.'

Kim and Debbie looked better than they had the previous day. Although still in the same clothes they were noticeably cleaner, the colour back in their cheeks. But there was no mistaking the unease they felt at their surroundings. Debbie's arms were wrapped round her while Kim's eyes flitted across the room.

'Where are Gav and Alan?' Kim said when Clare greeted them. Debbie lifted her gaze and the pair waited for Clare to reply.

'Right now, we're not sure.'

The women exchanged glances. 'You're not sure?' Kim said. 'What do you mean you're not sure?'

'We'll explain everything when we sit down to talk properly.'

Kim didn't look convinced but Clare steered them towards the interview rooms, explaining they would be questioned separately.

'Don't see why,' Kim muttered. 'We've done nothing wrong.'

Clare hastened to reassure her. 'Of course not. But it's important we learn as much as possible about your ordeal and we often find two people recall quite different things.' This seemed to placate them and Max was despatched to make coffees.

Clare stopped outside the interview rooms. 'We'd also like your permission to take a DNA sample from each of you.'

The women exchanged glances.

'Why?' Kim asked.

'It might help us secure a conviction. If we can link your DNA to the men who abducted you, or to the van they used, it strengthens our case; and we'll destroy the samples when the investigation's over.'

Kim shrugged. 'Suppose,' she said and Debbie gave a slight nod.

She installed them in separate rooms and went to find Ben.

'Might be better if we see Kim first,' she said.

'Because?'

'My guess is we won't get much out of Debbie. She looks scared out of her wits. Kim seems more inclined to talk. If Debbie does clam up we can use some of what Kim tells us to prompt her.'

He nodded. 'Makes sense.' He rose from his seat, shutting down his laptop. 'Let's see them then.'

Kim's face was set in a scowl when they entered the room. 'I can't believe you're treating us like this,' she said as Ben, Clare and Max sat down.

Ben smiled. 'Kim,' he began, 'I'm sorry if it seems a bit formal. We do appreciate you and Debbie are the victims here. You've been through a dreadful ordeal and we'll do everything we can to find those responsible. But we have to do things formally.' He glanced at Clare for confirmation and she nodded. 'If we don't,' he went on, 'and this ends up in court, a clever advocate could run rings round you and make it sound like we didn't question you properly. Any evidence you gave could be struck out. So we have to make sure everything's done by the book.' He indicated a digital recorder on the desk. 'Unfortunately, that means we will be recording this interview. You can have a solicitor present if you wish but I must stress you are not here under suspicion. We simply want to find out what happened.'

Kim's head drooped and the fight seemed to go out of her. 'Sorry. It's just…'

He gave her a moment to compose herself then he began. 'Perhaps we could go back to before Saturday night. Could you tell us how you came to be in the same house that evening?'

'We're friends.'

'You and Debbie? Or your husbands? How did you become friends?'

'Through the boys' work. Alan and Gav work together at the prison.'

'Did they know each other before working there?'

'No,' Kim said. 'That's where they met. Must be nearly four years now. They're about the same age and there's not many staff live out this way. Most stay nearer Perth.'

'So they struck up a friendship?'

Kim nodded. 'Anyway, one night Gav and Debs invited us over for a meal.' She smiled at the memory. 'It was a good night. Had a few drinks, good laugh. So we started doing it once a month.'

'At your house?'

'No. We took turns. Just happened to be our house this time.' She shivered. 'Maybe if we'd been at Debs'…'

'So, Saturday night,' Ben went on, 'Did anyone else know about it?'

Kim frowned. 'Like who?'

'Family, friends, workmates. People at the prison, maybe?'

'I suppose. I mean I'm not sure. I don't know if Alan told folk at work. Why would that matter? You can't think it was someone

133

from the prison? Alan's always saying how careful they are not to mention anything about their families. I'm sure he wouldn't have said, not in front of a prisoner. They wouldn't even know where we lived.'

She doesn't know, Clare thought. *About Paul Devine. She doesn't know why they were taken.* She glanced at Ben, and he went on. 'Maybe we could go on to what happened on Saturday night.'

Clare saw Kim swallow and she caught her eye. 'Take all the time you need,' she said. 'There's no rush.'

Kim wrapped her hands round the plastic cup of coffee and sipped at it. Then she put it down and took a breath in and out. 'We'd ordered a takeaway,' she began. 'Chinese. It came just before eight. We started opening the containers and realised they'd forgotten my rice.' She shook her head. 'Like that mattered.' She broke off and they waited a few moments. When she didn't carry on, Ben prompted her.

'What happened next?'

Kim looked down. 'The door went again,' she said, her voice small. 'I thought it was my rice. Thought the guy had realised his mistake. I think I heard voices—'

'Male or female?'

Kim frowned. 'A man, I think. Must have been. Next thing, Alan's coming into the room with a gun pointed at his chest.'

'How many of them were there?'

'Two. At least, two in the house.'

'Can you describe them, Kim?'

'Sorry. They had those head mask things on.'

'Balaclavas?'

'Yeah, that's it. Black. And they wore jeans and black jackets.'

'Blue jeans? Black?'

'Erm, just denim colour.'

'And the jackets?'

Kim closed her eyes, as if recalling then she opened them again. 'Like black fleeces.'

'Any logos?'

She shook her head. 'Sorry.'

Ben smiled. 'Kim, you're doing brilliantly. You really are.'

She nodded. 'I want to help. I want you to get them. Bastards.'

'Think about Alan for a minute,' he went on. 'How did the men compare to him, height-wise?'

'About the same, I think. Maybe a bit shorter.'

'And how tall is Alan?'

'Five eleven.'

'So they might have been, say, five ten?'

'About that. Well one was. The other was a bit shorter.'

'What about build? Were they slim? Stocky?'

She thought for a moment. 'Average I suppose. I honestly didn't notice.'

'Okay. I'm sorry to ask, but can you think about the man holding the gun, please?'

Kim shivered and wrapped her hands round the coffee cup again.

'Were his hands bare or was he wearing gloves?'

She took a moment before answering. 'Gloves, I think.'

'You didn't see his hands?'

'No, sorry.'

'What about shoes?'

She shook her head. 'I'm sorry. I was looking at his face, at the gun. I didn't notice his shoes.'

'That's fine,' Ben said. 'You're doing really well.' He hesitated then went on. 'I need to ask about the gun now. Can you tell me anything about it?'

'Like what?'

'Was he holding it in one hand, or two?'

'One.'

'So it was a handgun? Not long, like a shotgun?'

'Definitely a handgun.'

'That's good. After we're done here one of the other officers will show you some photos of guns. You might recognise it.'

Kim nodded, and Ben continued. 'What happened next?'

'He made us all sit down and put our hands out in front. Then he said we – that's me and Debs – that we'd have to go with them. Gav tried to stop them, but he waved the gun and said he'd use it, or something like that.' She stopped for a moment, moistening her lips, then went on. 'They pulled us up and tied our hands behind us.'

'How did they tie them?'

'Cable ties.' Kim held out her hands and Clare saw the faint traces of marks left by the ties. 'Bloody sore too. And they put something over our eyes.'

'A blindfold?' Clare asked.

'Sort of. Maybe a scarf. I can't remember. They led us out to the hall and one of them tapped on the front door. I heard another voice saying it was clear outside. So they took us out – Debs tripped on the step and bumped into me but the man must have caught her.' She stopped, as if reliving it, then she went on. 'There was a noise like a van door sliding. And I dug my heels in. Cos I thought if they got us into a van…' She sipped from the coffee again. 'Anyway, they lifted me in and Debs came in after me. Then a voice said if we made a sound they'd kick our heads in. So we lay there for a few minutes. I tried to listen. To hear anything. But it was all quiet. Then I heard the van doors slamming. Someone said "Go" and the van began to move.'

'Were there seats in the back of the van?' Ben asked.

Kim shook her head. 'No, we kind of rolled around a bit. I tried to move myself so I was facing the engine noise. I thought if I paid attention to the direction they took I could work out where we were going.'

Clare smiled. 'That was very quick thinking of you, Kim. Especially given how frightened you must have been.'

Kim's face darkened. 'I was angry by now. Debs, she was pretty upset. Crying, you know. But I wasn't giving up without a fight. Problem was, I didn't see the van when they put us in so I couldn't tell which way it was pointing. But I know the roundabouts on the estate and I think they took us along the Craigtoun Road.'

Clare tried not to react. The van must have gone right past her house. What had she been doing between eight and nine on Saturday evening? Watching TV? Or out walking Benjy, perhaps. Had the van passed her?

Ben was speaking again. 'Can you recall how long you were on that road?'

Kim wrinkled her brow. 'I'm not sure. Maybe ten or fifteen minutes. After that we seemed to slow down with a bit of stopping and starting.'

'As if you were in a town?'

'Yeah. Exactly like that. But, by this stage, I was disorientated.'

'And then?'

'We must have left the town 'cause it speeded up again. Then it slowed down and turned sharply. I remember because Debs rolled into me. It was bumpy after that. We were shaken all over the place. That went on for a few minutes until it slowed right down and the engine stopped. I could hear the men talking and opening the van doors. After a bit they slid the side door back and I felt the cold air. One of them helped me out and took my arm, making sure I didn't trip.'

'What was the ground like underfoot?' Clare asked.

'Bumpy. I remember because I stumbled into him a couple of times. I heard a door open and he told me to step up. I thought it must be a house because it was suddenly warm. And, even with the blindfold, I could see it was lighter.'

'What happened next?'

'They put us in a room – Debs and me. They took the blindfolds off and undid our hands. They said they'd bring us something to eat then they went out and we heard the door being locked.'

'Was there a window?' Ben asked.

'There was. But it was boarded up. And it was dark anyway.'

'Okay,' Ben said. 'What about the room?'

'Pretty basic. One of those Calor gas heater things so it was warm enough. There was a carpet on the floor too, but it was old, you know? A bit worn.'

'Colour? Or pattern?'

Kim thought for a moment. 'A sort of swirly pattern. Brown and orange, I think.'

Clare noted this down and Ben went on.

'What else?'

'There was a bed against the wall. A double with a wooden headboard. There weren't any chairs so we sat on that. After a bit one of the men came back with a carrier bag. He said it was food and drinks for us and later on they'd take us to the toilet, one at a time. I was pretty pissed off by now. Debs was crying and shaking and I was worried about her. I told him she wasn't well and he'd better do something.'

'And did he?'

'No. He brought us some blankets and said we'd get out sooner if we behaved ourselves. So, after we'd eaten and they'd taken us to the loo we lay down on the bed and tried to sleep. Debs fell asleep before me so I lay as quietly as I could, listening, in case I could hear what they were saying through the wall. But it was too muffled.'

'And the next morning?'

'Just the same. They brought us food, took us to the toilet. I asked why we were there, but the man said the less we knew the better and they wouldn't hurt us unless we tried to get away. I asked how long we'd be there and they said *a bit longer.*' She lifted the coffee cup and drained it. 'They wouldn't say any more than that.'

Ben nodded then said, 'How long did they keep you there?'

'I think it was five nights,' Kim said. 'Five or six. It's hard to be sure with the window boarded up. After a while, you lose track. But I think it was five. Wait, is this Wednesday or Thursday?'

Clare smiled. 'It's Friday. I'm not surprised you're a bit disorientated.' She glanced at Ben then said, 'Is there anything else you can tell us about where you were held?'

Kim shook her head. 'Not really. I mean we kept hearing a car – or maybe it was the van – doors slamming, sound of an engine – that sort of thing.'

'And how did you manage to get free?' Ben asked.

'It was yesterday,' Kim said. 'Two of them came in. One with the gun and the other with the blindfolds and more cable ties. They tied and blindfolded us like before and we were led out to the van again. They drove us around for a bit then the van stopped. Debs was hysterical. She thought they were going to shoot us. They took us out of the van and walked us over some bumpy ground – like a field, you know? They snapped the ties off our hands but left the blindfolds on. They told us to wait ten minutes before taking them off. They said they'd be watching and if we did it any sooner they'd shoot us. So we stood there and I listened for any sound. I wasn't sure if they might still be there – like a test, to see if we did what we were told. And then I heard the van engine start up and I tore my blindfold off.' She tapped her pocket. 'Still got it,' she said. 'Thought it might have DNA or something like that.'

Clare smiled. 'That's great, Kim. If you could avoid handling it any more we'll get an evidence bag for it.'

Kim nodded at this. 'It took a moment, you know? After the blindfold – everything was so bright. I looked all round but there was no sign of the men. They must have gone off in the van. So I took Debs' blindfold off too and tried to calm her down.'

'You did well,' Clare said, 'keeping Debs going.'

Kim shrugged. 'One of us had to be strong. Anyway, I heard a couple of cars in the distance so I knew we were near a road. I took a minute to get my bearings then we started walking. Ten minutes later we found a road. I can't tell you what a relief it was to get out of that field. After a bit a car stopped and Debs started to scream. I could tell he wasn't one of them. He took his phone out and said he'd call the police and I gave him a thumbs up. But Debs, she wouldn't wait. She ran off in the opposite direction so I had to go after her. We found a hedge near the road and we hid behind that. Then I heard the siren and I knew we were safe.' She shook her head. 'Honestly, I've never been so glad to see anyone in my life.'

Ben seemed to be happy enough with Clare's input and he agreed she and Max could sit in on Debbie's interview as well. As Clare had predicted, she was less forthcoming than her friend. But, with gentle prompting, she confirmed most of what Kim had said.

'What can you tell us about the place you were held?' Ben went on.

Debbie thought about this. 'It was quiet – like in the country. We could hear the birds, you know? And sometimes a car went past. Not that close, but it was quiet enough to hear.' She paused again then said, 'I think it was an older house.'

'What makes you say that?'

'Well, the bathroom for a start. It had an old turquoise bath and the loo had a seat that didn't match the rest. Like it had been replaced, you know? And the doors had those panels – two at the top, two at the bottom. Like old houses. The windows were the old-fashioned kind, too. I mean they were boarded up on the outside but we could see the inside.'

Clare noted all this down. 'Anything else, Debbie? Anything at all?'

Her brow creased as she recalled. 'I tried to see out of the window – through the boards, you know? There was a tiny gap. And we had nothing to do so I kept looking through it. Just for a glimpse of the outside.' Her brow furrowed as she seemed to be recalling. Then it cleared. 'I remember,' she said. 'There was a kind of tower – in the distance. Up on a hill.'

Max sat forward. 'What kind of tower?' Ben threw him a glance but Max was intent on what Debbie was saying.

'Quite tall, I think,' she went on. 'Kind of thin, with a sticky-out bit at the top.'

He took out his phone and tapped at it. Then he held it out for her to see. 'Did it look like this?'

Debbie nodded. 'Yes, I think so. In fact, that looks really like it. I mean, sometimes it was hard to see, if the sun was in the way. But I'm pretty sure that's it.'

'It's the Mount,' Max said. 'The proper name's The Hopetoun Monument but the locals know it as the Mount. It's between Cupar and the A92 at the top of Mount Hill.'

'I don't think I know it,' Debbie said.

'Depends where you live,' Max began, but Ben made a warning gesture with his hand and Max took the hint.

Ben gave Debbie an encouraging smile. 'That's great. So helpful. Can you think when the sun was in your eyes? What time of day?'

Debbie frowned. 'Later on,' she said. 'A few hours before it got dark.'

'Late afternoon?'

'I think so.' She looked at them. 'Does that help?'

He smiled. 'It does. Thanks, Debbie.'

Chapter 18

Clare sent the women home with a couple of officers to check their houses. 'I've arranged for family liaison officers to come up but they won't be here for an hour or two yet so you'll need to stay with them. I don't want them left alone.'

When the officers had gone she tapped on Ben's door and went in. Again, he closed down his laptop and waited for her to speak.

'Family liaison officers are on their way up,' she said. 'They'll stay in the women's houses. And there's a car parked outside each of them.'

'Thanks, Clare.'

When he didn't volunteer anything further she said, 'What about the hunt for the men? Any progress?'

He smiled. A polite smile. 'Some.'

She couldn't make him out. Was there something he was keeping from her? He seemed curiously detached from the investigation. 'Is there anything I should know?'

'No. I've officers working on it. They have pretty good intel on who we think the gang are. But the fewer folk who know about it the better. Rest assured, we'll get them.' He glanced down at his laptop. 'So, if there's nothing else?'

Clare stood her ground. 'I want to search the area around that monument Debbie saw from the cottage.'

'Sounds like a good idea.'

'You've no objection?'

'No. It won't affect my investigations. And, in any case the women have been released so the house will be empty now. They'll have moved on.'

He had a point. But, if they did find the house, there might be valuable evidence.

'I'll get on with it then,' she said and he simply nodded, one hand on his laptop as though waiting for her to go.

She left him, none the wiser, and sought out Max. 'Let's see if we can pin down that cottage.' They went into the incident room and studied the map on the wall.

'There's the Mount,' Max said, indicating a contour ring on the map. 'It's not high but the land around it's pretty flat so the monument stands out.'

'Debbie said the sun was in her eyes around late afternoon,' Clare said. 'That means they must have been kept somewhere to the east of the hill.'

'Maybe even south-east,' Max said.

Clare drew a finger along the route she guessed they'd taken. 'Kim said she thought they drove through a town. Could that have been Cupar?'

Max nodded. 'Has to be. If they were heading for somewhere south-east of Mount Hill, I'd say we start from Duffus Park in Cupar and spread out to the north and west.' He drew an imaginary arc on the map with his finger. 'That's your area, boss.'

'Right,' Clare said. She looked round the incident room. Only Bill and a few other officers were there, heads bent over laptops or phones clamped to their ears. 'Ask Jim to get on the radio please. I want as many bodies as possible back here. We're going to comb every inch of that area.'

Within half an hour the incident room was packed. Jim had called Dundee, Cupar and Glenrothes, and begged extra staff. Those who were within a reasonable distance of St Andrews had come straight over and more were on the way.

'Traffic cars are setting up road blocks on all the junctions in the area,' Jim said. 'We're still a few cars short. So many back roads round the Mount. But we're nearly there.'

Clare thanked him and set about allocating officers to stretches of road. 'I want every single building checked,' she said. 'You're looking for an older property, possibly in need of an upgrade. At least one window will be boarded up or show recent evidence of boards. The women also said the approach to the cottage was bumpy so it could be up a farm track.'

'What do we do if we think we've found it?' Nita asked.

'Keep a low profile. Check for vehicles and, if there's none outside, approach carefully. But do not enter the cottage. It's likely to be a crime scene so I want any potential evidence preserved.'

Max raised a hand. 'It's pretty open countryside out there. Might be hard to keep out of sight.'

Clare frowned. 'Good point. Okay, folks, if you think you've found the cottage only plain-clothes officers should approach. Uniforms to block any roads further back. Every vehicle to be checked. Ask the occupants for ID and insist on seeing in car boots and in the back of vans.' She checked her watch. 'I want regular reports please; and remember, at least one of these men has a gun. No heroics.'

'Do you want armed response on stand-by?' Jim asked.

Clare nodded. 'Just alert them for now. No point in bringing a team out until we have something concrete.'

—

Within ten minutes the station was almost empty. Jim remained at the public enquiry counter while Ben stuck to his room, tapping away at the laptop, although Clare had absolutely no idea what he was doing. Max was chatting to Zoe and, for once, Clare didn't quite know what to do with herself. She wandered into her office and sat down. Then she took up her phone and typed a message to the DCI.

> Weird day
> Fancy a takeaway later?
> C x

The mention of a takeaway made her think again of the two women and she lifted her phone to check on them. Janey confirmed the family liaison officers had arrived so she was heading across to the Mount to help with the search. Clare's phone buzzed and she saw the DCI had sent a reply.

> Sounds good.
> What do you fancy?
> Al x

She tapped back,

> Anything but Chinese!

She'd almost given up hope of any news when, just before five, Jim burst into her office.

'Bill on the phone. He thinks he's found the cottage.'

Clare shoved her chair back. 'Any sign of life?'

'Nope. But there's a boarded-up window at the back. He shone a torch through a gap in the boards and he said there's a bed and a brown and orange carpet.'

—

'Take a left after the park,' Max said, and Clare swung the car off Cupar's Balgarvie Road onto a narrower one. She slowed for an officer who held out his hand then, recognising Clare, waved them on.

'See the Mount?' Max said as she picked up speed again.

The road was mostly straight and Clare took her eyes off it for a few seconds to squint at the skyline. The sun had dipped behind a cloud but it was still clear enough to see the slender outline of the Hopetoun Monument. 'How much further?' she asked.

'From what Bill said, another mile or so.'

She drove on, as fast as she dared, passing officers stationed at every junction. The road was peppered with farm cottages but she knew from Kim's statement the one they were after was along a rough track. As the gradient increased, the monument loomed larger; and then she saw a police car parked on the verge opposite a break in the hedgerow. The officer recognised Clare's car and directed her through the gap. She changed gear to negotiate the track, swerving to avoid a pothole. It was tree-lined on one side and as they bumped further along it curved round to reveal a single-storey cottage built in sandstone. The roof was missing a few pantiles and there was a crack on the chimney stack. The front door paint was peeling and the windows had seen better days. Clare took it in. It looked all but abandoned. Was this really where Kim and Debbie had spent the past few days?

Bill was in the process of setting up a cordon and Clare turned the car onto a patch of grass, clear of the tape.

'I've kept the rest of them back,' he said. 'But I did walk round the cottage to check for a boarded-up window.'

'Do we know who owns it?'

'Not yet. Robbie's checked with a farm further down the road but they say it's not one of theirs. They thought it hadn't been lived in for years.'

'You didn't go in?'

He shook his head. 'Thought I'd wait – see how you want to play it.'

'Thanks, Bill. I will have to check it matches the women's story. There's no point in dragging SOCO out here if it's not the right cottage.' She nodded to Max. 'Let's get suited up.'

A few minutes later the cottage door was forced and they stepped inside. It felt cold but when they pushed open the first door off the hall they saw a half-filled coal scuttle and a box of firelighters. There was a sofa in a red jacquard fabric, worn at the edges, an ashtray full of dog ends perched on one arm. In front of this stood a tiled coffee table strewn with empty beer cans and foil takeaway containers. Clare stooped to sniff at one of them.

The remains of something dark yellow were congealing and she caught a faint whiff of curry.

'Someone's been here recently,' she said. 'SOCO might get DNA off that lot,' and Max nodded.

She retraced her footsteps back to the hall and opened the next door to find a small kitchen. It was bright enough, thanks to a curtainless window and a half-glass back door, but it didn't look as if it had functioned as a kitchen for some time. A free-standing gas cooker was thick with grease, the control buttons cracked or missing. The Formica worktop was chipped and the units below had old style sliding doors, one of which had come off its runner. A stainless steel sink was piled with dirty dishes.

'Ugh,' Max said 'They're not exactly houseproud.'

Clare laughed. 'That's an understatement. Heaven help SOCO sorting this lot out.' She backed out of the room and opened a door at the top of the hall. A curtain was drawn over the window and, not wanting to touch the light switch, she took a moment to adjust her eyes. And then she saw it was a bathroom. It was a bathroom with a turquoise suite and a toilet seat that didn't match. 'This is where they were kept,' she said. 'No doubt about it.'

Two other doors led to bedrooms, one of which had a bed with a wooden headboard and a Calor gas heater in the corner. She looked down and saw the brown and orange carpet. 'Get onto SOCO,' she said. 'And tell them it's urgent.'

–

Raymond and his team arrived as it was growing dark.

'You're in for a treat,' Clare told him, and he shook his head.

'Just what I need at the end of a busy day.' He began pulling on a white forensic suit. 'Anything particular you're after?'

'DNA, ideally. It's possible the people who abducted the women are on our system and there's plenty of food and drink containers in the cottage. Cigarette ends, too. I sent the women's DNA over earlier. And there was a scarf used as a blindfold. Oh, and any notes or receipts that might show where they've been.'

Raymond sighed. 'I'll get on, then.' He went to the boot of his car and took out his case. As he closed the boot the lighting rig came to life and the cottage was bathed in a harsh light which made the surrounding countryside seem all the more dark. Clare picked her way carefully over the rutted track towards her car. As she clicked to unlock it her phone began to ring. She glanced at the display and swiped to take the call.

'Jim?'

'Alan Carter,' he said. 'He's just walked into the station.'

Chapter 19

'I've called the doctor,' Jim said as Clare walked in the station door, 'but he's declined medical attention. Says he won't see him.'

'He'll see him,' Clare said, her face grim. 'Have you told Chris?'

'Aye. Warned him not to come to the station but you know what he's like.'

Clare's lips thinned. 'He is not to see Alan.'

'Don't worry. I'll make sure of it.'

'And the prison van?'

'In the car park. I've phoned SOCO.'

Clare nodded. 'Thanks, Jim. Where is he?'

'Interview room two.'

'Ben?'

'On his way.'

The station door opened and the duty doctor appeared. Clare introduced herself and explained the situation. 'He's been missing since Monday and we do need to interview him.'

'If he's anything like the two women I saw yesterday—'

'I gather he's not,' Clare said. 'In fact, he told my sergeant he wouldn't see you.'

'That could be part of his trauma.'

'Would you allow me to come in with you?'

The doctor considered this. 'I suggest you come in to start with, introduce yourself and explain the situation. Then leave him with me and I'll see how he is.'

'Perfect. Thanks, doc. Only, this time it really is important.'

He smiled. 'Come on, then. Let's see what he's like.'

Alan Carter had been slumped in a chair. As they opened the door, he sat up, adjusting his position. Clare pulled out two chairs for herself and the doctor. Then she took her first look at Chris's cousin, one of the officers who'd allowed Paul Devine to escape. His sandy hair was closely cropped, his eyes blue. A scruffy beard was, she guessed, the result of five days without access to a razor. He was still wearing his prison officer uniform, although the white shirt was grubby and the clip-on tie absent. His hands were grimy and Clare wondered if he'd been sleeping rough. She introduced herself and the doctor. But before she could say anything else, Alan spoke.

'Don't need a doctor.'

Clare regarded him. 'All the same, Alan, I'm sure you know enough about the justice system to know we have to check you over before taking your statement.'

'I'm fine.'

'That's good. Now, I'm going to leave you with Dr Gillespie here. If he judges you need medical attention we'll send you to Ninewells. You'll have a police escort and someone will be with you at all times. But you will have to go if that's the doctor's recommendation. Do you understand?'

He exhaled audibly. 'Whatever. When can I see Kim? That sergeant out there said she's okay.' His voice cracked as he spoke and Clare saw his eyes were shining. 'I need to see her,' he said.

'Kim's fine,' Clare said. 'She spent a night in hospital, mainly to allow her to rest and get some fluids. We've interviewed her and she's at home now with a police officer.' She met his eye. 'She is fine.'

'And Debs?'

'She's at home too.' She scraped back her chair. 'I'll leave you now but I'll be back as soon as the doctor's finished.'

Outside the room she found an agitated Chris pacing the front office. He rushed towards her when she emerged.

'You've seen him? Is he okay?'

Clare took his arm and steered him towards her office. She gestured to Max to make some hot drinks. 'And ask Jim to organise a solicitor,' she added. 'In case he is fit to be interviewed.' She propelled Chris into the room. 'Take a seat,' she said, closing the door behind him.

He hovered, looking at the seat. 'I need to see him, Clare.'

She smiled. 'And you will. But I'll repeat what I said when Kim and Debbie were found. Whatever Alan's testimony turns out to be, we can't have it influenced by your presence. You don't need me to tell you that.'

He sank down in the chair, running a hand through his hair. Then he met her eye. 'How is he?'

'The doc's with him now. I have to say he looked tired and a bit grubby but he seems in pretty good shape. Refusing to go to hospital. Wants to see Kim. Much as you'd expect.'

'Has he... has he been knocked about?'

Clare shook her head. 'Not that I can see. No bruises on his face. No cuts on his hands. I'd guess he's been sleeping rough. Apart from that, he seems in reasonable shape.'

The door opened and Max appeared with two mugs. He set these down on Clare's desk. 'Sorry,' he said, 'I couldn't find any of those biscuits you like. But I can nip to the shop.'

Chris forced a smile. 'Nah, it's okay. Coffee's great. Thanks.'

'No problem.'

Clare waited until Max had left, then she picked up her coffee. 'Get that while it's hot.'

He sipped at it. 'I'll give him this much – he makes a better cup than you.'

She laughed. 'I think he grinds his own beans.'

'Tastes like it.' He put down his cup. 'What next, then?'

Clare glanced at the door. 'We wait to see what the doc thinks. With luck he'll clear Alan for interview and we'll find out what did happen on Monday.'

'Will he be charged?'

Clare didn't answer at first. Then she said, 'You've been in the job long enough to know the answer to that. If he facilitated the escape he could well be charged. On the other hand, if he acted under duress...'

'There's no way Alan would have done it any other way.'

'I'm sure you're right, Chris. And now, I'm going to ask you to leave the station. You can't be here when I speak to him.'

He looked at Clare but didn't answer.

'You know all this,' she said. 'So, drink that coffee and get off home for a couple of hours. You've another night of tractor hunting ahead of you.'

—

'He's refusing medical attention,' the doctor told Clare.

'Is he fit to be questioned?'

He nodded. 'Yes. He's not showing any indications of shock or confusion. He's orientated in time and place, perfectly lucid. I'd say he's tired and I wouldn't want you questioning him all night. But there's no reason to suppose any statement he gives would be unreliable, medically speaking.'

Clare thanked the doctor and went back to her office to wait for the duty solicitor. Ben, having gone home earlier, had returned now and told Clare he would lead the questioning.

'But I've no objection to you sitting in,' he said.

Half an hour later the solicitor arrived and was shown to the interview room. After five minutes alone with Alan he indicated they were ready to begin. Clare introduced Ben and began the recording, delivering the standard caution. Alan said he under-stood, and she sat back, waiting for Ben to begin.

'How are you, Alan?' he asked.

'Fine,' Alan said. 'I'm fine.'

'If you need a break at any time, just say and we'll pause the interview.'

Alan acknowledged this and Ben went on.

'Can we go back to Saturday night, please?'

Clare glanced at Ben. Surely they should be asking where Gavin Gates was.

He ignored her, his gaze fixed on Alan. 'Saturday?' he repeated.

Alan looked down for a moment then he said, 'We had a takeaway delivered. Only there was a mistake and when the door went a few minutes later we thought it was the guy back with our missing stuff. So, I opened the door and these two lads were there.'

'Can you describe them?'

'Not really. Big lads, dark jackets, jeans. Balaclavas and gloves.'

'Any logos?'

Alan shook his head. 'Nah. Standard stuff.'

'Okay. Go on.'

'One of them had a gun.'

'Type?'

He shrugged. 'Handgun. Maybe a Beretta.'

Ben noted this down then he went on. 'So you opened the door and saw two men. What happened next?'

'They forced their way in and shut the door behind them. They made us all sit down and one of them – the one without the gun – he tied the girls' hands and put blindfolds on them.'

Clare saw Alan's knuckles grow white as he recounted this. 'That must have been awful for you,' she said, and he nodded.

'What happened next?' Ben asked.

'The one without the gun – he took the girls out to the hall and I heard him bang on the front door. A voice outside said it was clear. And they were gone.' He rubbed a hand through his hair. 'I didn't know if we'd ever see them again.' His voice cracked as he spoke and Ben gave him a moment to compose himself.

'Could you hear the van at all?' he went on.

Alan shook his head. 'Triple glazing.'

'Okay. Then what?'

His brow wrinkled. 'He came back into the room and one of them – can't remember which one – said they knew we were taking a prisoner to a funeral on Monday.' He looked at Ben and Clare. 'I dunno how he knew that.'

'Do you and Gavin often work together?' Ben asked.

'When we can. Makes sense, both of us coming from St Andrews.'

Clare sat forward. 'Do you lift-share?'

'Depends. Sometimes one of us is going somewhere after work, that sort of thing.'

'Did you share a car on Monday?'

'No. After what happened, Gav said we'd be better not arriving together.'

Clare nodded at this and indicated he should continue.

'So, like I said, they knew about Paul going to his uncle's funeral, down at Pittenweem. They said we'd to make it look like the van tracker was playing up.'

'How did you do that?' Ben asked.

He shrugged. 'Gav did it. He said he knew how to fiddle with the fuses. Make it look like it was intermittent. The prison would call to check we were okay and after that he'd take the fuse out altogether. They'd just think it was broken.'

'So they told you to interfere with the tracker,' Ben said. 'Then what?'

'We were to head back via Anstruther. Up the B9131. Just past Dunino they'd have another van waiting. We'd to pull in and take the cuffs off Paul. Let him go.'

'And after that?' Ben asked.

'They said they'd hold onto Kim and Debs for a couple of days. There was a job they had to finish and they'd let the girls go after that.'

'What did you think they meant?' Ben asked.

Alan shook his head. 'No idea.'

'Okay. Go on.'

'After we let Paul go they said we'd better keep our heads down. They'd leave us with the van and we could buy a newspaper every day. Soon as the papers said the girls were out we could hand ourselves in.'

Clare sat forward. 'Alan, surely in the prison service you have protocols for this kind of thing? Some way of indicating you're under duress?'

'Course we do.' He met Clare's eye. 'But if they'd taken the person you loved more than anything in the world, would you chance it?' He glared at her. 'They said they'd mess the girls up so badly we'd need an instruction book to put them back together again.' He folded his arms. 'Total no-brainer.'

Ben flicked a glance at Clare and she sat back. 'Let's move on to Monday,' he said. 'You arrived at work. What then?'

'The usual. Paul was ready in his cell. We collected him about ten and headed off down the coast.'

'And the funeral?'

'Standard stuff. Not many there. Paul wanted to hang at the back, not get into anything with the others. Then his brother came over for a chat.'

'What was the chat about?' Clare asked.

'Just the uncle. How they remembered him, what would happen to his house. Usual stuff.'

Clare sat forward. 'Alan, this is important: was anything said about Paul escaping custody? Did you get the impression his brother knew about it?'

'I'm not sure that's relevant,' Ben interrupted. 'We can question the brother when we pick him up. Let's move on to Dunino.'

Clare didn't dare look at Ben. She clenched her fists under the desk and forced a smile. Alan looked from one to the other.

'Dunino?' Ben reminded him.

'So, we'd done the tracker stuff and that. The prison phoned and we said it was all cool, just the tracker playing up. They seemed okay with it. We got near to Dunino and Gav took the fuse out while I drove. There's a left turn just after the houses. They'd told us to take that. Bit further along we saw a farm track. I slowed to check it and saw the van. They waved us in off the road. Soon as we were there they told us to get out. I handed them the van keys and the keys for the cuffs and they got Paul.'

'How were they dressed?' Ben asked.

'Pretty much the same as Saturday. Dark clothes, balaclavas.'

'What then?'

'They put Paul in their van. Reminded us to stay off the radar for the next few days. And they drove off.'

'Which way?'

'Same way as we'd been heading.'

Ben noted this down. 'What happened to your mobiles? We tried tracking them.'

'Smashed. They didn't want you lads finding us.' He shook his head. 'Brand new phone, too. Not that it matters.'

'Where have you been since Monday?' Ben went on.

'Here and there. Moved about. We had the van to sleep in and we both had some cash. They'd said it could be a couple of days so we found a village shop and bought some food. We'd been warned not to use bank cards or anything like that. Said they'd be watching the news to make sure we were still missing.' His face darkened. 'Smart bastards. They had it all worked out.' He exhaled, then went on. 'We got some food and we drove around until we found somewhere to spend the night.'

'Where was that?'

'Industrial estate on the outskirts of Cupar. Lots of warehouses with white vans outside. We knew we could sit there without attracting attention.'

It was all Clare could do not to react. Cupar. If they'd only realised how close they were to Kim and Debbie. But what could the two of them have done against an armed gang? Not a thing. 'Did you stay there all week?' she asked.

He shook his head. 'Didn't want to attract attention by staying anywhere too long. So we moved about. There was plenty of petrol in the van and we stopped in a different place every night. Glenrothes, Kirkcaldy – it's not hard to find white-van-land. Anyway, next day I said to Gav we should find a newsagent's. He agreed so we headed along to Dairsie. There's a wee shop on the main street. Gav stopped a bit further down the road and I went in. I did my jacket up so they wouldn't notice the white shirt and I bought a paper. But when I came out, the van was empty. I thought Gav had maybe gone for a wander – stretch his legs. I had a look round and found he'd left the keys on the front wheel but there was no sign of him. So I jumped back into the van and flicked through the paper to see what was being reported. But Gav never came back.'

'Where did you think he'd gone?' Clare asked, but he simply shrugged.

'Not a clue. I wondered if they'd been watching us and lifted Gav while I was out of the way. Or maybe he'd gone after them. Maybe he knew something I didn't and he'd gone to find them. In the end I moved the van further along the road, hoping he'd see it and come back. But he never did. I still don't know where he is.'

Clare had the sense that Ben was preparing to wind the interview up but there was so much more she wanted to ask. He'd clicked his pen off and laid it down on his notepad. Clearly it was his interview and he now judged it was over. And then the figure of Maggie White lying dead in her garden shed came into Clare's mind. *Oh what the hell*, she thought. 'Just one more thing, Alan,' she said, angling her head slightly so she couldn't see Ben's face. 'What do you know about Paul Devine?'

Alan looked surprised. 'Not much. Doing a stretch for armed robbery. Held up a jeweller's, I think.'

'I think Alan's had enough,' Ben said, but Clare wasn't to be put off.

'The woman who identified Paul and testified against him at his trial was killed,' she said. 'Probably on Monday afternoon or evening.'

The colour drained from Alan's face. 'You think that's why he escaped? He went after her?' He sank back in his chair, shaking his head. 'Oh God,' he said. 'That poor woman.'

Ben shot a warning glance at Clare. 'We'll end it there,' he said, and Clare nodded.

Alan seemed relieved the interview was over but his face fell when he was told he'd be held in custody.

'I can't go home? I want to see my wife.'

Ben shook his head. 'Sorry. I don't doubt a word of what you've said but we have to verify your account. We'll check for cameras at the industrial parks where you stayed overnight. Hopefully that'll match what you've told us. Meantime, we need to hang onto you. Besides, the men who abducted your wives are still at large so it's vital we keep you safe.'

He nodded, accepting this. Then, as Clare was about to end the interview, he said, 'Funny thing, though.'

Clare stopped, watching him. 'Yes?'

'Paul Devine.'

'What about him?'

'What you said about him going after that woman.'

'Yes?'

'Well, I'm not sure it adds up. I mean, I might be wrong but I could swear he didn't know he was being sprung.'

Chapter 20

'You do know what's meant by *leading an interview*?'

Clare had the grace to blush. 'Sorry. I've said all along I thought the two killings were linked. I couldn't let Alan go without asking about Maggie.'

Ben shrugged. 'We'll find out when we pick Devine up.'

'About Paul Devine.'

'Yep?'

'If he didn't know he was going to be sprung...'

'Doesn't matter,' Ben said. 'He's not handed himself in so he's as guilty as the gang who got him out.'

It was on the tip of Clare's tongue to say escaping custody was hardly the same as abduction at gunpoint but she thought better of it. Instead, she said, 'I'm not sure where that leaves my murder investigation. I started out thinking Devine killed Maggie White. But now I'm not so sure.'

'I don't see why,' Ben said. 'He could easily have done it. Dunino to your victim's house can't be more than, what, twenty minutes by car? He gets the gang to drive him over there, hides in the garden and waits for her to come outside. A few blows with a hammer – job done.'

'I doubt the gang would have sprung him just so he could kill Maggie. It feels more like an opportunistic killing,' Clare said. 'Not planned.'

Ben nodded. 'Yeah. Could be. Chance to settle a score.'

Clare was silent for a moment, mulling this over. Then she said, 'Why do you think Gavin Gates disappeared?'

He shrugged. 'Any number of reasons. He could have decided to go after the women himself. Or there could be something

Alan's not telling us. We only have his word for it Gavin disappeared in Dairsie. Either way, we're still looking for a prisoner and a prison officer.'

'And Anthony Devine,' Clare added.

'Of course.'

'So what now?'

'I'm going to update my team.' He took out his phone and began tapping at it.

Clare wondered about that. Since Ben's arrival they'd scarcely been in the station. 'Where are they working from?'

'Erm, Dundee mostly,' he said. 'Look, Clare, I need to get on. There's not much more we can do tonight.' And, with that, he strode off to his room, leaving her to wonder why he seemed so casual about this whole investigation.

She saw Max hovering.

'Update on the Devines,' he said.

'Oh yeah?'

'I spoke to the community liaison officer. Seems there were a couple of barneys. Usual stuff. Too much drink and they set about each other in the street.'

'Were they lifted?' Clare asked.

He shook his head. 'No. First time given a talking to. Second time a formal caution.'

'When was this?'

'Last one was about eight months ago. Not long after Paul was convicted. Before that it was a couple of years.'

Clare considered this. 'Might be significant. But it might just be one of those things. Families falling out. Thanks, Max.'

He hesitated. 'How did it go? With Alan, I mean?'

'Good question,' Clare said, and she related the content of the interview.

'Bit odd about Gavin Gates. If he'd decided to go after the gang himself, why wouldn't he tell Alan?'

'Probably afraid Alan would stop him. Remember they were warned the wives would suffer if they didn't do as they were told.'

Max stifled a yawn. 'Sorry,' he said.

Clare glanced at her watch. It was almost eight. 'No, I'm sorry, Max. You've been on duty for twelve hours. Time to call it a day. We'll look at it fresh in the morning.'

She called the DCI as she headed out to the car. 'I'm on my way home now so I'll pick up something. Fish and chips okay?'

'Definitely. Want some wine?'

'Better not.'

'Big mug of tea, then.'

'You're on.'

The Tailend Fish and Chip restaurant was busy but there wasn't much of a queue at the takeaway counter and she was soon on her way, the smell of chips filling the car. As she drove along the Craigtoun Road towards Daisy Cottage she thought about Saturday night. Had Kim and Debbie been driven along this very road, blindfolded and rolling around the back of a van? What time had she been out with Benjy? Probably before eight, now she thought about it. All the same, the idea of the van with two terrified women in the back was a chilling one.

She turned the car into her drive and her heart lifted, as it always did, at the sight of her cottage. It was dark now, the front room curtains drawn, but she could see the light was on in the hall. As she stepped out of the car she smelled wood smoke. He'd lit the fire. Benjy began to bark and she heard the DCI's voice, unusually stern. Then the door opened and Benjy rushed towards her, sniffing at the bag of food.

'He's in disgrace,' the DCI said, taking the bag from her.

'Oh dear. Should I ask?' She closed the door behind her and put down her work bag.

'Your new oven gloves,' he said, picking up the remains of the gloves to show her.

'Benjy?' Clare said, taking the gloves from him. 'What's this about?'

Benjy read the room and slunk off to a corner, eyeing Clare as he went.

'I give up with that dog,' she said. 'Honestly I do.'

'Why don't you ask Moira to walk him for a bit longer?' he said. 'It might help.'

She yawned. 'Good plan. I'll speak to her at the weekend. Oh, wait. That's tomorrow. Cancel that. I'll be working. God, but I'm tired.'

The DCI put the teapot on the table and went to fetch milk from the fridge. Clare opened the fish and chip boxes and pushed one across the table.

'Can we do without plates?' she said.

'We certainly can.' He lifted the teapot and began pouring out two mugs of tea. 'So, no progress?'

'Well, yes and no. We've had statements from the two women and we managed to find where they were held. It's deserted now but SOCO are going over it.' She speared a chip and dipped it in ketchup. 'And one of the prison officers turned up tonight.'

'Really? Just one?'

She nodded. 'Van, too. He claims the other one disappeared on Tuesday while he was in a shop getting a newspaper.'

'So they weren't being held by the gang?'

Clare shook her head. 'Only the wives. When they sprang Paul they reminded the men they had Kim and Debbie. Told them to stay out of sight until they saw in the news the wives had been released. Only then were they to hand themselves in.'

'But one of them disappeared? That's odd.'

'Isn't it? Ben reckons the other one – Gavin – maybe he went after the wives. Thought he could find them. If he'd told Alan what he was planning, Alan would've stopped him.'

The DCI picked up his tea and sipped it. 'Do you believe that?'

She exhaled. 'I'm not sure what to believe.' Then she said, 'Ben, what do you think of him?'

He shrugged. 'I barely know him. Why?'

'You've not come across him this week?'

'No. Should I have?'

'I'm not sure.' She munched on a piece of fish. 'He said his team's been working mainly out of Dundee. And he has been out a fair bit.'

'It's a big station, Bell Street. And my office is tucked away at the end of a corridor. It's not likely I'd have run into him.' He looked at her. 'You having problems with him?'

She shook her head. 'Not really. I just find him a bit – it's hard to say. A bit detached, I think. Almost casual.'

'Everyone's different, Clare. We all have our own way of managing an investigation.'

'Yeah, you're right. It's just, I've never worked with anyone like him.'

Benjy padded across the room and sat beside Clare, his face upturned.

'Do not give that dog a chip,' the DCI said. 'Not even one.'

'I wasn't going to,' she lied, then she turned and regarded the little dog. 'Two words, Benjy: oven gloves!'

–

It seemed to Clare she'd only just fallen asleep when she felt the DCI shaking her shoulder. Surely it wasn't morning already?

'Your phone,' he was saying. 'Your phone's ringing.'

She forced her eyes to open and tried to focus on the bedside clock.

'Your phone,' he said again.

Suddenly, she realised what was happening and reached out for the phone plugged in at her bedside.

Chris.

She swiped to take the call, easing herself up and swinging her legs round out of bed. Her feet found her slippers and she stood, padding round to the bedroom door to avoid disturbing the DCI any further. 'Chris?' she said, her voice low.

'Clare, there's something going on here.'

'Tractors?'

'No. I think it might be to do with Paul Devine.'

She closed the bedroom door behind her and pulled a dressing gown round her shoulders. 'Tell me?'

'We had a tip-off a farm near here might be targeted.'

'Where are you?'

'Brunton. Tiny village off the A92. We were talking about it the other day. One of the funerals Anthony Devine helped at.'

She was starting to remember. 'Go on.'

'We're up a hill looking down towards the farm and I thought we'd spotted the tractor thieves. Car headlights half an hour ago but they never came as far as the farm. Then one of the lads noticed torches so we watched where they were going, thinking they might be recceing the farm for another visit. But they headed off in a different direction. They're there now. I don't have night vision glasses but I think they're digging.'

'Where? Where are they?'

'It's a graveyard, Clare. They're digging in a graveyard.'

It took Clare a moment to realise the significance of this. And then she got it. 'Anthony Devine.'

'Exactly.'

'Can you see him?'

'Too far away to recognise anyone. But there's five or six of them, at least.'

The bedroom door opened and the DCI emerged, yawning.

'Brunton,' Clare said to him. 'Know it?'

He nodded and Clare put the phone on speaker. After a brief conversation with Chris he said, 'Sit tight where you are, Chris. And, if they move get back to me.' He turned to Clare. 'You're going to need a lot of cars and officers. That area's full of little roads. They'll all need to be blocked off.'

Within five minutes they were on their way, the DCI driving, Clare poring over a map on her phone. She tried calling Ben but it went straight to voicemail and she left a brief message telling him where they were heading. Then she called Jim.

'I want two cars down on the coast road, eight officers. That's the most likely escape route. Block Brunton off from the south and let's have a couple of cars on the road to Creich; and I need you to cover Hazelton Walls, Luthrie and let's have cars on the A92 as well. But no sirens or blue lights. We don't want them to know we're onto them.' She glanced at the DCI. 'Have I missed anything?'

'No,' he said, accelerating past the Strathkinness junction. 'But I'd want a good few officers on the ground as well. There's a lot of countryside to cover. They could easily abandon the vehicle and head cross-country.'

'Got that,' Jim said through the phone. 'I've a couple of minibuses heading from Dundee and Glenrothes. More from Cupar, hopefully.'

The DCI nodded and Clare ended the call.

'How do you know the area?' she said.

'I've cycled it a few times. Lots of hills. Good for the quads. You should try it sometime.'

She raised an eyebrow. 'You know me and bikes.'

'Yeah, fair point.'

They were almost at Pitscottie now and he slowed to turn right towards Cupar. 'Explain the graveyard connection to me.'

'Our escaped prisoner's brother, Anthony. He works for an undertaker. But he rarely does burials – he's only done three, one of which—'

'Brunton?'

'Yep. And just yesterday Anthony Devine was snatched off the street by a couple of men who sound similar to the ones who abducted Debbie and Kim. It's too much of a coincidence.'

Clare's phone buzzed and she squinted at the message. 'Jim says he'll have all routes covered in the next twenty minutes. How far away are we?'

They were driving through Cupar now, the streets deserted. He checked over his shoulder and swung the car round to the right. 'Ten, maybe fifteen minutes.' He tore up Balgarvie Road, ignoring the traffic-calming signs. Clare glanced towards the road she and Max had taken a few hours earlier. It was too dark to see the Mount, of course, but she knew it was there.

'How many did Chris say there were?'

'He thought five or six.' Clare put a hand out to steady herself as he negotiated a series of tight bends. 'I'm guessing both Devine brothers, the two men who snatched Kim and Debbie plus their driver. Could be—'

The DCI glanced at her. 'What?'

She turned to look at him, his face illuminated by the lights from the dashboard. 'Gavin Gates,' she said. 'What if one of them's Gavin Gates?'

They were approaching the A92 now and he slowed the car as they neared the junction. Turning left Clare saw blue lights illuminating the night sky.

'What the...'

'Thought you told Jim no blue lights.'

Clare's lips tightened. 'I did. But someone's obviously not got the memo.'

The DCI began to slow as they neared the road that led up to the villages of Luthrie and Brunton, clicking on his indicator. An officer in a fluorescent jacket stepped into the road and Clare saw his car was blocking the junction. He approached them and the DCI wound down the window.

Clare leaned across to tell him to kill the blue lights but he cut across her. 'Sorry, you can't go up there.'

She fished out her warrant card. 'I'm DI Mackay from St Andrews and I'm in charge of this operation. This is DCI Gibson,' she added almost as an afterthought.

'Sorry,' the officer said. 'I've instructions not to let anyone up this road without my boss's say so.'

Clare opened her mouth to object but her phone began to ring. Jim. Glaring at the traffic officer she swiped to take the call.

'Sorry, Clare. We've been stood down.'

'You've what? Says who?'

Before he could answer Clare's phone buzzed again. 'Hold on, Jim. Chris is trying to call.' She clicked the phone. 'Chris?'

'Clare, I don't know what the fuck's going on but some DCI has ordered us to leave.'

'Hold on, Chris. Just stay where you are. I'll call you back.' She returned to the other call. 'Jim, who's telling you to stand down?'

'The DCI. Ben Ratcliffe.'

'Doesn't he know we're here to help? God sake, we've enough cops to cover every road.'

'He's brought his own.' There was a noise in the background and Clare heard Jim speaking then he returned to the call. 'We have to go. He's said it'll be a discipline issue if we don't.'

The DCI had pulled the car into the verge now.

'If you'd like to move on,' the traffic cop said.

'Listen, sonny,' Clare began, leaning over, but the DCI forestalled her.

'We'll move as soon as we've clarified this. We're not interfering with your operation parked here so give us a minute, please.'

The officer gave a nod and moved back from the car.

Clare tapped furiously at her phone until she found Ben's number. To her surprise he answered.

'Clare.' His tone was curt.

'Ben, what the hell's going on?'

'I've told you. The hunt for Devine is my operation. I've sent your troops home and I'll explain it in the morning but, for now, you are to go home too. Got it?'

'That's ridiculous. We're here now. Are you actually turning down dozens of extra officers?'

'I am. Now, if you don't mind we're about to move in.'

She opened her mouth to protest but he'd ended the call. She felt her cheeks hot and she sat, trying to process what had happened.

'Want me to try?' the DCI said. 'I'm happy to have a go at him.'

'No point.' She jerked her head back towards Cupar. 'Might as well go home.' She picked up her phone again. 'I'll just call Jim and Chris. Apologise for wasting their time.'

Half an hour later they were back at Daisy Cottage. Benjy wandered sleepily from his basket and Clare bent to ruffle his ears.

'Mug of tea?' the DCI asked.

'Please.' She sat down heavily on the sofa and bent forward to pick up the poker, raking the embers in the fire until they began to glow. Then she added some kindling and when it had caught, placed a small log on top. Benjy moved to stretch out on the rug and she sank down beside him, her back against the sofa.

'What's going on, Al?' she asked when he brought the mugs over.

'Clare, I don't know!'

'But this guy Ben – I don't understand it. Who the hell is he? I've never worked with anyone so secretive.'

He shrugged. 'Maybe he's getting his orders from above. Maybe he's not allowed to say any more.'

The log sparked making Benjy jump and Clare stretched out to pull the fire guard across. 'I'll tell you this much, Al Gibson. I'll get to the bottom of this if it kills me.'

He reached across and kissed the top of her head. 'Drink your tea so we can get back to bed. We're looking at three hours sleep if we're lucky.'

Saturday

Chapter 21

Given the late night call-out, Clare had sent a message round telling the team to come in for nine. But she'd lain awake until nearly dawn, running over things in her head. What was Ben Ratcliffe playing at? Why all the secrets? It's not like Paul Devine was a risk to national security. Or was he? What was it Ben wasn't telling her?

She'd called in all her favours last night, drummed up every spare officer. So where had Ben found a similar number to move in on the gang? And, more importantly, had he caught them?

If he's let them slip through his fingers, she thought as she drifted off to sleep.

She'd forgotten to adjust her alarm and it went off as usual at half past six. The DCI raised himself up on his elbow and picked up his phone.

'It's six thirty,' he said. 'Let's at least have another hour.'

She fumbled with the alarm, eventually switching it off then she lay down again. But sleep wouldn't come and, in the end, she hauled herself out of bed, bone weary, and went for a shower. As she stood, head bowed against the deluge, she wondered again about last night. There had to be more to Paul Devine's escape than she was being told.

'I'll find out what's going on if it's the last thing I do,' she said, turning the shower off and reaching for a towel.

She arrived a bit after eight. The station was quiet except for a red-gowned student reporting a stolen bike. She wandered through to her office and sank down behind the desk, shaking the mouse to bring her computer to life. She was scrolling through her inbox when the door opened and Chris entered. He had dark circles under his eyes, his hair was standing on end and her spirits lifted at the sight of him.

'You seen your hair?' she said. 'Looks like you've been plugged into the mains.'

He came in and sat down heavily opposite her. 'Don't look so hot yourself.'

She laughed. 'God, I've missed you.'

He shrugged. 'Of course you have. Serves you right for replacing me with a newer model.'

'Noted. So, not that it isn't lovely to see you…'

'Oh I dunno. I mean last night, we had good intel and suddenly I'm getting pulled off the op. What's that about?'

Clare shook her head. 'I wish I knew. I'm as much in the dark as you.' She regarded him. 'You going out again tonight?'

'No point. All that fuss, blue flashing lights. Anyone planning a farm job will be lying low for the next few nights. Thought I'd look back through convictions for farm stuff instead. See if any of them are living in the area.'

'Good plan,' Clare said. She scraped back her chair. 'Let's grab a coffee first.'

They took their drinks into the incident room and stood looking at the photos on the board. She had thought all these crimes were connected: the abduction of the wives, the coercion of the prison officers, Paul Devine's escape, Anthony being seized; and, of course, Maggie's murder. But now she wondered if they were. The longer this went on the less likely it seemed. And, if Paul Devine wasn't responsible for Maggie's death, who was?

Officers began drifting into the room and just before nine she suggested to Chris he use her office to look back over the farm machinery convictions. 'You'll get peace in there,' she said.

'You mean I'll be out of the way.'

She opened her mouth to protest but he held up his hands.

'It's fine. I get it. Only, when you find out what the hell happened last night, let me know, will you?'

She left him to his crime reports and went back to the incident room. When she was sure they'd all arrived she closed the door and looked round at them, an uneasy feeling in her stomach. For the first time in, well, as long as she could remember, she was about to start a briefing without a single idea of what to say. She smiled round and began.

'First of all, thanks everyone for your efforts last night. I'm sorry we weren't able to see the operation through but I'm very grateful for the quick response and particularly for the efficient way you conducted yourselves. I have no doubt, had we been left to progress things as planned, we'd have our bodies in cells this morning.'

Janey raised a hand. 'Were they apprehended? The men in the cemetery.'

Clare spread her hands. 'I can't even tell you that, Janey. I don't know.' She looked round for Jim. 'Don't suppose there's any news on that?'

He shook his head, and Clare pressed on.

'I did have a brief conversation with DCI Ratcliffe last night. But, other than confirming it was his operation, I'm none the wiser.' She hesitated, choosing her words. 'Let's hope they were successful.'

She glanced back at the board. 'We'll move on, then. We're still hunting Maggie White's killer. If Paul Devine was apprehended last night I will seek to interview him. Otherwise, it's back to checking Maggie's bank statements and phone records.' She stood thinking for a moment. 'We never did find her mobile, did we?'

Max shook his head.

'Was there a laptop?'

He nodded. 'On a shelf in the bedroom. Went to SOCO on Thursday, I think.'

'Chase it up, would you, Max? Might be something on it.'

Max indicated he'd do this. Clare was about to speak when Bill raised his hand. 'What about Alan Carter?'

So much had happened over the past twenty-four hours it took Clare a moment to recall. She frowned. 'Is he still in custody?'

'Aye. Over in Dundee. But we can't keep him much longer without arresting him.'

He was right. The clock was ticking on Alan's detention. She stood thinking for a minute then she said, 'Let me talk to Ben. I have an idea.'

She ended the briefing and went out to the public enquiry area. Chris was working away in her office and the incident room wasn't private enough. 'Back in a minute,' she called to Jim and walked through the front doors, heading for her car. Once inside she took out her phone and dialled Ben's number.

'Alan Carter,' she said.

'Yeah?'

'Have you found CCTV to verify his story?'

'Not yet.'

'The clock's ticking on his detention, Ben. We'll have to release him soon. But I'm keen to keep him apart from Kim. Just until his story's checked out.'

'Seems sensible. What are you thinking?'

'I think there's somewhere I can put him. Leave it with me.'

She ended the call and clicked to search through her contacts.

Steve Robins was an officer with the Serious Organised Crime Squad. Clare had met him briefly when she'd been tasked with keeping a witness safe prior to giving evidence. Maybe he could return the favour.

'Steve Robins.' His voice was clipped, as though he had no time to waste.

'Steve, it's DI Clare Mackay at St Andrews. You might recall we co-operated over—'

'Our witness, yes I remember. What can I do for you, Clare?'

'The safe house where we kept the witness. Is it still in use?'

'Think so. I'd have to check. Any reason?'

'I could do with it. Just for a day or two.'

'Usually these things come through us,' he said. 'What's the situation?'

Clare started to tell him about the prison officers and their wives but he interrupted.

'I know the case.'

'One of the officers has handed himself in and he's spent the night in a cell, partly while we verify his story but for his own protection as well. I've got to be honest, Steve, and say it's not strictly my enquiry so I may be talking out of turn. We've no reason to arrest him, as far as I can tell. But the abductors may still be at large.'

'May?'

'Okay, full disclosure. We thought we had them last night. Maybe the escaped prisoner too. We had troops in place to close in on them then we were told to back off.'

'By whom?'

She hesitated. The last thing she wanted to be accused of was going behind Ben's back. After last night it might seem like childish retaliation.

'I can't help you if I don't know who took over your op.'

She took a deep breath. 'DCI Ben Ratcliffe.'

'I see.' There was a silence. Then he said, 'But you need this prison officer kept, let's say, safe for a few days?'

'I do.'

'And you will inform DCI Ratcliffe of this?'

'Oh yes. I'm not trying to conceal anything. I've suggested to him that I arrange something.'

'Very well. I'll authorise it for forty-eight hours, on condition DCI Ratcliffe confirms he's happy with the arrangement.'

Steve Robins agreed to send an officer to St Andrews with the keys to the flat and Clare ended the call. She was about to

173

climb out of her car when a silver Lexus drew into the staff end of the car park. She sat on, wondering who it was, then realised it was Ben; and there was another man with him. They walked into the station and she climbed out of the car, following them in. After stopping briefly to speak to Jim, letting him know an officer would be there in a couple of hours with a set of keys, she went to tap on Ben's door. He opened it himself, standing in the doorway as if trying to come to a decision. Then he ushered her in and closed the door behind her. There was something in his manner that made her uneasy. She took in the other man. He was younger than Ben. Thirties, maybe. His hair was short, dark with the odd strand of grey. He was lean and looked athletic. There was something familiar about him but, on a few hours' sleep, she couldn't put her finger on it. He nodded at Clare but said nothing.

Ben indicated a seat and, after a moment, Clare eased herself down, perching on the edge. She waited for him to speak, to introduce the other man and when he didn't she decided she'd nothing to lose.

'About last night.'

Ben held up a hand. 'Hold on, Clare. Before we go any further, I need your assurance what I'm about to tell you will go no further than these four walls.'

She was watching him as he spoke and saw the other man was watching him too.

'Agreed?'

'Of course. So, last night?'

'All in good time. But first, let me introduce you. Clare – this is Gavin Gates.'

Chapter 22

She stared at the two men, looking from one to the other. Then she found her tongue.

'You're Gavin Gates? The missing prison officer?'

He glanced at Ben. 'Yes, that's me.'

Clare sat for a moment, taking this in. Then she said, 'Would one of you like to catch me up?'

Ben sat forward, his hands clasped. 'Gavin, as you know, is a prison officer. What you don't know is, he was involved in a sting operation.'

She looked at them as she processed what she was hearing. 'What sort of sting?'

'You doubtless remember the Elzinga heist in London?'

For a moment Clare was transported back to the footage none of them would ever forget. It hadn't been released to the media but had gone out to every force in the country to help track down the gang. They had gathered in the incident room, silent to a man as they watched the raid on one of London's most exclusive jewellers. The terrified staff forced to unlock cases at gunpoint, then the unprovoked attack on the security guard, felling him with a blow to the head. He had lingered on life support for two weeks until his wife had taken the inevitable decision. She'd given a heart-rending interview to the media, appealing for anyone with knowledge of the gang to come forward. But no one had.

Every available officer had been drafted in, every informant interviewed, but the trail had gone cold. No one knew who the four men were and, for that reason, they'd become known in their absence as the Elzingas, a name Clare disliked. It implied a kind of glamour, like the so-called Great Train Robbers. In Clare's experience there was nothing great about violence.

The only bright spot – if you could call it that – was the estimated haul turned out to be far less than it might have been. The sound of the security guard's head striking one of the glass cases had panicked them into grabbing what they could before fleeing.

A sick feeling was developing in Clare's stomach. 'You're not telling me—'

'We had some reliable intel from the Met,' Ben went on. 'Long story short, we believe the Elzinga lot went on to carry out the raid on Jardine's.'

'That gang,' Clare began slowly, 'the men who killed that security guard, you're saying they're the ones who robbed Jardine's? You're telling me Paul Devine is one of the Elzingas?'

Ben nodded. 'We think so; and, if we're right, the intel suggests the rest of the gang are back in the area.'

She stared at him. 'How long have you known?'

'Couple of months.'

'Then why the hell weren't we out looking for them?'

He frowned. 'It's a bit more complicated than that.'

'Go on then,' she said, before she could stop herself. 'Astound me!'

Ben raised an eyebrow at the rebuke, but he went on. 'Our intel suggested they were planning to skip the country.'

'And that's why they sprung Paul Devine?' Clare said.

Ben and Gavin exchanged glances. 'Not exactly.' Ben paused, then he said, 'I organised Paul Devine's escape.'

She blinked a couple of times, wondering if she'd heard correctly. 'I don't understand.'

He hesitated for a moment. 'Let's get some coffee. Then I'll explain.'

Clare escaped to the loo while Ben made mugs of coffee. She locked herself in the cubicle and perched on the seat, trying to process what she'd been told. Paul Devine the leader of the

Elzinga gang? She felt sick at the thought of what might have happened if Maggie or Finlay had fought back.

She heard the door open and quick footsteps which she recognised as Sara's. She turned to flush the loo and waited until she heard Sara lock the neighbouring cubicle. Then she opened hers, made a pretence of washing her hands and fled before anyone else could appear.

Ben and Gavin were chatting in low voices when Clare re-entered the room. Gavin indicated one of the mugs and she drew it across the desk.

'It's just instant,' Ben said. 'Couldn't find your DS to ask for the good stuff.'

'It's fine.' She looked from one to the other. 'So?'

Ben took a draught from his mug, then laid it down. 'The haul from Jardine's was a big one. Seems your Mr Jardine is well thought of in the industry. It's a small shop but the stock he keeps is pretty high end. The gang knew what they were doing. Perhaps we should have connected it to Elzingas at the time, but the fact is we didn't. Devine, as you know, exercised his right to silence and the rest of the gang melted away; and so did the jewels.'

Clare sat silently, taking this in. Should she have made the connection? Asked the Met for help tracking the gang down? Might things have been different if she had? And then she remembered she'd been away on a course. By the time she'd returned, her head full of *A 21ˢᵗ Century Approach to Leadership*, Paul Devine was on remand and a team from Edinburgh charged with hunting the rest of the gang. With over three hundred emails in her inbox she was simply relieved someone else had dealt with the robbery.

'And then our CHIS at Perth prison got in touch,' Ben was saying. 'He's pretty good. Knows how to bide his time. Gain a bit of trust. And he told us two things.'

'Which were?'

'First, as I said, that Devine was head of the Elzingas gang.'

'Devine wasn't feeding the CHIS a line?'

Ben shook his head. 'Nope. It was good intel.'

'And the second?'

'That Devine had hidden the jewels before his arrest, just until the fuss died down. None of the others knew where, and we'd picked him up before he'd time to recover them.'

'So the jewels were still where Devine hid them?'

'That's what we think.'

Clare was starting to see. 'So, you thought if Devine escaped custody he would lead you to the jewels?'

Ben nodded. 'The jewels, yes. But, more importantly, the rest of the gang. We had to get them before they skipped the country. So we devised a plan that would draw them out of hiding.'

'Which was?'

'We whispered in the right ears that Paul Devine had taken against his Elzinga mates – that he was planning to reveal the location of the jewels to another gang. We reckoned that would be enough to tempt them into the open. But they needed Paul to take them to the spot; and that's why we arranged for Devine to attend a funeral.'

'You *arranged*?' Clare said. 'But his uncle had died. Please don't tell me we've started killing relatives to help our investigations?'

'Of course not. We simply told Devine his uncle had died.'

'Does he even have an uncle?'

'Probably.'

'But the funeral?'

'We had the brother Anthony on board. Not that he knew he was helping us. Simple enough to organise a funeral when you have someone working for an undertaker.'

Clare frowned. 'Hold on, go back a step. How did Anthony become involved?'

'Sorry,' Ben said. 'I'm going too fast. We had Gavin in the prison but, as I said, we've intel sources on the outside as well. Once we'd worked out a plan our CHIS whispered in the right ears that Paul Devine was planning an escape. The CHIS made sure this got back to Anthony, adding there'd be a few quid in it if he arranged a family funeral. Eventually Anthony agreed to help and he falsified the paperwork. Then he called the prison from the undertaker's number saying Paul's uncle had died and could he attend the funeral. Normally the prison would be pretty strict over checking this but Gavin here made sure it went through on the nod. All he had to do after that was adjust the rota so he accompanied Paul to the funeral.'

'But who was in the coffin?'

'Twenty-odd house bricks,' Gavin said. 'Taped up and padded to stop them moving. Same weight as an average man, apparently.'

'And Alan?' Clare asked. 'How did he come to be involved?'

'He's a good lad,' Gavin said. 'I knew he'd follow my lead, whatever happened. The plan was we'd head to Anstruther after the funeral. Get some chips. The road between Anstruther and Perth's a quiet one. Ideal for a hold-up. We'd come round a corner, somewhere north of Dunino and find the road blocked by a van – men with guns – that sort of thing.'

Clare's eyes narrowed. 'Surely, your wives – you didn't deliberately involve them?'

Gavin shook his head. 'No. That wasn't part of the plan. Pretty awful, to be honest. Poor Debs.'

'You didn't know they would burst into Alan's house and abduct your wives?'

Gavin shook his head. 'No way I'd have taken that kind of risk.' His eyes narrowed. 'There's obviously a leak in the prison we didn't know about. Otherwise they wouldn't have known I was rostered with Alan, or where we'd be on Saturday night.' He flashed a glance at Ben. 'We'll have to get that plugged,' and Ben nodded.

Clare's expression darkened. 'Your own wife. Anything could have happened to her.'

'We knew where the women were,' Ben said. 'We were tracking them.'

She was struggling to take this in. 'Hold on, you were tracking them? How? Like in their shoes? If you'd done that you must have suspected they were at risk. How could you do that? Your own wife, Gavin?'

'Clare, you're not listening,' Ben said. 'We did not know the gang would abduct Kim and Debbie. That was categorically not part of the plan.'

'Then how did you manage to track them?'

Gavin sat forward. 'That was down to me,' he said. 'When I started doing undercover work I bought a pair of watches for Debbie and I.' He rolled up his sleeve to show Clare a sleek black watch. 'I said it was a his-and-hers kind of thing and she thought it was romantic. But the watches have location tracking switched on by default. Great battery life, too. It's the kind of thing you can use for people living with dementia – helps you find them if they wander off.'

Clare considered this for a moment. Then she turned to Ben. 'So, all this time, the man-hours spent hunting Paul Devine and the wives, all the resources ploughed into it, and you knew where they were all along?'

Ben shrugged. 'I told you it was my operation. Told you to concentrate on the murder.'

'A murder Paul Devine had both motive and opportunity for. Probably the means as well.'

'Pure supposition,' Ben said. 'There's nothing to place Devine at your victim's cottage.'

This was true. Technically it was possible Paul Devine had escaped custody, somehow found out where Maggie lived and made his way to her cottage. But it was looking less and less likely. She looked back at Gavin. 'You knew where Kim and Debbie were all along?'

He nodded. 'We had eyes on the cottage and we used lasers to monitor sounds in the front room.'

Clare shook her head. 'I can't believe I'm hearing this. You used lasers?'

Gavin smiled. 'Pretty cool bit of kit, to be honest. We point it at a window looking for a reflective surface inside. A picture on the wall is ideal. Usually these old cottages are single glazed so it's easier for the beam to go through. It reflects off the picture glass, detecting minute vibrations when there's a sound in the room. We can't hear the actual words spoken – not yet at least. Maybe one day. But we can tell a lot from how the voices sound. It's easy to pick up shouting, or distress. If we'd heard anything to suggest they were at risk we'd have moved in.'

Clare thought back to the cottage. Had there been a picture on any of the walls? She vaguely recalled something in the sitting room. Some awful thing with a stag in the foreground and mountains behind. And then her mind went back to Kim and Debbie's faces when they'd stumbled into the station. She studied Gavin, trying to work him out. 'You knew where they were but you didn't pick them up. You let them go through five days of hell. I can't believe it.'

'With good reason,' Ben said. 'There were only two of the gang members staying in the cottage with Kim and Debbie; and we wanted all of them. The longer they remained captive, the better our chances of picking the whole gang up. You maybe don't realise how dangerous it is to try and break hostages out. There would have been far more risk to Kim and Debbie if we'd gone storming in.'

His remark, casually made, stopped Clare in her tracks. He clearly didn't know she'd been involved in a hostage situation herself. It was years ago, now. She'd shot and killed a young lad who'd come swaggering out of the house where a terrified woman was being held. He'd brandished a gun, aiming it right at her and made as if to fire. Clare had responded, shooting him dead. She'd been one of the best officers on the squad and it had only taken one shot. Problem was the lad's gun was a replica. A good one but entirely harmless. She'd been exonerated. Hell, she'd even been given a commendation. But none of that changed what she'd done – what she'd live with for the rest of her days.

They were looking at her now and she forced her mind back to the case. 'How the hell did you get authorisation for something like this?'

'Straight from the top,' Ben said. He leaned forward. 'These men have killed, Clare. And they would do it again. I'm in no doubt about that. A man died and he deserves justice.'

Clare turned to Gavin. 'And Monday? How did that play out?'

He hesitated. 'As you can imagine the weekend was pretty awful. Thanks to Debs' watch I knew where they were. And Ben assured me he had eyes on the cottage. So I went to work as usual on the Monday. But I wasn't sure what would happen after we handed Anthony over. So I left my car at the back of Tesco's car park, just up from the prison, and I walked down to work. I thought I might need to come back for the car and I didn't want anyone at the prison seeing me. We went to the funeral, as planned. Paul knew nothing about what was going to happen, of course. We let him have a chat with Anthony after the burial and I heard Anthony tell him nobody had died. That it was a ruse to get him out for a bit. He seemed to swallow it okay. Had a good laugh about it. Alan and I made like we were talking and didn't hear. Five minutes later we were on our way.' He picked up his mug and drained it. 'We'd been told to turn after Dunino and head along until we saw a farm track. They were there, sure enough. Balaclavas and guns. Devine just about shat himself. Didn't want to go with them. We played along, uncuffed him and they were gone.'

Clare looked pointedly at Ben. 'You knew where the ambush would happen,' she said. 'Why not pick them up there?'

'You're forgetting they had Kim and Debs,' Gavin said. 'And there were only two of them at Dunino. The other one must have been keeping an eye on the girls, and we wanted them all.' He smiled. 'What they didn't know was I'd slipped a small tracker into Devine's jacket pocket when we put him in the van. So I knew where he was too.'

'Which was?'

'Different cottage. Near Pitscottie. Again Ben had a team keeping an eye on it, although they didn't use lasers on that one.'

Clare sat back, weighing all this up. Then she said, 'That's why you left Alan?'

Gavin nodded. 'I needed to be free to communicate with Ben and his team. I made sure Alan knew not to come out of hiding until they'd released the girls.'

Clare frowned at that. 'Why did they keep Kim and Debbie so long? Why not release them as soon as they had Paul?'

'It's a good point,' Gavin said. 'My guess is they thought it was too risky to let them go before they knew where the jewels were. They might have noticed something that would lead us to them.'

'Debbie did,' Clare said. 'She helped us find the cottage. Mind you, that was a waste of time, given you knew where it was all along.' She turned to Ben. 'I still don't know why you couldn't have told me.'

He shook his head. 'The fewer people who knew about it the better. It's not you; more the chance one of your officers might have let something slip. We needed to keep it tight.'

'I agree,' Gavin said. 'Especially when they had Kim and Debs.'

Clare looked at Gavin, studying him for a moment. What made a young man like him want to involve himself in this kind of work? She guessed he wouldn't go back to his job at Perth. Not with it all likely to come out in court. 'What happens to you now?' she said.

He shrugged. 'I'll move on. Another job, another nick. Different name at work so nobody connects me to Perth.'

'And your wife?'

'Debs knows the score,' he said. 'We've moved before. She quite likes it. Change of scene.'

Clare was silent for a minute. It seemed a high price to pay, moving home, jobs, finding new friends and, all the time, worrying about the next operation. Police work had its dangers; but this was on another level. She wondered if Gavin was right about his wife, if she would be happy to move again. But that wasn't her problem. Her only concern was finding Maggie White's killer. Then she remembered she still didn't know if Ben had arrested the gang. 'Last night,' she said, 'after we left. Did you catch them?'

The men exchanged glances.

'Oh please don't tell me they got away?'

'Not exactly,' Ben said. 'We picked up the three gang members. They're in the cells down at Methil.' He checked his watch. 'They should be back up here later today to be interviewed.'

Clare regarded him. 'Why do I sense a *but*?'

Ben took a moment to answer. 'Paul and Anthony Devine were not apprehended.'

She stared. 'You mean you let them go? Deliberately?'

Ben shook his head. 'No. Definitely not. But we were so focused on catching the other three, they slipped away. We'll get Devine, though, and I doubt he'll have much added to his sentence. Gav and Alan will state he was released against his will. He might even agree to testify against the others, now we have them under lock and key. It'll go in his favour when he comes up for parole.'

Clare stared at them. 'I had every road covered,' she said. 'I even had men on the hill behind the cemetery. I could have brought them all in.'

'With respect,' Ben said, 'you can't say that.'

She scraped back her chair and rose. 'Well, we'll never know now, will we?'

Chapter 23

Clare emerged into the front office, her cheeks burning. What the hell was wrong with Ben, planning an operation like that on her patch and not a word of warning? And, despite what Gavin Gates had said about not realising they would abduct the wives, what a risk to take. She looked round the office and spotted Jim.

Keeping her voice low she said, 'Do we still have officers on the Jardines' house?'

'Aye. You want to stand them down?'

'No. Quite the reverse. I want two officers on the house and two on the shop at all times. Ben brought in three of the gang last night but the Devines are still at large.'

He nodded. 'Leave it with me.'

'When you've done that I want a full briefing, say, half an hour? Get everyone back except the ones keeping an eye on the Jardines.'

The door opened and a uniformed officer Clare hadn't met before marched up to the public enquiry desk. 'Looking for DI Mackay.'

'That's me,' she said. 'Can I help?'

The officer held out a jiffy bag. 'You're expecting this.'

Clare took the bag, weighing it in her hands. The keys for the safe house. But did she need them now? Was there any reason Alan Carter couldn't go home? The officer seemed keen to leave and she decided she might as well hang onto the keys, meantime. She gave him a smile. 'Thanks. Appreciate it.'

He acknowledged this and left as quickly as he'd arrived. Clare watched him go then she caught Jim's eye. 'What's happening with Alan Carter?'

He checked his watch. 'We really need to release him.'

'That's fine. Can you ask Dundee to bring him over please? I was planning to put him in a safe house but now that—' she broke off, unsure how much she could reveal of what Ben had just told her. 'I, er, think he can go home. But let's keep someone on both officers' houses, meantime.'

–

Alan arrived an hour later clutching a plastic carrier bag. He was dressed in fresh clothes, wearing a light grey tracksuit, although he still had on his black work boots.

'I know one of the lads over at Dundee,' he said. 'Brought me in a change of clothes.'

Clare glanced at the carrier bag. His grubby prison uniform, she guessed. 'You'll be able to shower in a bit.'

His face lit up. The first sign of emotion she'd seen. 'I can go home?'

'You can. But first we need to have a chat.' She indicated her car keys. 'I'll explain on the way.'

'Something wrong with Kim?' he said, following her out into the car park. 'Is she okay?'

Clare clicked to unlock the car and waited for him to climb in. Then she got in beside him and gave him a smile. 'First of all, Kim is fine. We had an officer staying with her and she's okay.'

'So?'

'You'll be relieved to know you won't be charged with facilitating the escape. There's enough evidence that you acted under duress.'

'Damn right I did.'

'And you can go home to Kim but I need you to stay there. I don't want you going out. Not anywhere, got it?'

His face darkened. 'What is it? What's happened? Is it Gav, then? Did something happen to him? Fucking hell. This is a nightmare.'

Clare looked at him, his face etched with worry. She wished she could tell him everything. He'd been through hell and he really deserved the truth. But if she told him about Gav's involvement, Ben would see to it she was suspended. And that wouldn't help any of them. 'Gav, Kim and Debbie are all fine,' she said. 'Kim and you can talk as soon as you get home but there's two things you have to know.'

'Okay...'

'First of all, you are not to contact Gav. That's a condition of your going home, Alan, so I need your assurance.'

He frowned. 'Why not?'

She shook her head. 'I'm sorry. I'm not authorised to say any more. I'm sure at some point someone will fill you in but, for now, steer clear.'

'What if he contacts me?'

Clare smiled. 'He won't.'

He stared at her for a moment then he said, 'And the other thing?'

'The men who abducted Kim and Debbie are in custody.'

His face relaxed, his shoulders down. 'Seriously? You've got them all?'

'All except Paul Devine.'

He exhaled. 'Oh, thank God. Devine isn't a problem.'

Clare met his eye. 'Alan, he may have been a model prisoner but it's possible he's more dangerous than you realise. Just bear that in mind, yeah?'

He shrugged. 'If you say so. He was no bother inside, though. I reckon he'll come in once he knows the others are under lock and key.'

Clare wondered about that. She thought back to the cemetery where Chris had observed the gang. *Digging*, he'd said. Almost certainly for the jewels from the robbery. But Ben hadn't mentioned that. She'd been so stunned to hear they'd set the whole thing up she'd forgotten to ask about the missing jewels. Could the Devines have got away with them? A haul like that could easily buy them safe passage out of the country. Surely Ben's team had checked where the gang had been digging? He hadn't said anything about it. Maybe they'd been too focused on the arrests. She took the key out of the ignition again. 'Won't be a minute,' and she stepped out of the car, moving away a little. She tapped Chris's number and he answered immediately.

'Chris, I want you to do something but I don't want anyone else to know.'

'Go on.'

'Can you head back to that graveyard please? It'll likely be taped off but I need you to see where they were digging. Given Anthony's involvement, I'd guess the jewels from the robbery were stashed in one of the graves. If they were, they might still be there.'

'Surely Ben's lot would have checked.'

'Yes they would. But the Devines managed to slip away. Maybe they'd just dug the jewels up when Ben's team closed in. Or maybe they're still there. Either way I'd like to know where they were digging and how far they got.'

'What if Ben's stationed a cop at the cemetery?'

'If he has it'll likely be a different shift from last night. Flash your badge and say you're in a hurry. Make something up.'

'And if I find anything?'

'Call me.'

–

'What's he doing here?' Alan asked, indicating Robbie, who was on duty outside the Carters' house.

'It's just until Devine's back in custody.'

'I told you, he's no threat. He's a pretty decent lad – for an armed robber.'

'All the same.'

'To be honest, if I can hug my wife and sleep and in my own bed tonight, I'll stay in the house as long as you want me.'

Clare smiled then she reached over to the back seat of the car and retrieved a mobile phone, one of the older models they handed out to anyone whose phone had been seized. 'Use this for now,' she said.

He stared at it. 'How old is this?'

'Dunno. But it works. I've put my number in and there's ten quid on it so call me if there's any problem.'

Her eye was caught by a movement and she saw that Kim had come to the window. Kim's hand went to her mouth and Clare thought she might be crying. 'I'll leave you to it,' she said. 'And, remember, stay in the house.' She indicated the mobile phone. 'Ring me if you need anything.'

She watched him walk quickly to the front door which was opened by Kim. He rushed in and scooped her up, kicking the door closed behind him. Clare nodded to Robbie and turned back to the car. She felt cold suddenly and started the engine, turning up the heater. It would be winter soon. Already a few shops had Christmas displays in their windows and she wondered idly what she might do this year. They'd always made the annual pilgrimage through to her parents. Maybe she should offer to host Christmas. She pulled on her seat belt, mulling it over. She'd never cooked a turkey before. She wasn't even sure her oven was big enough. Maybe she could buy it ready cooked. Just heat it up. Her mother would be appalled, but as long as she kept her out of the kitchen.

She felt her phone buzz in her pocket and took it out, glancing at the display. Chris.

'Any luck?'

'Yes and no. They'd got right down to the coffin.'

'Is it intact?'

'Yeah, apart from a couple of marks where I'd guess the spade's struck it.'

'Is that it?'

'It could be nothing,' Chris was saying, 'but there's what looks like the remains of a plastic bag.'

'So there could have been something down there.'

'I can't see why else there'd be a plastic bag buried with a coffin.'

'Is there a bin nearby? Could it have blown across and maybe got caught when the grave was being backfilled?'

There was a pause and the sound of wind buffeting Chris's phone. 'Not that I can see.'

'Any sign the coffin's been interfered with?'

'I'd have to get right down to be sure, but it doesn't look like it.'

Clare was about to speak again when Chris said, 'Hold on. I've another call coming in.'

She sat on, waiting while Chris took his call, her thoughts drifting back to the Devine brothers. The gang were in custody now. All except Paul; but she didn't share Alan's optimism that he'd hand himself in. She thought he might take advantage of his new-found liberty, especially if he'd recovered the jewels. But where was Anthony? Why hadn't he reappeared? Had he planned to disappear with Paul all along? Somehow get him away from the rest of the gang, dig up the jewels and share the proceeds? It was a hell of a risk but it was starting to look as if it had paid off. Maybe the Devine brothers were a lot smarter than she'd given them credit for. Made a run for it with the jewels. Or maybe they were hiding out somewhere near Brunton. Somewhere they knew they could remain concealed until the searchers had given up. Maybe—

Chris cut across her thoughts. 'Okay I'm back. I'll have to head over to Motray Farm.'

'The one down from Maggie White's cottage?'

'Dunno. I wasn't there, remember? You took the boy wonder.'

'Ah yes. Please tell me it's not another robbery?'

'No, it's vandalism, actually. I'd spoken to the farmer about his GPS unit so he had my number. I could pass it to the uniforms but it's kind of on my way back so…'

Clare thought for a moment then she said, 'I'll meet you there. I'd like another look round Maggie's place.'

Chapter 24

She saw the reason for Eric McGovern's call as she drew into the yard. Red spray paint across the front of a large steel barn. Clare drew in alongside Chris's car and climbed out. She squinted against the sun, and read,

Meat is murder

Dickhead

'It's quite cleverly done,' she said, indicating the shadows on the bubble lettering.

'It's bloody vandalism. You'd be raging if they'd spray painted the front of Daisy Cottage.'

She shrugged. 'Suppose. But I'm a lot nicer than our Mr McGovern.' She clicked to lock the car and stood, taking it in. 'There are courses you can do now,' she said. 'Learn how to do it well.' She studied the lettering. 'I'd say our artist's done a bit before. I've certainly seen worse.'

They headed off towards the farmhouse. As they approached the front door Eric McGovern strode round the side, wiping his hands on an oily rag. He nodded towards the barn.

'You've seen it then? Little shits. If I get my hands on them.'

Clare smiled. 'Maybe we should speak inside.'

He led them into the kitchen and indicated the kettle. Clare suddenly felt weary and Chris didn't look much better. She'd had next to no sleep and Gavin's sudden appearance plus the revelation about his involvement in Paul Devine's escape had made the day seem very long already.

'That would be lovely,' she said.

A door opened and Eric McGovern's daughter strolled in. She was dressed this time, in jogging bottoms and a cropped top.

'Get the biscuits, Tan,' he said without looking at her.

She glanced at Clare and turned her gaze on Chris, looking him up and down. Then she bent to open a cupboard door and put a gaily decorated tin on the table. 'Help yourselves.'

Chris reached into the tin and took out a piece of shortbread. The kettle came to the boil and Eric poured water into a large cream-coloured cafetiere, stirring it before replacing the lid. He carried this over to the table.

'Mugs,' he said to his daughter.

She rolled her eyes. 'Wha'd your last slave die of?'

'You what?'

She held up her hands. 'Nothing. Didn't say a word.' She strolled languidly back to the cupboards and took out four mugs, setting them down on the table. Then she sat down on the bench seat opposite Chris.

'Haven't you homework to do?' Eric said.

'Done it.' She shoved the biscuit tin towards Clare. 'Help yourself. Mum made it. It's pretty good.'

Clare smiled and took a piece of the shortbread. Eric plunged the cafetiere and began pouring out mugs.

'What you gonna do about that out there?' he said, easing himself down next to his daughter.

There was a tap on the door and it opened a little. A man in a tartan shirt and combat trousers stood as if unsure whether or not to come in. He shot a glance at Clare and Chris then turned back to Eric. 'Gotta minute, boss?'

'What is it?'

'Don't wanna come in with these boots. Better if I show you.'

Eric stood, stepping back over the bench seat. 'Back in a minute,' and he followed the man out.

Clare watched them go then she looked round the room. 'Nice kitchen.'

The girl followed her gaze. 'Suppose.'

'Tan,' Clare said. 'Unusual name.'

'Short for Tansy.'

'Pretty.'

She shrugged. 'S'all right.'

'Sorry about the vandalism,' Clare said. 'Pretty rotten for your dad.'

Tansy's eyes narrowed. 'He's not my dad. He's my stepdad.' She sipped at her coffee. 'Dunno why mum married him.'

'You don't get on?'

She inclined her head. 'You've heard him. How he speaks to me. He's a pig.'

Clare wondered about that. The graffiti, while cleverly done, had struck her as quite childish in character. Not the kind of thing animal rights extremists might do. 'You don't know anything about the paint out there, do you?'

Tansy laughed. 'Hah, no. But I could make a guess. School's full of folk that do it.'

Chris helped himself to another piece of shortbread, ignoring Clare's look. 'Might save us time if you gave us a few names.'

She shook her head. 'Nah. I'm not a grass. Anyway, I couldn't care less. It's his farm. Nothing to do with me.' She finished her biscuit and licked her fingers clean. Then she said, 'He was hopping mad, though. Not seen him so angry since the tractor thing was taken.' There was just the hint of a smirk.

Clare thought back. 'That was Monday, yeah?'

Tansy nodded. 'Late afternoon. 'Cause he was out on the tractor and he came in about half four. He went out again after tea and it had gone.'

'Did you notice anything?' Clare asked. 'Anyone hanging about?'

'Nah. It's a quiet road. Not many cars use it; and the ones that do fly up dead fast. Well, most of them.'

'Did you see any cars on Monday, maybe going more slowly?'

She considered. 'Dunno. Maybe.'

Clare put down her coffee. 'Tansy, it's really important. If you did see any vehicles driving slower than usual.'

She sighed. 'I mean, I don't care about his GPS thing. Serves him right for being such a pig.'

Chris smiled at her. 'It would help us a lot,' he said.

She regarded him. 'See your job…'

'Yes?'

'Do you like it?'

Chris thought for a moment. 'Yeah, on balance, I do. It's pretty cool most of the time.'

She was quiet for a moment, then she said, 'Think I could do it?' She glanced at him and away again, the colour rising in her cheeks.

'Don't see why not. If you like we could set up a time for you to come into the station. Have a look round. Chat to some of the cops.'

Her eyes lit up. 'Seriously? I could do that?'

'Sure. If you're really interested.'

Her gaze drifted towards the window and the voices outside. 'He says I should go to uni. Get a degree. I'd rather do something useful. Like you guys.'

Clare said, 'We can definitely set up a time for you to look round the station, as long as your parents agree, of course.'

'I'm sixteen,' she said. 'Do what I like.'

'Well, being a responsible citizen would certainly help us,' Clare said. 'And that would include reporting anything suspicious. So, Monday afternoon. Any vehicles we should be looking for?'

'Okay,' Tansy said. 'There was this car. Driving slowly, like it was lost, you know?'

'Did you notice the type of car?' Clare asked.

'Yeah, it was a Megane.'

'Renault?' Chris said.

Tansy nodded. 'My friend Ella's mum has one. Different colour, though.'

'What colour was this one?'

'Like a metallic blue.'

'You didn't notice the registration?' Chris went on.

'Sorry. Just the colour. There was a van, too.'

'Van?' Clare sat forward.

The outside door burst open and swung back on its hinges.

'You'd better come and take a look at this,' Eric McGovern said. 'And bring one of those bag things you lot use.'

Clare rose from her seat. 'What is it?'

'Hammer. Chucked into one of my fields. Just as well the lad here spotted it.' He glanced at their shoes. 'You can use our wellies,' he said, indicating a boot room off the kitchen. 'Field's pretty muddy.'

He led them across the yard and over the road towards the farm gate down from Maggie's cottage. 'Further up this field,' he said. He opened the gate and waited for them to go through before looping it shut again. Then he led them across the field, stepping from furrow to furrow. Clare followed, her feet awkward in the oversized boots. She could see they were nearing Maggie's cottage and, as they drew close, he stopped and pointed at the ground.

'I'm no detective,' he said, 'but did you lads no' say Maggie was hit with something like a hammer?'

She looked down where he indicated and saw an ordinary hammer — the kind she had in her toolbox at home. Glancing towards Maggie's cottage she imagined the killer throwing it, perhaps in a panic after an adrenaline-fuelled attack. It was possible. But, if it was the murder weapon, would there still be blood or DNA on it after so many days in the open? Might the evidence have been washed off by the weather or destroyed through contact with the soil?

Clare stooped to examine it. There was some discolouration on the steel head and she squinted at it. Was it blood? Or soil? Hard to tell, here in the field. It had rained a few nights ago. That could have washed away any evidence. The ground didn't seem waterlogged, though, and the hammer lay across the furrows. Maybe the underside had been protected from the elements. She had to hope so.

She didn't dare move it for fear of destroying anything that might still be there. Reaching into her pocket she took out her phone and dialled Raymond's number.

Chapter 25

'Dunno how your search party missed it,' Chris said.

Clare ignored the jibe. He was clearly still smarting from being side-lined. 'I told them to concentrate on the field margin. Further than that, well you saw how it was. Sheer chance that man spotted it.'

'Suppose. What about that grave – you want to apply for an exhumation order?'

Clare considered this. 'I really don't. Not if we can avoid it.'

'It is possible there's something in the coffin itself,' he pointed out. 'Could be Ben's lot moved in before the gang were able to get to it.'

They were driving back to St Andrews now, approaching the Guardbridge roundabout. 'That's true. But the plastic bag makes me think they did retrieve something.'

'Still worth putting a cop on the grave,' Chris said.

'Fair enough. I'll send someone up before it gets dark.' She turned left at the roundabout, crossing the River Eden. She sensed Chris was about to speak, but when he didn't she said, 'Something on your mind?'

'I was just thinking.'

'Spit it out.'

'Alan – he's not been charged with anything, has he?'

'Nope.'

'Where is he?'

'Home. Back with Kim. I've told him to stay in the house, meantime. We've a cop on duty outside.'

'And the other lad – Gavin?'

Clare hesitated. She couldn't tell him about Gavin Gates. Not yet, at least.

He picked up on the hesitation. 'There is something. Fucksake, Clare, tell me!'

'Chris, it was far from being a straightforward operation. At the moment I'm not authorised to tell anyone the details. All I can say is it's better for Alan if he's out the way while we're looking for the Devines.'

He regarded her for a moment. 'And that's it? That's all you're going to tell me?'

'Yup.'

'Well can I at least help with the search for the Devines?'

They were nearing the town and Clare slowed as they approached a roundabout. She considered this. Alan had been entirely blameless in the whole affair. They knew that now. He was back home safely with Kim. There was no reason Chris couldn't step in to help with the hunt for Devine. Clearly it was still Ben's operation but, now he'd taken Clare into his confidence, might he welcome her involvement? She decided it was worth a try.

'Don't see why not.'

'And you'll send the boy wonder packing?'

She glanced at him. 'I will not! He makes the best coffee I've ever tasted. I'm hanging onto him for as long as I can. And besides, he seems very taken with Zoe.'

Chris laughed. 'She'll eat him alive.'

'You'd be surprised. They have the makings of a pretty cute couple. They make you and Sara look positively middle-aged.'

'I'll never be as old as you, though.'

–

Jim caught Clare's eye as she entered the station. 'Might be something and nothing but that funeral home called a wee while ago. Said one of their vans is missing.'

'Oh?' Clare was suddenly alert.

'Aye. I've sent Sara along to get the details.'

'Let me know when she comes back. Could be there's a connection to Anthony Devine.'

She made her way to her office and sat down behind her desk, bone weary. She stifled a yawn as the door opened and Max came in. 'Done you a coffee,' he said, placing a mug on her desk. 'And Zoe gave me a peanut butter cake to bring in. Told me to hide it under her desk. I'll cut you a bit.'

Clare smiled. They really were the perfect couple. He made wonderful coffee and Zoe supplied the cakes. 'You two should start a café,' she said. Then she added, 'Any chance you could do Chris a coffee as well? I'd like the three of us to have a chat. See where we are.'

Max went off to make two more coffees and Clare sought out Chris. 'Come on, you,' she said. 'Max is doing coffee.'

He trudged after her. 'Bet it's not all that,' he said.

'You wait.'

Five minutes later the three of them sat round Clare's desk munching on Zoe's cake.

'Coffee's nice,' Chris admitted, and Max's face lit up.

'So,' Clare began, 'let's pool what we know. Start with the Devines.'

'Three of the gang in custody,' Max began.

'But no sign of Paul or Anthony,' Clare said. 'Last seen – we think – at that cemetery in Brunton.'

'Christieson,' Max said.

'Eh?'

'It's the Christieson family cemetery. Private and not used much. Only when a family member or someone connected to them dies.'

'It'd make sense for Anthony to stash the jewels there,' Clare said. 'If it's private there wouldn't be many burials. Quiet enough for a bit of midnight excavation. Let's assume his brother told him he needed to hide something valuable. Anthony realises there's a burial coming up in Brunton and he thinks it's the perfect place.

The family turn up, burial happens and he hangs on to help with the backfilling.'

'Wouldn't that be done by council employees, though?' Chris said.

Clare frowned. 'I'd have thought so. Maybe it's different when it's private ground. Or maybe he offered to help the lads. He could have distracted them. Or even slipped them a few quid to turn a blind eye.'

'I found the remains of a plastic bag down near the coffin,' Chris said to Max. 'Could be the jewels had been in some kind of container then put in a bag. Make it easier to spot it when they came to dig it up.'

'The bag had perished?' Max said.

'Yeah. It was in bits but you could still tell it was a bag.'

'But there was no sign of a box, or anything that could have held the jewels,' Clare went on. 'So we think they might have reached the box just as Ben's team closed in. The gang members were detained and, somehow, the Devines slipped away, possibly with the jewels.'

Max nodded. 'That makes sense. They'd know where to go.'

Clare looked at him. 'How would they know?'

'I checked up on them while you were out,' he explained. 'Seems they were brought up in Brunton. Stayed there until the boys were teenagers, then they moved to St Andrews.'

'So they'd know the area?'

'They definitely would.'

Chris fell silent. 'We need to get their photos back on the front pages again. Before they escape the country with the jewels.'

Clare avoided his eye. 'I'll have to clear it with Ben.'

He stared at her again and she met his gaze, daring him to push it. For a moment it seemed as if he might. Then he looked down at his coffee, shaking his head. 'And the murder?'

Clare glanced at Max. 'I haven't had time to update you. A hammer was found in the field near Maggie White's cottage. SOCO examined it in situ and they've taken it back to the lab now.'

'Do we have Anthony Devine's DNA or prints?' Chris asked.

Clare shook her head. 'No. Ben could authorise a warrant to access his house – get DNA from his toothbrush or something like that. But it would take time. Better to focus on finding him.' She turned to Max. 'Did you turn up anything else that might help?'

'Not so far.'

'Okay. Have a look at Anthony's social media. Check his likes, photos, any check-ins.'

'What about the men in custody?' Chris asked.

'Ben will interview them,' she said. 'I'll ask to sit in, depending on when it happens.'

Chris frowned. 'Thing is, can anyone identify them? They were all masked up for the robbery and the abduction.'

'They were,' Clare said, 'and, if we don't find the Devines or they can't be persuaded to give evidence against the men, we'll have to hope for DNA.'

'But where?' Chris asked.

'There's the cottage the women were kept in for a start,' Clare said. 'There were food containers, an ashtray too. We should be able to get some DNA from those; and your cousin's wife, Kim.'

'What about her?'

'Smart cookie. She pocketed a blindfold they'd used on her. Might get something off that.'

Chris smiled. 'She's great, Kim. Sparky, you know?'

'Yeah, I got that. So, let's move on to Maggie's murder. Any thoughts?'

'Hammer might help,' Max said.

Clare sighed. 'I'm not getting my hopes up. There could have been DNA. Prints, even. But it's been lying in that field since Monday. Maybe longer.'

There was a tap on the door and Sara looked in. 'Boss, that van.'

'The undertaker's?'

She came in and stood, her back to the wall. 'Yeah. Seems the keys have gone from the box in the office.'

'Have they checked with all the employees?' Clare said. 'Could be one of them's taken it and forgotten to check it out.'

Sara shook her head. 'No. They've all been asked about it. All except Anthony Devine, of course.'

'He must have taken it,' Chris said. 'Has to be him.'

Max nodded. 'I agree.'

'Hold on,' Clare said. 'He was at Brunton last night, at that cemetery. That was, what, two or three in the morning? How's he got to St Andrews to take a van?'

'Any number of ways,' Chris said. 'He could have nicked a bike, thumbed a lift, walked to a bus stop and caught a bus… Remember, it's Paul's face that's been splashed all over the papers. No one would look twice at Anthony. He leaves Paul hiding – gets over to St Andrews. Probably had his office keys with him when he was lifted. If he did still have them he'd be in and out in minutes; and, if not, he'd know how to get in. Where there was a window – that sort of thing. Don't forget who his brother is.'

'It's possible,' Clare said. She broke off. Something was worrying away at the back of her mind. Something about a van. And then she remembered. 'Chris, do you have the number for Motray Farm? Not the farmer's mobile. The farmhouse.'

He reached into his pocket. 'Give me a minute.' He tapped at his phone and held it out.

Clare took the phone and clicked to call the number. It rang out and she was about to give up when it was answered. The voice sounded young, female.

'Tansy?' she said, hoping she'd guessed correctly.

'Yeah – who is this?'

Clare introduced herself. 'I just need to ask one more thing, if you can remember? You spoke about a couple of vehicles driving slowly past the farm on Monday afternoon.'

'Yeah I remember. The Megane and that van.'

'Can you recall anything about the van?'

'Not much. It wasn't huge. But bigger than the ones that are like a car.'

'A Transit, maybe?' Clare suggested.

'I dunno. I remember the colour, though. It was green. Dark green.'

Clare muted the phone for a moment. 'Sara, get onto the funeral home. I want a photo of that van. Then see if you can get some images of different vans, green if possible. I want to see if Tansy picks this one out.'

Chapter 26

Clare and Chris were on their way again within half an hour, armed with a bank of photos. They were met this time by a woman in a Barbour jacket and Hunter wellies. She was about forty, with thick blonde hair tied back, her cheeks flushed in the cool afternoon air.

'Elspeth McGovern,' she said, holding out a hand. 'Eric's wife.'

She led them into the kitchen. The sun was low in the sky now, the large room warm and welcoming. A delicious smell wound its way round Clare's heart and she realised she'd missed lunch.

'Something smells good,' she said.

'Chicken casserole.' Elspeth shrugged off her coat and stepped out of her boots. 'I'll fetch Tansy.'

Minutes later Tansy appeared and Clare explained she would like her to try and identify the van she'd seen driving slowly past on Monday.

Elspeth frowned. 'That's the day the GPS was nicked. Tansy, why didn't you say something earlier?'

Tansy rolled her eyes. 'Dunno. Didn't think it was important.'

Elspeth raised an eyebrow but said nothing further. Clare spread out photos of six green vans, all different in style. It took Tansy seconds to pick out the funeral director's van.

'That's the one,' she said. 'I'm sure of it.'

'Can you recall the time at all?' Clare asked. 'Even roughly?'

'Maybe four; or a bit later.'

'And did you see it again? Going back down for instance?'

She shook her head. 'No, sorry. I think mum called me to help with tea.' She looked from Clare to Chris. 'Does that help?'

Clare scooped up the photos. 'It does, Tansy. Thank you.'

As they left, they saw Eric McGovern climbing down from a tractor.

'You back about that damned graffiti?' he shouted.

'Not this time,' Clare called. 'But I'll check with the station.'

Back in the car, Chris said, 'The green van – I'm not sure where it gets us.'

She held up a finger. 'Hold on.' She took out her phone and swiped until she found the number for the mobile she'd given Alan Carter. He answered after a few rings, his voice sleepy.

'Sorry, just having a nap. Catching up, you know?'

'Of course. But I need to ask you something.'

'Yeah?'

'The funeral on Monday. Was it well attended?'

'Nah. Not really. Just Paul and his brother, and the undertaker's lot.'

'Did you notice any cars?'

'What, like the hearse?'

'Well, yes. But any others?'

He was quiet for a moment, as though thinking. Then he said, 'We pulled in next to an old Nissan. Micra, I think. And there was something white beside that. Didn't notice the make.'

'Any vans?'

'Like a workman's van?'

'Any kind of van.'

'There was, now you come to mention it.'

'Can you recall anything about it?'

'Pretty average van, I'd say. In good nick. Didn't notice the reg, though. Think it was green.'

Clare ended the call. Ignoring Chris drumming his fingers on the side of the car, she dialled the number for Hardman and Son, Anthony Devine's employer. The receptionist wasn't keen to give out details of Anthony's work pattern, but when Clare said she was concerned for his safety she relented.

'So, Monday,' the receptionist said. 'He clocked on at eight but he took a few hours leave. Think it was a funeral. Not one of ours, though.'

'Time?'

'He left here about eleven. Mr Keys said not to hurry back, as it was a funeral, you know? Sometimes people find it hard to go back to work afterwards.'

'And did he?' Clare asked. 'Hurry back, I mean?'

There was a silence then she spoke again. 'Looks like he didn't clock back in. He must have taken the rest of the day. It's gone through as a half-day holiday. Mind you, I think he did come back briefly, about six o'clock.'

'But not to work?'

'No. He was only here a minute.'

'Do you know why?'

'Probably to return the van keys. He'd taken one of our vans down to the funeral, you see. I think his car was playing up.'

'Which van was it?'

'The dark green one. It's a Volkswagen. I can get the registration if you like.'

Clare ended the call, her mind racing. She needed to talk this through with Chris but she had to be careful not to mention Gavin's role in Paul's escape.

'You want to catch me up?' Chris said, eventually.

She turned to him. 'Chris, there's stuff I've been told not to share. With anyone, including you. Especially you.'

His jaw tightened. 'Stuff about Alan?'

'Not exactly. But, if I do tell you, you absolutely cannot tell anyone. Not even Sara. If you did, I'd probably lose my job. So, agreed?'

He was looking at her, as if trying to try and work out what was going on.

'Agreed?' she repeated.

He nodded. 'Agreed. So?'

'Anthony Devine knew about the plan to spring Paul from custody. After the funeral.'

Chris stared. 'He knew? What about Paul?'

She shook her head. 'From what I can gather it was a surprise for Paul.'

'So how did—'

'Anthony got wind an escape was planned. Don't ask me how, or who told him; and I don't know how they sold it to him. Maybe the jewels were mentioned. Either way it doesn't matter. But he knew. And there's more.'

Chris sat back and rubbed his chin. 'Go on.'

'The funeral was a put-up job. Nobody died.'

'Who the hell did they bury?'

'House bricks. Enough for the weight of a man. Wrapped up so they didn't shift.'

'And Anthony Devine arranged this?'

'Looks that way. It was a ploy to get Paul out of prison.'

'So he could kill Maggie?'

Clare frowned. 'No. I don't think so.' She paused then said, 'I don't think Paul Devine did kill Maggie.'

'Wait – what?'

She shook her head. 'I started out thinking he was our man but I'm pretty sure now he's not the killer.'

He frowned. 'So, if Paul didn't kill Maggie, and he didn't know he was going to be sprung, why the hell is he out?'

'It looks like the gang organised Paul's escape so he could lead them to the jewels. But he must have held out on them.'

'So they grabbed Anthony?'

Clare nodded. 'I think so.'

'That means Paul wouldn't have been free to kill Maggie?'

'Nope. He went from one set of captors to another; and, unless the whole damn lot of them turned up at Maggie's cottage and killed her, I don't think he's our man.'

Chris was silent for a moment. 'Where does the green van fit in? Are you thinking—'

'Anthony. I think he's our killer.'

'Anthony? Why would he kill Maggie? And why now?' Chris shook his head. 'Sorry, Clare. I don't get it.'

'Revenge, Chris. Revenge for putting his brother away.'

'What? After all this time? Plus, he'd know Paul would be our chief suspect now he's out. Killing Maggie might actually make things worse for him.'

'Depends. If he managed to get Paul away from the gang and they dug up the jewels they could be out of the country before we caught up with them.'

Chris considered this. 'He'd have to work fast. Once the prison raised the alarm he'd know we'd check on Maggie. Maybe even station a cop at her cottage.'

Clare didn't reply.

'Oh God,' Chris said. 'We didn't, though, did we?'

'No,' she said, her voice small. 'All the worry over the prison officers going missing – I overlooked the basics.' She met Chris's gaze. 'I probably cost that woman her life.'

'No, I won't have it,' Chris said. 'If it's anyone's fault, it's mine. I was so shocked Alan was involved. I made such a fuss; and anyway, there was nothing to suggest she was in danger. No threats or intimidation during the trial.'

She shrugged. 'Either way, it's a bad miss, and one I'll have to account for.' She sighed 'Let's get back to Anthony.'

Chris put a hand on her arm. 'I'll back you all the way,' he said, 'if it comes to it.'

She smiled. 'Thanks, Chris. But it was my op. My mistake. So, Anthony?'

He watched her for a moment then carried on. 'You think he went straight to Maggie's after the funeral?'

'I think so. Only he doesn't realise Tansy's off school, sitting at her window, clocking any cars that go past.'

'Hold on, though.' Chris frowned. 'Tansy said she saw the van about four. The funeral would have been over by one.'

'I dunno,' Clare said. 'Maybe Maggie was out somewhere. Maybe he'd something else to do first. He could have been up and down that road when Tansy wasn't looking. Or she could have been wrong about the time. But it makes more sense for Anthony to have done it than Paul. He had the van and all afternoon to wait for her.'

'But, if he kills Maggie around four,' Chris said, 'why didn't he carry on to Brunton? He had the van. Could have kept it till morning. Hang about till after midnight then start digging?'

'Dunno. Digging's hard work. Graves are deep. Maybe he needed Paul's help.'

Chris sat weighing this. 'So he goes back to St Andrews. Waits to hear from Paul.'

'But the gang grab him before Paul can get away,' Clare finished.

'You could be right.' He shook his head. 'I dunno, Clare. So, what now?'

'Now,' Clare said, 'we wait to see if Raymond can get any DNA from the hammer.'

'We don't have Anthony's DNA on file. Do we?'

'Nope. But I'm going to ask Ben for that warrant after all. I'll find his DNA in that house if it's the last thing I do.'

Chapter 27

Ben requested the warrant to search Anthony Devine's house. 'I've gone for phone and bank records too and asked for it to be rushed through,' he said, 'but don't get your hopes up.'

Clare smiled her thanks. 'What about the gang?'

He glanced at his watch. 'Just about to start the interviews.'

'Will you question them about the Elzinga raid?'

'Not at this stage,' he said. 'The Met retrieved some forensic evidence at the time. If there's a match they may want to be involved. Meantime, these lads aren't going anywhere.'

'I'd like to sit in. If you don't mind,' she added.

'That's fine. But you leave the questioning to me, okay?'

Ten minutes later Clare and Ben entered the interview room and came face-to-face with the man she believed to be one of Kim and Debbie's abductors. He was stockily built, aged about forty with thick brown hair and sideburns that reminded Clare of Noel Gallagher. He sat slumped in his chair, arms folded, and barely reacted when they introduced themselves. A younger man Clare recognised as one of the duty solicitors sat beside him, a notepad and fountain pen on the desk. She nodded to the solicitor and started the recording.

Ben introduced himself and Clare, and the man spoke only to confirm his name as Alex Rogerson. The solicitor then said his client would exercise his right to silence.

'That's a pity,' Ben said. 'You'll be out of here far quicker if you answer our questions.'

There was no response to this, so Ben went on. 'You were apprehended on Friday night at the Christieson cemetery at Brunton in north-east Fife. Can you tell me why you were there?'

The man muttered, 'No comment,' and Ben carried on.

'One of the graves was partly excavated. Can you explain this please?'

Again there was no response.

'We have you at the graveside,' Ben said, 'clearly engaged in its excavation.'

'Violation of sepulchres,' Clare put in. 'Carries a maximum life sentence.'

The solicitor and Ben both looked at Clare, but she continued staring at Alex. He met her eye.

'Like you'd get life for that.'

Clare shrugged. 'Depends on the judge. You get one who's just buried his mother.' She watched him, waiting to see if he would respond, but he lapsed back into silence.

'Where were you last Saturday?' Ben went on.

No response.

'Monday?'

Again, no response. It was only when Ben mentioned they'd recovered a handgun from the cemetery that Alex showed a spark of interest.

'Nothing to do with me.'

'The gun has gone to our forensic lab,' Ben said. 'They'll test it for DNA and fingerprints.'

There was the hint of a smirk on Alex's face and Clare remembered Kim stating the gunman had worn gloves. *He knows we won't get anything off the gun*, she thought.

'We have your clothes as well,' Ben said. 'And you know the interesting thing about guns? It's the tiny traces of residue. If that gun had been fired in the past, there might still be traces on the gun itself. And that stuff – it's so fine. Gets everywhere. Clothes, fingernails – even if it wasn't you who fired it.'

Alex inclined his head but he said nothing.

Ben carried on asking questions, Alex staring at the table in front of him. In the end he gave up and said Alex would be charged with abduction. 'You'll be up in court on Monday and I'd expect you to be remanded in custody.'

He made no response to this and the interview was terminated.

The second member of the gang, Colin Pirie, was no more forthcoming and he too was soon charged and on his way back to custody.

The third man was younger than Alex and Colin. He gave his name as Ross Pettigrew and, unlike the other two, he looked alarmed by his surroundings. Again the solicitor present stated Ross would be answering no comment to all questions. But when Ben mentioned the likely penalties for abduction the colour drained from his face. Seeing this, Ben softened his tone.

'Obviously if you are able to help us identify your co-conspirators that would be taken into account by the sentencing judge. We can also make sure you wouldn't be sent to the same prison as the others.'

'A few years off your sentence can make the world of difference,' Clare added.

The solicitor put a hand on Ross's arm. 'Perhaps we should have a chat in private.'

Ross looked at the solicitor for a moment then shook his head. 'Sorry,' he mumbled. 'No comment to all of it.'

They emerged from the interview room half an hour later.

'Reckon we can make any of it stick?' Clare said as they headed to the kitchen to make drinks.

'Hopefully. That house where the women were kept might throw up something. There should be DNA on those takeaway containers.'

'And we have the scarf, remember,' Clare said. 'The one Kim had over her eyes.' She picked up the kettle and went to the sink to fill it.

'That violation thing.'

'Violation of sepulchres?' She plugged the kettle in and switched it on to boil.

'Yes, that. How do you come to have something like that on the tip of your tongue? I was racking my brains trying to think what the offence would be.'

'Used to live with a solicitor,' she said. 'Helped him study for his exams.'

'You're not with him now, though?' he asked.

'No, he's married.'

'Didn't think so. You and Al Gibson.'

She turned, surprised. 'You're very well informed.'

He shrugged. 'I keep up. Nice guy,' he added.

'You know him?'

'We served together for six months. Long time ago now.' He smiled. 'Thought he'd have mentioned it.'

–

The warrant for Anthony Devine's house, phone and bank records came in as Clare was thinking of going home. The lack of sleep was catching up with all of them. She looked at the warrant and lifted the phone to call Raymond Curtice.

'This had better be good,' he said. 'I was just about to go home.'

'It might not take too long,' she said. 'We have a warrant to enter a house. The occupant has gone AWOL and I really need his DNA to compare with that hammer.'

He yawned. 'Go on, then. I'll send a couple of officers over. If there's a toothbrush or a hat, even, we might get something there.'

Clare gave him details of Anthony's house and said she'd send a couple of cops to assist with entry. Then she handed over to the duty inspector at Cupar, asking if he could request the phone and bank records, and she stood the team down. 'Back in at eight tomorrow,' she said. They trooped off wearily and she followed them out to the car park, Ben's words ringing in her ears. *We served together for six months. Thought he'd have mentioned it.*

The DCI was detaching Benjy's lead from his collar when Clare pulled into the drive at Daisy Cottage. He walked across and opened the car door for her, Benjy jumping into the car before she could step out. He leaned down and kissed her then, pulling Benjy back, he held the door for her to climb out.

The cottage was warm and she shrugged off her coat, throwing it over the banister. Leaving her work bag in the hall, she wandered through to the kitchen.

'Stir fry okay?' the DCI asked.

'Anything. I'm so tired I'm not even sure I have the energy to eat.'

'It's all ready. Just be five minutes. Sit down and I'll pour you a glass of wine.'

She watched him moving about the kitchen, striped apron tied round his middle. He was humming to himself and seemed entirely relaxed. She picked up her glass and drank from it setting it down on the kitchen table. 'Thought you said you didn't know Ben Ratcliffe.'

He shook the wok and the vegetables jumped and spat. 'I don't really.'

'So you didn't work with him for six months.'

He turned off the gas and reached down to fetch plates from the oven. Then he glanced round. 'That's going back a bit. Where did you find that out?'

'He told me himself. Said you were a decent bloke.' She picked up the wine again and drained her glass. 'I'm starting to wonder...'

He began spooning the stir fry onto plates and handed her one. 'It's a bit hot.'

Clare carried her plate to the table and sank down. 'Why didn't you tell me?'

He brought his plate across and sat opposite. 'Does it matter?'

She regarded him. 'It does when I find out he's been keeping information from me. Information which I can't even tell you; and that makes me wonder who this guy even is.' She held out her glass for a refill. 'And I'll tell you something else, Al Gibson. It makes me think you know exactly who he is. What I don't get is why you don't trust me enough to tell me.'

He had half-filled her wine glass and put the bottle down. She reached across and picked up the bottle, topping up her glass. Then she set it down and stared at him. 'Why the hell didn't you tell me?'

Benjy, hearing the sharp tone in her voice, barked and Clare held out a warning finger. Picking up her glass she glugged the wine. 'Well?'

He looked at her for a moment. 'You allowed Sara to work on this enquiry, didn't you?'

'Yeah. So?'

'Despite the fact she lives with and is engaged to Chris; Chris who was so closely connected to the enquiry you removed him from it.'

Clare picked up her fork and began to load it with vegetables.

'Correct me if I'm wrong, Clare, but I imagine you had a conversation with Sara about not taking information back to Chris.'

'What if I did?'

'My point is you trusted Sara not to tell Chris how the operation was going.' He reached across the table and took her hand. 'I was in a position of trust too. I knew as soon as they put Ben in charge there had to be more to it than a straight abduction. But if I'd told you can you honestly say it wouldn't have affected your relationship with him? He'd have sussed you out in no time.'

'You're saying I can't be trusted,' she said, her tone mulish.

'No. I'm saying I *can* be trusted.' He withdrew his hand and picked up the bottle to top up his own glass. 'I've my job to consider as well, you know?'

Clare sighed. 'Yeah, okay.'

'See my point?'

She rolled her eyes. 'I always do. You're so damned reasonable.' She picked up her fork again. 'So, who is he? And don't tell me he's just a DCI for hire.'

'Okay. But you didn't get this from me.' He took a slug of wine, then said, 'He heads up an undercover unit. Embeds officers in Organised Crime Groups so they can gather intel on upcoming jobs. It's dangerous stuff, Clare. The fewer folk who know about it the better.'

'Jesus,' Clare said. 'Seriously?'

'Yup. They've had some good results too. But it's high-pressure stuff. He'll likely do it for a couple more years and move on. There's a high turnaround. Needs to be for officer welfare.'

Clare sat back considering this. No wonder Ben had been so secretive, always closing his laptop when she entered the room. She wondered how many officers he had working undercover. Had she come across any of them without realising who they were? It certainly explained how he'd managed to put his hands on so many officers for the Brunton operation.

'But you can't breathe a word of that,' the DCI was saying. 'It could cost lives, Clare.'

She nodded. 'Yeah, I get that. Don't worry.'

He smiled at her and took her hand again. 'I'll tell you this, Clare Mackay: there are times when you are bloody hard work!'

Sunday

Chapter 28

As she drove into work Clare was glad to see a newspaper hoarding bearing the words,

Police Still Hunt Escaped Con

Hopefully the front pages would have Paul Devine's photo and perhaps one of the green van too. She entered the station and made for her office. A minute later her door opened and Max entered, notepad in hand.

'Morning Max,' she said. 'What's new?'

'Phone message from SOCO. They've taken a few things from Anthony Devine's house.'

'Did they say what?'

He consulted his notepad. 'Apparently a toothbrush, hand towel and the crust from a bit of toast.'

'Yeuch.'

'Yes, I don't envy them that.'

'Anything else?'

'A laptop. Should be at Tech Support now.'

'Thanks, Max. I'll give them a call.'

Clare dialled the number for her friend Diane Wallace who ran the Tech Support unit, twenty miles away in Glenrothes. The call was answered by Craig, her assistant.

'Sorry, it's Diane's day off,' he explained.

Clare asked about the laptop and he confirmed they had it. 'I presume you're calling to say it's a rush job?'

'I'd really appreciate it,' she said. 'If you can get past the login, have a look at his internet search history. Maybe any recent online shopping or emails. He's gone AWOL and I'm worried he plans to skip the country.'

Craig promised to look at it that morning and Clare turned to her inbox. There was one from the inspector at Cupar saying he'd requested phone and bank records for Anthony Devine and she sent back a quick message of thanks. As she clicked *Send* another email popped up. Raymond Curtice. She opened it and digested the contents. Then she rose from her seat and went through to the incident room.

Chris was perched on a desk chatting to Sara and Max.

'Good news,' she said. 'SOCO found traces of Maggie White's blood on the head of the hammer. Blood spatter down the shaft as well. It's definitely the murder weapon.'

'Any other DNA?' Max asked.

'Still testing. Raymond said not to get our hopes up, though.'

'What now?' Chris asked.

It was a good question. Strictly speaking, she should run anything to do with the Devines past Ben, but since he'd revealed Gavin Gates's role in events he seemed more relaxed about Clare's involvement. Surely he didn't still expect her to run everything past him?

'Check ANPR for that green van, please. I'm sure we'd have heard if it had pinged a camera but it's worth making sure. And let's dig further into the Devines' family and friends. See if we can turn up anyone else who might have helped them. Go back over Paul Devine's known associates. Check for any large withdrawals of cash or unusual behaviour; and I want every report of a stolen vehicle in Fife, Perth and Dundee checked. Registrations into ANPR.'

Chris groaned.

'I could always put you back on tractor night shift.'

It was mid-afternoon when Clare heard Raymond had managed to isolate a DNA profile from the hammer.

'It's a male,' he said. 'But not on our database. And before you ask about the mouldy toast and the toothbrush, that'll be another few hours.'

'And that's all you can say? That he's male?'

'Oh, I forgot to mention he has red hair, a glass eye and all his own teeth!'

'Sorry. Stupid question.'

Raymond sighed. 'No, I'm sorry. I shouldn't have snapped. I know you're under pressure with this one. It's, well, I don't need to tell you what it's like. I've just lost two of my best members of staff. Gone to the private sector and I can't blame them. More money, better conditions, and no crawling through mud in the middle of the night. I'm almost tempted to join them.'

Clare had never heard Raymond sounding so down. 'I'm sorry,' she said. 'Look, how about coming over to Daisy Cottage one night. When this case is over. Have a meal, few drinks. There's a spare room. You could stay the night.'

'Will the dog be there?'

'Oh yes.'

'Then it's a deal. But I want decent wine, mind. None of your supermarket bargains.'

She ended the call and sat back, mulling over their conversation. She had an excellent relationship with the forensic service. Raymond was usually quick to respond and he always turned Clare's requests round as fast as he could. But if they were struggling for staff, what did that mean for the future? Her phone began to ring again, cutting across her thoughts and she glanced at the display. Craig from Tech Support.

'Got into the laptop okay,' he said. 'Still downloading stuff but it doesn't look like there's much in his emails. They'll be up on the server in the next few hours. But I've checked his browsing history and it might be more helpful. I'll email over a link.'

Clare ended the call and waited for the email to arrive. It appeared a couple of minutes later and she clicked on the link Craig had sent. A record of Anthony Devine's browsing history since the Monday of the funeral appeared and she scanned the list of web addresses. One or two looked particularly interesting and she clicked to view them. She studied the contents for a few minutes then rose from her desk. Chris, Max and Bill were in the incident room. 'Come and look at this,' she said, and they followed her back to her office.

'Boats.' She tapped the screen. 'He's been looking up boats for hire. They're planning to skip the country.'

Bill nodded. 'Looks that way.'

Clare was scribbling on her notepad. 'These three phone numbers – the boats for hire. They're all mobiles. Let's get them tracked. Don't call them, mind. If one of them has been booked by Anthony Devine I don't want them knowing we're onto them.' She lifted her phone. 'I'm going to call Ben Ratcliffe now and get him to authorise this. Top priority. I want locations for all three with covert surveillance in place. If one of these guys is planning to ship the Devine boys abroad, we'll catch them.' She sat, holding her phone, wondering if she'd covered everything. 'Check with the Maritime and Coastguard Agency for quiet spots to leave from. Tide tables too.' She looked round at them. 'We're getting close, guys. Let's throw everything at this.'

Ben agreed to authorise the phone traces and Clare read out the numbers from the weblinks Craig had found.

'I'll get it rushed through,' he said, 'and I'll call the coastguard.'

'Already done.'

'Good,' he said. 'Keep me posted.'

She thanked him and ended the call. And suddenly there was nothing to do. She wandered through to the incident room and stared at the map on the wall, tracing her finger round the Tay Coast. Where might they leave from? If only they knew where the van was. Then a horrible thought struck her. The Devine brothers had been missing since Friday night and now it was Sunday. What if they'd already gone? Chartered a boat on Saturday, paying for it with stolen jewels? They could be in North Africa by now, or anywhere with a coastline. She had to hope not.

–

It was five o'clock when the call came.

'We might have the van,' Jim said. 'Parked outside a sports centre. Woman phoned it in. Her house overlooks the car park and she saw exhaust vapour from the van last night. They've had a problem with folk parking campervans overnight so she was right onto it. But she didn't say anything about it being green and the local lads were pretty stretched with it being Saturday night. It was only this morning they went to check on it.'

'Is it still there?' Clare asked.

'Aye. Nobody inside, though. Engine cold.'

'Get a photo, Jim.'

'I've got better than that,' and he reeled off the registration.

Clare checked her notepad but she didn't need to. She'd committed the number to memory. 'Where's the sports centre?'

'Newport-on-Tay. It's Waterstone Crook Sports Centre. Car park just beside it. I've put Robbie and Gillian in an unmarked car at the other end. If the Devines return to the van they'll call it in.'

Clare shook her computer mouse and opened Google maps. She found Newport-on-Tay and zoomed in. 'I see it here,' she said. 'Top of Castle Brae.' She zoomed out again, looking along the coastline.

'Way ahead of you,' Jim said. 'There's a harbour half a mile along the coast at Woodhaven.'

She frowned. 'That's in Wormit, right?'

'Aye. It runs on from Newport-on-Tay.'

'Okay, we need eyes on that van but covert, mind. The same at the harbour.'

'There's a clubhouse down at the jetty,' Jim said.

'Too public. Any houses we could use?'

'I'm sure there will be.'

'But subtle. I don't want guys in shiny suits knocking on doors and flashing their badges. If those two have left the van and they're hanging about Woodhaven waiting on a boat, they'll be on the lookout for plain-clothes cops.'

'Leave it with me.'

He turned to leave but Clare called him back. 'Who's been in touch with the Maritime and Coastguard Agency?'

'Think it was Bill. I'll ask him to alert them.'

Jim left the room and Clare sat on, thinking for a moment. She looked at the map of Wormit on her phone. Would they be in time to pick the Devines up?

It was Max who burst into her office with the news they'd tracked one of the mobile numbers to Newport-on-Tay. 'It has to be Woodhaven. The van and the mobile – it's too much of a coincidence.'

'I agree,' Clare said. 'What about the coastguard agency?'

'Standing by with a boat and we have eyes on the jetty and the van.'

Clare decided she could sit in her office no longer. 'Let's head over there,' she said. 'We'll stay out of the way. But I'd like to be close to the harbour, just in case. And ask Jim to let Ben know. He'll want his team out.'

She was pulling on her coat when her phone rang again. Another call from Raymond.

'Hi,' she said, putting the phone on speaker and setting it down on her desk. 'Any news?'

'Yeah, but you won't like it.'

An uneasy feeling began to form in her stomach. 'Go on.'

'We managed to get DNA from those three items – the tooth-brush and so on. All yielded the same profile.'

'Oh God.' Clare sank down into her chair. 'It's not a match for the hammer, is it?'

'Sorry Clare. Another male profile but definitely not the same as the hammer.'

Chapter 29

They raced through the streets, Chris at the wheel of an unmarked car, Clare and Max clutching their seats as he took the corners at speed. He roared past St Michael's crossroads, siren blaring, ignoring the thirty miles an hour sign. He carried on past the signpost for Wormit.

'Quicker this way,' he said. 'I've an idea where we can sit.'

At the roundabout he switched off the siren, heading across and down into Newport-on-Tay, muttering about the speed bumps. The road ran into the village, past a queue outside a fish and chip shop.

'Oh smell that,' Clare said.

'Chips on you if we get him,' Chris said.

He turned left down the High Street and, at the bottom took a sharp right into a small lane. 'There's parking here and a great view of the river.' He nosed into a space behind another car and killed the engine. A small car park lay before them, every space filled. He scanned the cars. 'All empty,' he said. 'No one hanging around either.' He took the key out of the ignition. 'Come on – I'll show you the Woodhaven pier.'

They crossed the car park and looked up the river. It was growing dark now but there was still enough light in the sky for them to see the coastline all the way to the girders of the iconic railway bridge, a mile or so to the west.

'Is that it?' Clare asked, indicating a sloping pier a short distance away.

'Nope. That's private. Generally locked up at this time on a Sunday. Woodhaven's further up. See?'

Clare followed where he pointed and squinted, trying to make out the pier. 'Yeah, I see it. Should have brought binoculars.'

'We won't need them,' Chris said. 'We should see the boat lights.'

'Nearly high tide,' Max said, studying his phone. 'Good time to go.'

Clare's phone began to ring and she snatched it up.

'Bill, hi. What's happening?'

'We're in place at the pier. Out of sight. No sign of them so far. No boat either.'

'Coastguard?'

'Moored further down, just off the road bridge.'

Clare looked down river towards the bridge. The coastline was irregular but it lacked inlets deep enough to conceal the coastguard's boat. Admittedly the light was fading now. That would help. Hopefully the Devines and their boatman wouldn't spot it. 'Is one boat enough?' she asked.

'There's another on standby, at the mouth of the river,' Bill said. 'With any luck it won't be needed.'

'You think they'll stop for the coastguard?'

'Hard to say. But…'

'Bill?'

'Hold on. I want to grab binoculars.'

She waited, listening to the sound of Bill fumbling with the binoculars. Then she heard him shout and other voices in the background.

'Bill?' she said again.

Seconds later he came back on the phone. 'There's a boat just coming through the rail bridge legs now. Motorboat. Moving at a fair speed.'

Clare squinted towards the bridge trying to make out the boat. She thought she could see a light half way across the river but it was hard to tell from this distance. 'Is it pulling in towards the Woodhaven?' she asked.

'No,' he said. 'If anything, it's heading out to the middle of the river. I'll alert the coastguard.'

Clare could hear a faint buzzing now as the motorboat passed the Woodhaven pier, heading for the road bridge.

'It's fairly shifting,' Chris said.

'Bill, get the coastguard moving.'

'Ben's on it,' he said. 'Coastguard's primed to intercept. They'll order it to stop and most likely force it into Tayport harbour.'

'We'll head along there now,' she said. 'Keep in touch.' She ended the call and nodded to Chris and Max. 'Tayport harbour. Quick as you can.'

They raced along the coast road towards the Tay Road Bridge, Clare's eyes trained on the river, where gaps between trees and houses allowed. 'I can see both boats,' she said. 'Can't tell which is which, though.'

'I reckon that's the coastguard in the rib,' Max said. 'They have bigger vessels but ribs are great for a quick response.'

They passed the war memorial, the trees and houses clearing to give an uninterrupted view. The two boats were racing along with no indication either was slowing. Chris swung the car round, blues and twos warning oncoming traffic to give them room. Their view was obscured by houses once more as they approached the legs of the road bridge. With no traffic ahead of them Chris gunned the car. They passed under the bridge, heading on towards Tayport. Again, the trees cleared and Clare saw they were a bit ahead of the boats. And then she saw another larger boat, moving towards the centre of the river to meet the others. The river was wide at this point. Almost a mile and a half. Would these two boats really be enough to stop the speedboat?

A sound that had been faint was coming closer and her spirits soared. Their view of the river was obscured once more as they entered Tayport with its houses either side of the road. But there was no mistaking the beat of helicopter rotors. Ben's doing, she guessed. Chris signalled left and he slowed dramatically to take the narrow road down towards the harbour. He glanced briefly at Clare, no doubt remembering the time they had made the same journey and Clare had jumped into the freezing harbour waters to save a woman's life.

'No heroics this time,' he said, and she shook her head. They reached the harbour and Chris drove across the car park, angling the car so the headlights shone towards the river. They climbed out and stood watching the lights from the boats and the spotlight that shone down from the helicopter. The sound of its rotors filled the air and people began drifting out of their houses to see what was happening.

'Somebody in the water?' a red-haired lad shouted.

'Don't tempt me,' Clare muttered.

'They're slowing down,' Max called, trying to be heard. 'I think they've agreed to come in.'

'Get on the radio,' Clare shouted. 'I want three cars. One for each of them.'

They followed the lights from the two coastguard vessels as they flanked the motorboat, now chugging slowly towards them. Overhead the helicopter marked their progress, the spotlight moving ever closer to the harbour. More people appeared or hung out of house windows, the babble of conversation lost in the cacophony. Along the coastline Clare saw the sky light up with blue flashes and she heard the sirens from approaching vehicles. Three police cars arrived a minute later, drawing up beside them as the speedboat drifted slowly through the harbour entrance.

'Perfect timing,' Clare said as the officers jumped out of their cars. Chris put a hand to his ear, indicating he couldn't hear over the noise from the helicopter but she just shook her head. She put up a hand to stop her hair blowing into her eyes and looked round to see if Ben had arrived with the officers. 'DCI?' she mouthed to one but he shook his head. 'Ten minutes away,' he shouted, and Clare nodded in response. 'I'll do the arrests, then,' she shouted back, 'and you can take one each to St Andrews. Keep them separate until I get there.'

'What will you charge them with?' Max asked, cupping his hands round Clare's ear.

'Good question,' Chris said, but his words were lost on the downwash from the rotors.

Clare turned towards them so they could hear her above the noise. 'Paul Devine is being returned to lawful custody. It's for the prison to deal with him under their disciplinary code. But Anthony, I'd say attempting to defeat the ends of justice is a pretty safe bet. I can always add charges later.'

Chris nodded. 'What about the boatman?'

'Same.'

'He could argue he was simply fulfilling a contract,' Max said.

The speedboat bobbed up to the pontoon and they walked round to meet it.

Clare's expression darkened. 'He can try. But I think the coast-guard will testify he didn't stop when first challenged.'

She walked along the pontoon until she was level with the boat and took her first look at Paul Devine. The glare of the spotlight from the helicopter cast shadows around the inside of the cabin, giving his face a ghostly quality. He was leaner than his brother, his hair closely cropped. His face was pock-marked and bore the grime of almost a week on the run. It was hard to be sure but she thought she could see faint bruising on his face and she wondered how he'd come by it. Then she ran her eye over the boat. It was larger than she'd expected, more like a cabin cruiser. She stood waiting for them to disembark. The Devine brothers hung back but the boatman stepped easily onto the pontoon.

'Polis?' he asked, unnecessarily.

'Detective Inspector Mackay.'

He held out his hands. 'Sorry, Inspector. I didn't realise these lads were coastguards. Thought they were just messing about. I'd have stopped sooner if I'd known.'

The helicopter was pulling away now, the light fading but it didn't stop Clare taking in the boatman's expression and deciding she didn't believe a word of it. 'I'd like you to come to the station,' she said. 'We'll take a statement then decide if any charges will be preferred. In the meantime,' she indicated his boat, 'I'll be carrying out a search of this vessel.'

He shrugged. 'I didn't bring anything on board. If there is anything dodgy it's down to the passengers.'

Clare stood by to let him move along the pontoon into the arms of two officers. Then she extended a hand to help the Devines out of the boat. Anthony came first, declining the hand. Clare stood, barring his way while she formally arrested him. He made no reply and she passed him to another pair of officers. Then she stood, waiting for the final figure occupying the small cabin to rise from his seat. But Paul Devine didn't move.

'Out you come,' she said, her tone brisk, but he sat on.

Chris stepped forward. 'I'll get him out,' but Clare sidestepped him and moved to the edge of the pontoon. It was dark inside the boat now, the boatman having turned off the interior lights. A faint orange glow told her he'd lit a cigarette and a wisp of tobacco smoke reached her nostrils.

'I'll just finish this,' he said, exhaling a cloud of fumes towards Clare.

'No, you'll come out now. Or I'll send someone in to get you.'

The helicopter had receded into the distance now and, despite the frantic activity of the past few minutes, an uneasy silence had descended on the harbour. Staring down at the gloomy interior of the boat, Clare tried to read his expression but his eyes seemed almost wholly dark; dark and dead, like a shark. Was that what this man was? An emotionless, solitary killer? Might he be armed? There was no way she could risk tackling him in the tiny cabin and nor could anyone else. But it was suddenly so important that she didn't back down. Didn't show any sign of weakness to this man who had killed a security guard and terrorised the staff of a jeweller's shop on Clare's own patch.

She summoned up her courage and, keeping her voice level, said, 'Fetch a taser, Chris.'

Devine blew out another cloud of smoke, his eyes never leaving hers. 'No need for that, officer.' He took a final drag then dropped the remains of the cigarette. She saw it glow briefly as it landed then heard him grind it beneath his foot. 'Finished my fag now.'

She stood her ground as he rose and began slowly to ascend the steps, dipping his head as he passed through the cabin door.

The boat swayed a little with the movement but he seemed barely to notice, drawing himself up to his full height. Then he stepped over the gunwale and onto the pontoon inches from Clare. His breath was sour, a noxious blend of beer and smoke, she thought, and there was a faint odour of stale sweat. She stepped back involuntarily, regretting that she'd allowed him to crowd her. She should have made room before he'd stepped out. He was taller than her and he stood, unmoving, an unnerving presence on the pontoon.

Chris was at her back now, taser in hand, Max beside him with a powerful torch and she was grateful for their presence. But still she kept her eyes trained on Paul Devine. He stood for a moment, perhaps prolonging his freedom from custody, taking in the scene before him. The ghost of a smile played on his lips then he turned back to Clare, the smile gone.

'I never forget a face,' he said. 'Never.' Then he lifted his hand and she thought he was going to strike her. She flinched and staggered back, only just keeping her feet. Chris leapt forward to grab his arm but he drew it back and brushed a strand of hair from his face. 'Calm down, son,' he said, laughing. 'Hair in ma eye.' Chris ignored this and reached for Devine's hand, snapping the cuffs on. As he did so Clare noticed a small tattoo on his wrist. The tattoo that had helped Maggie identify him, and her spirits lifted. They had their man. She moved forward again, fighting to keep the tremor from her voice as she arrested him and recited the caution.

He made no response and she delivered him into the hands of the uniformed officers. As he was led away, he turned his head, his gaze never leaving her face. 'Never,' he repeated, his voice as soft as it was deadly. She watched him go until he was stowed in a car then she turned and began walking off the pontoon, praying her legs wouldn't give way.

'Scary little fucker, isn't he?' Chris said, giving voice to her thoughts and she nodded. Was this really the same man Alan Carter had said was *no bother inside*? She'd certainly be glad when he was safely back in Perth prison.

'He'd better see a doctor,' she said. 'I don't want him to have any excuse not to be interviewed.'

Chris nodded. 'I'll phone ahead.'

'What now?' Max asked, his eyes shining with the drama of it all.

'Now, Max, you and Chris are going to search this boat. I have the feeling there may be something of interest on board.'

Chapter 30

'You're certainly keeping me busy,' the doctor said as he emerged from one of the interview rooms after seeing Paul Devine.

'How is he?' Clare asked.

'Nothing a square meal won't fix. It would have been cold out on the river but he was well wrapped up and his core temperature's fine. I'd get him some food before you speak to him, though.'

'Don't suppose you could glance at the other two? Particularly Anthony Devine. I don't want him wriggling out of charges, claiming he didn't know what he was saying. He's just the type.'

'No problem.'

Clare asked Jim to order pizzas for the three men, then she went to her office where Chris and Max were waiting, a large brown evidence bag on the desk in front of them. 'You've not touched it?' she asked.

They shook their heads. 'Okay.' She pulled on a pair of gloves. 'It'll have to go to SOCO but I want to be sure what's inside first.'

It was a metal box, dark grey in colour. There was a lock on the front but no key.

'I've seen these before,' Max said. 'I think it's called a Deed Box. People use them to keep documents safe.'

Clare clicked the latch carefully and lifted the lid. The contents were held in a clear plastic bag which had been secured with parcel tape. But even through the plastic they sparkled under the office lights. She brought her desk lamp over and they stood taking in what they guessed were the proceeds of the jewellery shop robbery.

Chris gave a low whistle. 'Bloody hell.'

'Wow.' Max's eyes were alight at the sight of the haul. 'Look at the shiny shiny!'

Chris raised an eyebrow at the expression and Clare suppressed a laugh. 'Okay, guys. This has to go to SOCO for prints and DNA but it'll have to be under escort. Chris, can you arrange that please?' She closed the lid carefully and replaced it in the evidence bag. 'I'll give Raymond a call. Max, keep an eye out for duty solicitors arriving.'

Raymond wasn't in the office so Clare tried his mobile.

'I'm just waiting on my souffles coming out of the oven,' he said. 'You have precisely eight minutes.'

'Seriously?' Clare was impressed.

'Pfft, no! I've phoned for a takeaway. Been a long week. So?'

'I need to send you a metal box to check for prints and DNA.'

'Doesn't sound like something you'd need to phone me at home for.'

'It's the contents.'

'Which are?'

'A bag of jewellery and watches. Potentially six-figures worth.'

'Ooh okay. In that case, speak to Samantha. She's on until ten tonight. We have secure storage. If your officers call her when they arrive they can go with her to the storage unit. She'll give them a receipt and I'll get onto it in the morning.'

Clare was thinking as he was speaking. 'I'll probably have to bring in an expert, Raymond. So the sooner you're finished with it the better.'

'First thing tomorrow,' he promised.

She sat for a minute to gather her thoughts, then dialled Ben's number. He answered immediately.

'You got them?'

'We did.'

'Good work, Clare.'

'The helicopter helped,' she conceded. 'Thanks for that.'

'Ach, it's what it's there for.'

'About the interviews…'

'I should be with you in an hour or so. Two at worst. Let them stew until I get there.'

She hesitated for a moment, then she said, 'Ben, look, I know this is your case but I would particularly like to interview Paul Devine myself.'

'Reason?'

'He – when we took him off the boat he was – well, he tried to scare me.'

'Ah. He tried that, did he?'

'Yep. And he damn near succeeded. I think if you led the interview,' she tailed off.

'He might think he'd rattled you?'

'Something like that.' There was silence at the other end and she waited to see what he would say.

'Okay,' he said at last. 'One condition.'

'Go on.'

'You can ask him about the prison break, about your dead woman, but you are not to mention the Elzinga raid. Clear?'

'If that's what you want.'

'No choice. The Met will send a team up, once the DNA results are back. They have their own line of questioning and have asked us not to interfere.'

'Seems a bit—'

'It's not a request, Clare.'

'Okay.'

'I presume you'll want to interview the brother as well?'

'Makes sense,' Clare said. 'And the boatman too.'

'That's fine. Just remember what I said.'

She ended the call and went to find Max and Chris. They were perched on a desk in the incident room, cradling mugs of coffee.

'Solicitor's with Paul Devine,' Max said. 'Should be able to start shortly.'

Clare thanked him and drew Chris over to the side. 'Sorry,' she began, 'but you can't be in there.'

He shook his head. 'I knew you'd say that. It's because of Alan, isn't it?'

'Yeah. I have to ask him about the hijack and I don't want anything to go wrong at this stage.' She smiled. 'You could take the boatman, though.'

'Suppose.' Then his brow creased. 'I don't like the thought of you in there with him. You saw how he was.'

She smiled. 'Thanks, Chris but I'll be fine; and I'll have Max with me.'

'Hah! Max.'

'Hah, what?'

'You know fine,' he said. 'He's a nice lad, Max, but we both know he couldn't knock the skin off a rice pudding.'

'Fortunately we're not interviewing rice puddings. Look, Chris, it'll be fine. His solicitor's in there so he's not going to do anything stupid. I bet he'll be as mild as milk.'

His face darkened. 'He'd better be.'

They entered the interview room quarter of an hour later. Paul Devine sat next to his solicitor, a woman in her late thirties. He looked better for the pizza and a mug of tea, the colour returning to his cheeks. She'd been right about the bruises. They were yellowing now but he'd clearly had a few knocks to his face. Where else, she wondered? Max began setting up the recording and Clare took a seat opposite Paul Devine. She met his eye, daring him to intimidate her. He stared back for a moment then shrugged, as if acknowledging the reality of his position.

Round one to me. Clare nodded to Max to start the recording.

She began the interview in the usual way, informing Paul he would be returned to custody. 'But first, I'd like to ask you about the events of the past week.'

He made no reply to this, and Clare went on.

'Let's start with the funeral. When did you first hear of your uncle's death?'

The corner of his mouth twitched, and Clare thought he must know by now no one had died. 'Got a message to see the

Governor,' he said. 'Probably a week before. Said about ma uncle and did I want to go to the funeral. I said of course I would.' He nodded. 'Anything to break the monotony.'

'And did you plan to escape custody while you were out of prison?'

'Naw. Nothing to do with me, that.'

'You didn't know it was going to happen?'

'Nope.'

'Did your brother Anthony say anything about it when you spoke at the funeral? Or at any other time?'

'What, the hijack? How would he know?' Paul said.

How indeed, Clare thought. He was certainly taking care not to drop his brother in it. 'What did you speak about – at the funeral?'

'This 'n' that.'

'For example?'

He exhaled audibly. 'I dunno. Like it was a nice day. He asked how prison was. I asked how he was. That sort of thing.'

Clare watched him carefully. Was he lying? She found it hard to tell. An expression of her father's came into her mind. *More faces than the town clock.* 'Was there anything on the journeys to and from Pittenweem?' she went on. 'Anything that made you think something might happen?'

'No' really. I mean one of the prison lads was fiddling with the tracker. Said about it being faulty. I wasnae bothered like. They're sound lads. I thought maybe they wanted a bit more time out of the prison. Maybe disable the tracker so they could take the long way back, ye know?'

'Was it your impression they were trying to disable it?' Clare asked.

Paul folded his arms. 'Well let's put it this way. I've never seen anyone bother as much about a tracker as those two did. But it wasnae ma concern. I was just glad to be out for a bit.'

'Okay,' Clare said. 'Let's move on to the point at which the van stopped.'

For a moment it looked as if the mask had slipped, the bravado gone. He looked down at the table and shook his head. Then he seemed to gather his wits and forced a smile. 'Thought they were gonnae kill me,' he said. 'Thought ma time had come. All balaclava'd up and that.'

Clare thought he was trying to make light of it. But she could see he'd been shaken by the question. 'Can you describe how it happened?'

'Van turned onto a side road. Bit further along it pulled into the verge. Next thing, I hear shouting and the officers are getting out. Then the back doors open and they haul me out too. The lads in the balaclavas shout at the officers to unlock the cuffs and they throw me in the back of another van.'

'Did you know the men?'

'No' at first. But once we were roaring along the road they took off their balaclavas and I realised who they were.'

'And who were they?' She saw him hesitate. 'If it helps, three men were arrested at Brunton cemetery on Friday night and they remain in custody.'

He nodded at this. 'Alex, Colin and Ross.'

Clare mentally checked off the names. The same names given by the three men she and Ben had interviewed yesterday. 'How did you know them?' She watched him carefully. He seemed to be weighing his response.

And then he said, 'Known them for years.'

She remembered Ben's instruction not to mention the Elzinga raid and she took a moment before speaking. 'Were they, perhaps, the men who had helped you rob Jardine's Jewellers in St Andrews?'

He regarded her for a moment. 'No comment.'

'You realise you'll face a disciplinary hearing at the prison,' Clare said. 'It might help if you co-operate with us.'

'Like I say, no comment.'

'Okay,' Clare went on. 'What happened next?'

'We drove for a bit. I wasnae sure where. Round Fife, I suppose. Then we pull up at this cottage.'

'Any idea where?'

He shook his head. 'Naw. Just fields and that.'

'Okay, go on.'

'One of the lads takes out a key, opens the door and we're in.'

'What was it like?'

'Nothing special. Warm enough. Warmer than prison, to be honest.'

'How many of you stayed in the cottage?'

He shrugged. 'Varied. Sometimes just two of us. The other lads, they came and went. Then Anthony arrived.'

'When was that?'

He shrugged. 'I cannae mind, now. One day kinda went into another. Maybe a couple of days ago.'

'So, you stayed in the cottage from the Monday afternoon with one or more of the three men, yes?'

'More or less.'

'Were you ever alone in the cottage?'

'Naw. Always at least one of them there. Stop me legging it, I suppose. Not that I could,' he added. 'They had me cuffed to a radiator most of the time.'

Clare paused for a moment, forming her next question. 'I'd like to go back to your trial.'

There was an expression in his eyes she couldn't work out. She waited to see if he would speak, but when he didn't she went on. 'How did you feel about the witness who identified you?'

His eyes narrowed. 'That woman in the shop? I dunno. Suppose I was annoyed with masel' for leaving ma face exposed. Just bad luck she happened to be working in the window when I got out of the car.'

'It was her testimony that resulted in your conviction.'

He shrugged. 'Suppose.'

'So, it's reasonable to say you probably weren't her biggest fan.'

The solicitor cleared her throat, a warning gesture Clare thought, but she pressed on.

'Mr Devine, did you kill Maggie White?'

His eyes widened. 'Eh? Did I what? You joking?'

'I'm deadly serious. Maggie died the afternoon you escaped custody.'

He glanced at his solicitor. 'Oh now, wait a minute,' he said. 'I never harmed a hair on her head. I didnae even know she was dead. Check my DNA. It'll be on file. Check it and you'll see. If she's dead it wasnae me that killed her.'

'Do you have any evidence to place my client at the murder scene?' the solicitor asked.

Clare's lips thinned. 'Our enquiries are continuing.'

The solicitor raised an eyebrow but said nothing further.

'Okay,' Clare said. 'We'll revisit that another time. Let's go back to the men who engineered your escape. Did you ask why they'd done this? Why they'd helped you escape?'

He laughed. 'Wasn't it obvious?'

Clare raised an eyebrow. 'Maybe you could explain it. For the tape.'

'The jewellery. They knew I'd hidden it. And they wanted me to tell them where.'

'To be clear, Paul, you are speaking of the jewellery stolen from Jardine's Jewellers, an offence of which you were convicted, yes?'

'Aye.'

'And did you? Did you tell them?'

He smiled. 'I didnae know.'

'Is that the truth? Or did you say that, hoping they'd believe you? I should tell you we have opened a box found in the boat tonight.'

'Like I say. I didnae know where they were.'

'And how did they react to that?'

'No' too pleased. Eventually they *persuaded* me to tell them Ant had helped. That he'd hidden the stuff, like. Until the fuss died down. Next thing I know, he's there too. In the cottage.'

'And did *he* tell them where the jewels were?'

He shook his head. 'No' at first. But in the end they said they'd kill me in front of him. Think he believed them. So he told them – about the cemetery, ye know?' He nodded. 'Pretty clever place.'

'What happened then?'

'Next night we headed over. Ant telling them where to go, like. Got to the cemetery and I saw where we were. Brunton.' He smirked. 'I don't think they realised we knew that place like the back of our hands. Anyway, they brought spades and Ant showed them the grave. They made him do the digging, me helping a bit; and then I saw something. Through the trees. Just for a second. Like a torch. It was there, and it was gone. So I whispers to Ant. Couldnae say much 'cause they were standing near us, looking into the grave.'

'What did you say?' Clare asked.

'We played this game when we were wee. Called it *Denny*. A chase game, ye know? But you couldnae catch someone if they went up on this rough bit of ground. Like a wee hill. All gorse and trees. That was the Den; and it was over the cemetery wall. It was pitch black and I knew, if we could get away, they wouldnae be able to follow us fast enough. So I whispered *Denny*. And Ant looks at me, like he understands. Then I hear his spade strike metal and I know he's hit the box. He crouches down and sweeps the earth off it. Then he stands up and hands it to me just as the spotlights go on and we hear shouting. A'm holding the box and Ant's hoisting himself up out of the grave. I said *Denny* again and we ran for the back wall. You lads had cops round the cemetery but there's a bit that's in the shade of a tree. So we made for that. The cops went after the other three and somehow we got away. Ant vaulted the wall behind the tree. I handed him the box and followed him over. I heard one of the cops shouting we'd got away, but once we were out of the cemetery we knew where to go. Years ago now but it comes back to you. We zig-zagged up towards the *Denny*. Once we were there we knew they'd never find us. We were up the top and down the other side before they realised where we'd gone. We kept going for ten minutes – something like that – then we knew we were safe.'

Clare couldn't help thinking if she'd been leading the operation she'd have had enough boots on the ground to stop them escaping. But maybe not. The Devine brothers certainly seemed resourceful. 'And then?'

'We lay low for a few hours – till we thought they'd given up. Saw the vans leaving. We gave it another hour and we moved on again. Made for an old barn we knew about. Ant told me to hide there and he'd be back with transport. Few hours later he turned up in a van. Then he said he knew a lad with a boat. Some'dy who'd get us away.' Paul rubbed his chin. 'I wasnae so sure. Thought you lads would catch up with me eventually. And I knew I'd done nothing wrong – apart from legging it at the cemetery.'

He stopped for a minute, rubbing his chin. 'Skipping the country, though – that's another matter. But Ant, he said how the insurance would've paid out by now so what was the point in handing the jewels back. Said he knew a lad abroad who'd handle them for us. So I thought, what the hell. Then you lads showed up. Never been in a boat chase,' he said. 'Almost worth it.'

'And this box, Paul, it contained the jewels stolen from Jardine's shop last year? The robbery you were convicted of?'

He looked at Clare. 'A'm co-operating, yeah?'

'So far.'

'If I tell you stuff, you'll make sure it's mentioned – to the prison, like? Might make a difference for me.'

'I'll make sure it's mentioned. So, are these the jewels you took from Jardine's Jewellers?'

He took a moment then he nodded. 'Aye. That's them.'

Clare noted this down. Then she scanned her notepad. Had she covered everything? Then Kim and Debbie's faces flashed into her mind. 'Just one last thing,' she said. 'Did you wonder why it was so easy for the three men to hijack the prison van?'

He looked at her for a minute, a smile spreading across his face. 'You mean those two were in on it?' He laughed. 'Well, that's a first.'

'No, Mr Devine,' Clare said, her voice level. 'That's not what I meant. Just answer the question please.'

He frowned. 'Mebbe. You'd think they'd have some kind of routine, like a panic button on their phones, that kind o' thing.'

'I'm sure they do,' Clare said, watching him carefully. 'Why do you think they didn't follow the protocol for these situations?'

His eyes widened and he seemed genuinely at a loss. 'No idea. Mebbe you could tell me.'

She considered this for a moment. She'd like to have seen his reaction. To see if his conscience would extend to sympathy for two terrified women. But if she didn't mention the abduction, and he let slip he knew about it in a future interview, it would prove prior knowledge of the escape. She didn't think he had known about it, but better not to mention it. 'I don't think that's relevant just now.' She glanced at her watch 'Interview terminated at 8:55 p.m.'

Chapter 31

Chris was typing up his notes when Clare emerged from the interview room.

'How'd it go with the boatman?' she asked him.

He leaned back in his chair and stretched, rubbing the back of his neck. 'Not much, really. Phone call asking him to pick up a couple of passengers down at Wormit bay.'

'Why didn't he suggest Woodhaven pier? The bay's pretty shallow at that point.'

'Apparently they said the beach was better for them so he went ashore to pick them up in a tender – an inflatable, you know? Then back out to the boat.'

'Did he confirm they brought the box of jewels on board?'

Chris yawned. 'He did.'

'Where did they want to go?'

'Ah now, there he was a bit vague. Eventually he said south of England.'

'Bit of an odd way to get to England. Believe him?'

He shook his head. 'I'm pretty sure he was heading abroad. But he wasn't going to admit it. Said he didn't do much trade at this time of year so he couldn't afford to turn them down.'

'Did you ask him why he tried to outrun the coastguard?'

Chris laughed. 'He said something about thinking the lads on board had upset someone. Soon as he realised who it was he slowed down. To be honest, Clare, I think he saw an easy way to make a few quid, taking the Devines to Europe, or North Africa. But I don't think there's much more to it than that.'

'Fair enough. Release him pending further enquiries.'

Chris hesitated. 'Can I ask—'

'Paul Devine? Meek as a lamb. No doubt putting on a show for his solicitor.'

'Tell you much?'

'Nothing we didn't already know. The rest of the gang sprung him so he could lead them to the jewels. Only, he didn't know where they were. It was Anthony's idea to bury them. I think Paul knew that much but he couldn't tell them where the grave was so they grabbed Anthony off the street.'

Chris shook his head. 'What a shower. Did Anthony corroborate Paul's story?'

'I'm just about to find out.'

She was heading for the interview room when Jim stopped her, notepad in hand. 'There's been a development.'

'Tell me?'

'That van at Waterstone Crook. A lad appeared about an hour ago. Seems the key was on the front wheel. He was just getting into it when Robbie and Gillian stopped him. They're bringing him in now; but you might want SOCO to go over the van.'

'Oh?'

He took out his phone and clicked to show Clare a photo. She peered at it. It wasn't the clearest image, taken in the dark with the flash bouncing off the van interior.

'What is it?'

'To be honest, Clare, I'm not entirely sure. But I've googled a few of the names on the boxes. There's at least six GPS Guidance Units in there, a couple of drones and I've no idea what the other stuff is. But from what I can gather I'd say it's high-tech farming stuff.'

'Our farmer's missing tractor GPS?'

'That and a whole lot more. I could be wrong but it's possible you've found your farm machinery thief. Or one of them.'

Clare smiled. 'Give Chris a shout please, Jim. He can grill the van lad while I tackle our gravedigger.'

Anthony Devine was less forthcoming than his brother. He denied having prior knowledge of the prison van hijack. But

243

when Clare asked about his uncle he shifted in his seat, avoiding her eye.

'Do you even have an uncle?' she said.

'Aye.'

'And he died?'

'Erm, aye.'

'What was the cause of death?'

He avoided her eye. 'No idea.'

She paused for a moment. 'We've checked, Anthony. You have one uncle. He lives in Yorkshire and, when we spoke to him today, he sounded pretty lively for a dead man.'

'He, erm, he wasn't that sort of uncle. Just someone you called uncle.'

His eyes were flitting back and forward. *He's trying to work out how we know*, she thought. 'Let's save some time, Anthony. We know and you know there wasn't a body in that coffin. Now we can apply to have the grave exhumed but it would save us all some time if you were straight with us.'

He sat for a few seconds, as though weighing this up. 'Okay. So it wasn't a body. Nobody died.'

'Thank you,' Clare said. 'Can you tell me why you invented a family death?'

'Thought Paul could do with a break. Get out of the prison for a bit.'

'You conceived this elaborate ruse simply so your brother could have a few hours out of prison?'

'Aye.'

'No other reason?'

'Like what?'

'Oh, I don't know,' Clare said, 'maybe the chance to dig up the jewels he'd stolen.'

'I did that under duress,' he said. 'The three men who grabbed me on Thursday – they told me where the jewels were. They knew I helped with graves occasionally. Especially where it wasn't easy to get a digger in. I guess they thought I was used to it.' He met her eye, his gaze confident. 'I was slave labour and that's all there was to it.'

This didn't quite match with Anthony's story. It sounded like he was trying to wriggle out of any involvement in the Jardine's robbery?

'I suppose that's why you ran for it on Friday night – taking the jewels with you?'

He shrugged. 'I was scared, you know? Didn't know who it was that had surrounded the cemetery.'

'But why take the jewels?'

'Dunno. Panicked I suppose.'

Clare sat, regarding him for a moment. Then she said, 'I'll tell you what I think. I think the package put through your door earlier in the week was a burner phone so the men arrested at the cemetery could communicate with you. I think you refused to help them and that's why you were abducted from outside your workplace on Thursday. I believe they threatened to harm your brother and, to protect him, you agreed to take them to the place where you'd hidden the jewels.'

He sat back and folded his arms. 'Never heard so much shite in all my life. If that's the best you can do…'

Clare watched him for a minute. Then she decided to change tack. 'What did you do after the funeral on Monday?'

His brow creased as though trying to work out where she was going with this. 'I dunno,' he said. 'Just drove around. It was hard, seeing Paul cuffed to those goons. Didn't feel much like going back to work so I drove for a bit.'

She was impressed at his ability to lie on the spot. It wasn't going to be easy catching him out.

'Where did you go?'

'Here and there. Can't remember, really.'

'Try.'

He shook his head. 'Sorry. I drive so much, you see – for work.'

'Might you have gone up the Toll Road? It runs from Guard-bridge to Balmullo.'

His eyes narrowed. 'Dunno. Might have.'

'I think you did,' she said. 'Your van was seen on that road on Monday afternoon. So I'll ask you again. Did you drive up the Toll Road on Monday afternoon?'

'If you say I did then I must have.'

'Did you stop at Maggie White's cottage? It's just beyond Motray Farm.'

His face cleared as he realised what she meant. 'The woman who was killed? You're barking up the wrong tree, there. I wouldn't know her if I fell over her; and, no, I did not kill her.'

'Did you speak to her? Knock on her door, perhaps?'

'Nope. Didn't even stop.'

'So you do remember being on the Toll Road.'

'I suppose so.'

'Did you stop anywhere?'

'Nope.'

She was getting nowhere. Admittedly it wasn't Anthony Devine's DNA on the hammer, so he probably hadn't killed Maggie after all; but he had been up there on Monday afternoon. She was sure of that now.

There was a tap at the door and Clare ended the interview, informing Anthony he'd be remanded in custody.

Outside, Jim was waiting. 'Anything else you need done? Or can I let the team get away?'

'Chris?'

'Still in with the lad from the van.'

Clare yawned. 'Tell him to detain the lad overnight and I'll go over his statement in the morning.' She glanced at the clock. 'You're right, Jim. We've all been here long enough. Send them home; and I think we can call off the supervision on the Jardines' house and shop. Pretty much everyone's in custody now. If you could give them a call and let them know?'

Jim said he would do this, and she went back to her office to shut down her computer.

Monday

Chapter 32

Clare overslept on Monday morning.

'Why didn't you wake me?' she said, buttering a piece of toast.

'You've been working flat out,' the DCI said. 'Anyway, pretty much everyone's in custody.'

'Everyone except Maggie White's killer. Honestly, Al. I'm going to be chasing my tail all day now.'

'Another hour won't make any difference. You'll be all the fresher for it.'

She crunched a mouthful of toast. 'Suppose.'

'So, what's the plan for today?'

Clare stood, her back to the sink, and considered this. 'Honestly? I haven't a clue. I mean the prison break's more or less wrapped up but I'm no nearer finding Maggie's killer.'

'Back to basics,' he reminded her. 'The person who's most likely is often the one responsible.'

She mulled this over as she drove into the station. It was raining now, the crisp autumn weather having broken at last. The rain grew heavier as she approached St Andrews and her wipers switched automatically to the faster speed. She pulled into the station car park and saw a familiar figure walking across the car park. Zoe was unmistakable with her red curls peeping out from her duffel coat hood, her yellow wellies sloshing through the puddles. A carrier bag swung from her hand. More cakes, no doubt. Clare patted her stomach, thinking of the takeaway meals and snacks grabbed over the past week. It was always the same when she was on a major enquiry. The diet went to pot. *Tomorrow*, she promised herself. *I'll start eating sensibly tomorrow.*

As she dashed across the car park, the DCI's words rang in her head. Who was the person most likely to have killed Maggie White? Who benefited from her death? The money they'd found in the garden shed was a tidy sum but surely not enough to kill for. It hadn't been taken anyway. Plus, Maggie had been hit from behind. There was nothing to suggest she'd been knocked about to make her disclose where the money was. But, if the motive hadn't been financial, what else could it be?

The cottage. It had to be. Eric McGovern wanted it for one of his workers and now he had it. Or he would have, once Clare had finished with it. But surely that wasn't enough of a motive for murder. Was it? She looked into the incident room, shaking the rain off her coat. Janey was tapping away at a laptop and she glanced up.

'Morning, boss.'

'Wonder if you could do me a favour, Janey?'

'Sure.'

'I want a sample of DNA from Eric McGovern. He's the farmer at Motray Farm, down the road from Maggie White's cottage.'

Janey regarded her. 'You fancy him for it?'

Clare shrugged. 'I'm honestly not sure. But it's an oversight. The DNA on the murder weapon is from a male. He wanted Maggie out of her cottage, and she wasn't for budging.'

Janey raised an eyebrow. 'From the sound of him he won't like it.'

'No, he won't. Take Bill along for moral support.'

'What if he refuses?'

Clare sighed. 'You know what? Just arrest him. We don't have time to play games. The Jardines' statement confirms he tried to intimidate Maggie into giving up her cottage. I'd say that gives us reasonable grounds to suspect him of involvement in her death. Get it voluntarily if you can, though. Hopefully the threat of arrest will persuade him to co-operate.'

Janey nodded. Then her brow creased. 'Hold on – didn't he come to get you when the hammer was found? Surely he'd have waited until you'd gone then buried it somewhere? In fact, if he'd killed Maggie, would he honestly get rid of the hammer in one of his own fields?'

It was a good point. 'I dunno, Janey. Maybe he knew the field was due to be ploughed and he was counting on the hammer being ground into the soil. Then one of his workers finds it and he's forced to tell us.'

Janey rose. 'Yeah, could be. I'll head over there now.'

Clare's phone began to ring and she squinted at the display. Ben Ratcliffe. *What now?* She swiped to take the call. 'Hi, Ben.'

'Wondering if you can spare me a few minutes?'

This sounded ominous. 'I've time now.'

'No. In person. I'll come over later. Say four-ish.'

Clare ended the call, none the wiser. She wandered into her office to find Max and Chris chatting over coffees. 'Make yourselves at home, guys, why don't you?'

Max jumped to his feet. 'Can I get you a coffee?'

She waved this away. 'Thanks, though.' She moved round the back of her desk and switched on her computer. 'I've asked Bill and Janey to head over to Motray Farm and take DNA from Eric McGovern.'

Max's eyebrows shot up. 'I don't envy them that.'

'Nor me,' Clare said. 'But they'll arrest him if there's any nonsense.'

Chris sipped his coffee and set the cup down. 'What about Anthony Devine?'

Clare shook her head. 'I think we can rule him out of Maggie's murder. His DNA isn't on the murder weapon and it's pretty clear he was up that farm road to steal the tractor GPS.'

'He uses that van for work, though,' Chris said. 'So his prints and DNA will be all over it.'

'That's true. But, if SOCO find them on the stuff inside the van, I'll charge him.' Then Clare remembered Chris's interview the previous night. 'What about the van lad? Any luck?'

'Jack Sneddon? Yes and no.'

'Go on.'

'Claims somebody called, asking him to pick up a van and drive it to St Andrews. A few quid in it for him. Key on the front wheel, kind of thing.'

'I'm guessing he didn't know the caller?'

'So he says. Interesting thing is he works at Motray Farm.'

'Oh really?'

'Yep. General farm hand, from what he said. So I arrested him on suspicion of reset and that got him talking.'

'And?'

'He admitted knowing Anthony Devine. Seems he and Anthony had a conversation over a pint one night. Anthony claimed to be interested in high-tech farm equipment. Said he was thinking of setting up in business so Jack told him about some of the stuff McGovern has. Said he suggested Anthony called at the farm for a chat with McGovern. And this is where it gets interesting.'

'Yeah?'

'He told Anthony not to come round on a Monday, late afternoon, as that was when McGovern did his paperwork. Said he'd be inside and wouldn't want to be disturbed.'

'In other words,' Clare said, 'Monday late afternoon would be a good time to nick the GPS unit.'

Chris nodded. 'Sounds like it. I'm guessing McGovern would lock stuff like that away at night but it might still have been sitting out in the yard at that time.'

'and no doubt he told Anthony exactly where to find it.'

Chris nodded. 'I mean he denies it all but I reckon that's what happened. He eventually admitted to seeing Anthony that afternoon. Anthony claimed he was out for a walk.'

Clare sat back. 'Good work, Chris. I reckon there's a fair chance Eric McGovern's GPS unit's in that van; and I wouldn't want to be in Jack Sneddon's shoes when McGovern finds out.'

'Do you think that could be something to do with Maggie's death?' Max asked. 'Maybe she got wind of the thefts. Could be they parked the van near her cottage. She saw Jack loading stuff into it and threatened to report him. Maybe she was blackmailing him and that's where the money came from.'

Clare frowned. 'Where would a lad like that get twenty thousand pounds in cash?'

'How about from selling those machines?' Chris said. 'Could have been going on for years. Maybe Maggie got greedy – wanted more and he finally flipped.'

She looked at him. 'You might have something there.'

He shrugged. 'I try.'

As they chatted, Clare's inbox began to fill and she saw an email from Raymond Curtice. She clicked the message and scanned it briefly.

'Both Jardines' prints on the money found in Maggie's shed.'

'It came from the shop, then,' Max said.

Clare frowned. 'Looks like it. I just don't know how. Or why.'

Chris shrugged. 'Out of the till, I'd imagine.'

'I doubt it. Most of their transactions would be card payments.'

'Maybe he paid Maggie in cash,' Max suggested. 'Avoiding national insurance and so on.'

Clare shook her head. 'No, remember he said he paid her by standing order? Straight into her bank account.'

'He could have been lying,' Chris said. 'Maybe not all Maggie's wages went through the books.'

Clare frowned. 'It's possible. He just doesn't strike me as the type.' She sighed. 'We'd better see them again.' She picked up her phone. 'I'll get onto them now. See if we can call round.'

There was no response from Sylvia Jardine's mobile. Clare tried calling the shop but it rang out. She put down her phone, thinking. 'Is Sara out on patrol?'

Chris shrugged. 'Dunno.'

'Get her on the radio, would you, Chris? Ask her to pop in to the jeweller's. Find out when they close for lunch and say we'll look in.'

As Chris went off to radio Sara, Clare's phone began to ring. It was Raymond.

'Clare, I'm a bit jumpy about having this metal box around the lab. It's full of rings, watches and goodness knows what else. Who knows how much it's worth!'

'Yes, I can see that,' she said. 'How soon do you want it picked up?'

'Now, if you can. I went over it early this morning. Easy enough to pick up DNA samples and there were clear prints on the box itself. I've another team on the van at the sports centre. Maybe by tomorrow we'll have the results for both. If we push it.'

'Okay,' Clare said. 'Give me an hour and I'll be across to collect it. And I'll bring my two minders with me.'

She ended the call. 'I need a diamond expert.'

Chris raised an eyebrow. 'Don't look at me.'

'I know one,' Max said, and Chris stared at him.

Clare shook her head. 'Max, how on earth do you know a diamond expert?'

'Just one of those things you pick up,' he said. 'Nice man. Office in Perth.' He smiled. 'Want me to see if he's free?'

—

Carl Menzies had an office on Atholl Place, an attractive Georgian crescent overlooking the quaintly named North Inch park in Perth. They collected the box of gems from the SOCO office in Dundee and headed west, along the north bank of the River Tay until the road joined the dual carriageway to Perth. The rain drummed down on the car and Clare had to keep the fan blowing to avoid the windscreen steaming up. Chris looked hopefully at The Horn Milk Bar as they passed it but Clare's eyes were focused on the road ahead. Although there were three of them in the car she still felt uneasy with such valuable cargo sitting on Chris's knee. She'd be much happier once it was in secure storage.

'Take the Queen's Bridge,' Max said as they left the dual carriageway and entered Perth.

He directed her along the south bank of the river until they came to Charlotte Street, a broad throughfare bordering the North Inch. She pulled into a parking space and Max jumped out. He crossed the road, dodging between the lanes of traffic and mounted a short flight of steps leading to a dark blue panelled door with a fanlight above. Clare watched as he spoke into an intercom. Then he signalled for them to join him. Chris took charge of the metal box as they dashed across the road and up the steps.

The office had an air of calm in contrast to the busy road outside. Carl Menzies was a small man with receding hair and metal-rimmed glasses. He was casually dressed in black jeans and a pale blue shirt, the sleeves rolled up. Clare introduced herself and Chris and he led the three of them into a brightly lit room. A large white table stood against a wall with equipment and lamps towards the back. Clare took it in, wondering what all the gadgets were. There was something that looked like a microscope, a small set of scales and several other machines she'd never seen before.

He smiled politely. 'I understand you have some items of value you wish me to examine.'

Clare nodded. 'We believe them to be the proceeds of a robbery from a jeweller's shop.'

'The one in St Andrews?' he said. 'I know the Jardines. They keep some very nice pieces.' He indicated a smaller table. 'If you could put it up there and open the case, please?'

Clare did as he asked and she pulled back the lid on the box. The jewels were still in the plastic bag but SOCO had peeled the tape back as part of their investigations.

Carl Menzies studied the contents without comment. After a moment he opened a drawer and withdrew a pair of fine gloves. Reaching inside the plastic bag he removed several rings, placing them on a white tray. He carried this across to the table, flicking on two lamps, and eased himself down onto a velvet-topped stool. Removing his specs he took a small eyeglass from a drawer beneath the table which he placed against his right eye, creasing his brow to prevent it slipping. Then he examined the rings, one by one, setting each aside as he moved to the next. When he had scrutinised these he turned back to the metal box and extracted several more along with two necklaces. Again he peered through the eyeglass, then he pulled one of the instruments Clare thought was a microscope towards him. He held a ring under the lens and bent forward to look through the eyepieces, repeating this process with each of the items from the tray.

They stood silently while he carried out his examination. Eventually he sat back and regarded Clare. 'What is it you wish to know?'

For a moment Clare wasn't sure how to respond. What did she want to know? 'I suppose we'd like confirmation these are the jewels stolen from the Jardines' shop last year; and it would be useful to know the value of what we have here.'

He looked down at the jewels. 'Might I ask how you came by these?'

'They were recovered when we arrested…' She hesitated. She didn't want to give away any details about the Devine brothers. 'When we detained a suspect.'

'I see.' He began replacing each item carefully in the plastic bag and when he had finished, he said, 'If I recall correctly, the loss to Jardines was put in the region of three to four hundred thousand pounds, yes?'

'I'd have to check,' Clare said, 'but I think so.'

He nodded. 'The contents of this box,' he said, 'should be passed to the insurers. They will want to ascertain they match the claim.' He indicated the box. 'We in the trade are always on the lookout for likely stolen property. We have lists, you know? So we can alert the police if any of them happen our way.' He indicated the box. 'In terms of what was stolen from the Jardines, I would say the contents probably match in type and number. In other words I would guess this box contains roughly the right number of rings, necklaces, watches and so on. However, the value of the pieces I have examined is considerably less than what was reportedly stolen.'

Clare frowned. 'So, these are not the jewels taken from Jardine's?'

'That's not what I'm saying. This watch, for instance – it's a lady's Rolex. Worth around nine thousand pounds. I happen to know the Jardines stocked this particular model. But the others, they are worth far less. And some of these rings: the diamonds have multiple inclusions.'

'What does that mean?' Clare asked.

'They are simply marks on the stone. The more marks, the lower the price; and all those I examined had inclusions. Two of the rings were actually cubic zirconia.'

'Is that bad?' Chris asked, and Max rolled his eyes.

'Well, it's not a diamond, officer. It's very much a cheaper alternative.'

Clare was struggling to take this in. 'So, how much would you estimate the contents of this box are worth?'

He shook his head. 'That, I'm afraid, would take quite some time. I may have been unlucky in the pieces I selected but, if these are typical, it could be anything from, say, fifteen thousand pounds to perhaps thirty thousand at the most. I suggest you contact the insurers and have their experts analyse the contents fully.'

Chapter 33

They drove back in silence, the only sound from the rain drumming incessantly on the car roof. Chris was the first to speak.

'So, what do we think?' he said. 'Are these the jewels from Jardine's shop or not?'

'That's what we need the insurers to tell us,' Clare said. She glanced at Max. 'Anything from Jim yet?'

He fished his phone out of his jacket pocket and glanced at it. 'Yeah. They're sending someone over in the morning. First thing.'

'There is a quicker way,' Chris said.

Clare checked over her shoulder as she accelerated up the slip road to the M90. 'Yeah?'

'The Jardines. They're bound to recognise the jewels.'

'Good point. Did Sara find out what time they close for lunch?'

Chris squinted at his phone. 'Note on the door,' he said. 'Shop's shut till further notice.'

Clare's expression darkened. 'We'll catch them at the house then. See what they have to say about that insurance claim.'

–

There was no reply when Clare rang the bell at the Jardines' house in Donaldson Gardens.

'He might be at the shop after all,' Max said. 'Maybe doing a bit of paperwork in the back.'

Clare nodded. 'I thought she might be at home, though.' She stood back scanning the upstairs windows for any sign of life but it looked like the bedroom blinds were drawn. Chris frowned at this.

'Funny time of day to draw the blinds,' he said.

The autumn sun, while low in the sky, was shining on the upper part of the house and Clare put a hand up to shade her eyes. 'Probably to keep the sun out. They might have nice paintings or furniture in those front rooms.'

Chris shrugged. 'Suppose. Check the shop, then?'

'Yeah.' Clare turned to walk down the drive but her eye was caught by an empty milk bottle on the front doorstep. She hadn't noticed it when she rang the bell and she walked back to the door, bending to examine it. A folded piece of paper had been placed under the bottle and she picked it up to read:

No milk on Tuesday or Wednesday please

Back to normal on Thursday

Thank you,

S Jardine

She held the note out for the others to see.

'They've gone away then,' Max said.

Clare nodded. 'Looks like it.'

'Should we check the shop anyway?' Chris said.

'Might as well.'

But the shop too was shut up, a note on the door, as Sara had said.

'We'll have their mobile numbers back at the station,' Clare said, heading for the car. 'If they're not too far away maybe we can take the jewels for them to examine.'

—

'Got the farmer's DNA,' Bill said when Clare entered the incident room.

'Any problem?'

'Not really. He wasn't happy, though. Said Maggie's death was nothing to do with him. I gave him the usual stuff about ruling him out. I also said it would help in identifying his stolen technology when we found it. That got his attention.'

'You didn't tell him we'd recovered his GPS unit, did you?'

Bill shook his head. 'No, but I did say our enquiries were progressing and having his DNA would be helpful.'

'Good thinking. Okay, let's station someone outside the farm. Just until we get his DNA back.'

'You're thinking if he is the lassie's killer—'

'That he might abscond,' Clare finished. 'Yes, I wouldn't put it past him; and I don't want to lose him at this stage.'

Bill frowned. 'You want to bring him in?'

'Wish I could,' Clare said. 'But we've no grounds. And I don't want to start the clock ticking on his arrest until I know if it's his DNA on the hammer.'

She found Jim at his desk and asked him to station a car on the Toll Road, outside the farm; and then she remembered the Jardines. 'Could you look up their mobiles?' she went on. 'They seem to have gone away for a couple of days and I could do with seeing them. Don't say anything about the jewels,' she said. 'Just that I'd like to check something.'

Jim noted this down and Clare went back to her office. She sat down on her chair, suddenly tired. They were well into the second week of this operation and, while the prison break and jewellery theft were pretty much tied up, she was still no nearer finding Maggie's killer. Admittedly she had the farmer's DNA now. It might just prove a match. She thought she'd like the killer to be Eric McGovern. There was something about him. Something about the way he spoke to Tansy, his stepdaughter. Did Tansy's mother realise how much her daughter hated him? 'Families, eh?' she said softly and turned back to her inbox which had filled up again with new emails.

She'd almost forgotten about Ben Ratcliffe when her office door opened and he appeared.

'Oh, Ben,' she said, rising. 'Sorry, I was deep in paperwork. Erm, coffee?'

'Your nice young sergeant's making it,' he said.

Clare decided he must mean Max and she cleared a space on her desk for the cups. A minute later Max appeared with, of all things, a tray. Clare wondered where he'd found it and whether he'd cleaned it before using. It looked vaguely familiar but she certainly hadn't seen it for a year or more. She thanked him for the coffees and waited until the door closed. Then she smiled at Ben. 'You wanted to see me?'

–

Clare lay on the sofa, toasting her feet on the fire which spat and sparked. She eased herself forward and pulled the fireguard over, to Benjy's evident disgust. 'I think these logs are a bit damp.'

The DCI picked one up from the basket and scrutinised it. 'Probably larch,' he said. 'It sparks a bit. Where did you buy them?'

Clare lay back again. 'Dunno. Some shop.'

He rolled his eyes. 'You need to buy from a proper log supplier. These nets you pick up from corner shops might not be properly dried. You'll end up with more smoke than fire.'

'Okay,' she yawned. 'Soon as this investigation's over I'll order some logs.'

'You really should think about a stove,' he said. 'The brochures are on the bookcase if you want a look.' He indicated the fire. 'Most of that heat's going straight up the chimney.'

'Yeah, okay, Al,' she said. 'Soon as—'

'I know. Soon as the investigation's over.' He rose from the hearth and flopped down beside her. 'You've still not told me what Ben wanted.'

She swivelled round so her head was on his lap and he began stroking her hair. 'He's offered me a job.'

'Really? A promotion?'

'No. Another DI post but heading up undercover ops.'

'Wow.' He'd stopped stroking her hair now and seemed lost in thought. 'You must have made quite an impression.'

'It was bringing in the Devine brothers,' she said. 'Tracking the boat, recovering the stolen jewels. He actually said he doubted anyone on his team could have done a better job.'

'I agree,' the DCI said. 'You do run a good operation, Clare Mackay.'

'Not so good at finding murderers, though,' she said.

'Maybe your farmer's DNA will be a match.' He hesitated, then went on. 'This job with Ben. Did he say where?'

'That's the thing. I could be working anywhere in Scotland really, but my base would be Gartcosh.'

There was a pause. Then he said, 'That must be sixty miles from here.'

'Sixty-four.'

'It's a helluva commute.'

She lifted her head and swung her feet round and down so she was sitting and turned to face him, her elbow on the arm of the sofa. 'Yeah. I couldn't do it daily.'

He frowned. 'So, how would it work?'

'Well, day-to-day, I'd probably leave here on a Monday and maybe come back Thursday night, work from home on Friday. Weekends off. But when there was an op I could be anywhere, any days.'

He didn't reply and she went on.

'I mean I know we wouldn't see each other from Monday to Thursday but sometimes, if you're away or I'm involved in an incident, it's a bit like that anyway.'

'Yes, that's true,' he said. 'But there's one thing you're forgetting.'

'Which is?'

'Benjy.'

At the sound of his name Benjy's tail thumped the rug. Clare was suddenly appalled at herself. How could she have forgotten him? Her faithful companion through all the ups and downs of the last few years. What was she thinking, even considering this job?

'It's not insurmountable,' the DCI went on. 'I'm here most evenings and your neighbour Moira takes him out twice a day anyway. But it's not really fair, giving him so little of your time, is it?'

–

She lay awake long into the night, despite the weariness of working eight days in a row. Was there a solution for Benjy? Might it even be possible to take him to Gartcosh with her on a Monday? Would he sit under her desk while she worked and be content with a lunchtime walk? She doubted it very much but more and more employers were allowing their staff to work flexibly. Might that extend to Ben Ratcliffe's undercover team? She doubted that too. But it could be worth asking on the basis that, if you didn't ask…

Eventually, she fell into a fitful sleep with no idea of how she would respond to Ben's offer.

Tuesday

Chapter 34

Clare drove into work, listening to the news on the radio. A brief statement had been issued to the press the previous night confirming the escaped prisoner had been recaptured and three suspected accomplices were also in custody.

> Police sources are still refusing to confirm that a
> quantity of jewellery stolen in an audacious robbery
> last year had also been recovered.

She sighed, wondering how they found these things out. She drew into the car park and backed into her usual space. In the station, Jim was at his desk tapping at a computer with two fingers.

'Any luck with the Jardines?' she asked.

He shook his head. 'Not yet. His phone went to voicemail, hers just rang out.'

'Keep trying please,' she said, and wandered into her office. Her head felt thick this morning, maybe from lack of sleep, Ben's offer running through her head most of the night. She'd asked for time to consider, and he'd agreed.

'Not too long, though. I'm keen to have another team up and running ASAP.'

But what were her options? Giving up Benjy was unthinkable. It wasn't his fault she'd been offered an exciting new job; but it did sound exciting. *You're wasted in a backwater like St Andrews*, Ben had said. Backwater? St Andrews? Sure, it wasn't a sprawling city with its dark corners and darker deeds. It was a traditional town with historic buildings and an ancient university; but scratch beneath the surface, and all human life was there. Admittedly the work could be tedious at times, repetitive even, but you could say that of most police work. Undercover, though, that was different. She felt a frisson of excitement at the prospect. Over the years she'd investigated all manner of crimes from the petty to the perverted. She'd even spent time as a firearms officer. But never anything like this. She thought about Gavin Gates. Not even his friend and colleague Alan had realised he was working undercover. What else went on that wasn't generally known among the ranks? It might be thrilling to be part of it.

A tap at the door interrupted her thoughts and Chris came in. He sank down in a chair opposite and she wondered suddenly how he'd deal with a new DI at the station. He could be lazy, difficult at times. But she'd learned to manage him over the years and, she believed, bring out the best in him. A new DI might not take the same approach. Would Chris cope with that?

'Insurance assessor's here,' he said.

Clare rose. 'Right. I want an officer with him while he works. He is not to be left alone with those jewels.'

'She, actually.'

'Eh?'

'The insurance assessor. It's a woman. Helen Cosgrove.'

'Where is she?'

'Interview room four. Janey's fetching the box from the store.'

Clare went to the incident room and found Gillian bent over a laptop. 'Job for you, Gill.'

She glanced up. 'I was checking the DVLA database,' she said. 'I thought if we put out an alert for the Jardines' cars...'

'Good idea but I need you for something else.'

Helen Cosgrove smiled as they entered the interview room. Clare introduced herself and Gillian, explaining someone had to stay with her while she examined the jewels. Helen seemed fine with this, and Clare went on to explain their visit to Carl Menzies the day before.

'Mr Menzies said some of the items were of low value,' Clare said. 'We're keen to know if the contents of the box are the items stolen from Jardine's Jewellers.'

Helen nodded at this. 'What I can do today is to count and categorise the items. I have some basic equipment with me and I'll analyse a sample from each type and make an assessment on that basis.'

'How certain can you be,' Clare asked, 'without properly examining every item?'

'If the number and type matches the claim submitted by Mr Jardine, we would consider that a strong indicator. I'll also look for the most distinctive pieces – those named specifically on the claim. Again, if I find these, that increases the likelihood they originated from the robbery. But a full analysis will have to be carried out at our lab.'

Clare offered Helen tea or coffee but she declined. She smiled at Gillian. 'You can help if you wish. Make the time pass more quickly for both of us.'

She left them to their tedious task and went back to her office, her mind on the Jardines' robbery. Away on a course at the time she'd missed the whole thing. Might there be something the investigating team had overlooked? On an impulse she lifted her phone and dialled the number for Tech Support. Diane Wallace who ran the department answered.

'Clare – great to hear from you. How are things?'

'Busy as ever.'

'You'll be after a favour then? Go on.'

'I'd like to access the CCTV from the robbery on Jardine's Jewellers, here in the town.'

'I remember it,' Diane said. 'Pretty frightening for the staff.'

'Do you still have it?'

'Oh yes. We kept it in case there were further prosecutions. It's probably archived but I can retrieve it for you.'

'Thanks, Diane. Will it take long?'

'Give me half an hour. I'll send a message when it's up on the network.'

Diane was as good as her word and half an hour later Clare had the footage from the robbery. She scrolled to the time when Paul Devine had entered the shop then she scrolled back to watch Maggie move to adjust the window display. Only her back was visible, as she bent forward. Then Clare watched as she straightened up, stood for a moment and backed out of the window moving quickly to the counter. Finlay came into shot and the two of them stood as the figure of Paul Devine entered the shop. Finlay moved as if to do something – press an alarm or perhaps deploy the fog device – but Paul Devine jerked the gun and they both raised their hands. Then he handed Maggie a sack. There was no audio but his instructions were clear and she began to fill the sack with items from the counter. Finlay moved forward as if to protect her and Paul waved the gun once more. Maggie stumbled back and with a glance at the gun she began unlocking one of the display cases. Finlay continued tipping trays of rings and necklaces into the sack. Then he reached below the counter and brought out more trays. Maggie was fumbling with the key, as though her fingers wouldn't work. Moments later she watched Paul turn back to the door as though hearing something. He grabbed the box of necklaces Maggie had taken from the display case and threw it in the sack. With a final wave of the gun he turned and fled for the door. Maggie ran after him and slammed the door shut. She stumbled back into the shop, weeping visibly. Clare watched as she approached Finlay, who seemed frozen with fear. In the end it was Maggie who took out her phone and tapped at it. A minute later the footage ended. 'Must be motion activated,' she muttered. She scrolled back and watched it again, trying to compare what Finlay was dropping into the sack with the haul she'd recovered from the bottom of the boat. He'd certainly tipped in a lot of rings. Some had been displayed in individual boxes but others had been set out on velvet pads, maybe fifteen on each. No wonder the haul had been so large. So many jewels in, what, less than a minute?

She paused the footage and sat back to think. Was there anything here that could help find Maggie's killer? Unless Paul

Devine and the rest of the gang were lying, they weren't responsible for her death. Their DNA had been sent to the lab and, although Raymond hadn't actually said, she presumed none of them was a match for the hammer. She looked again at the frozen footage from the jewellery shop then rose from her seat.

Bill was in the incident room, dipping a chocolate biscuit in a mug of coffee. 'Can you find me the footage from Jardine's Jewellers please?' Clare said. 'We requested it for the week leading up to Maggie's death.'

'Aye, no problem.' He set down his mug and reached for a laptop. 'Want me to email the link?'

'Please.' She wandered back to her office, lost in thought. Might there be something on the CCTV from Maggie's last day in the shop? She hadn't been in on the Monday but maybe the Saturday...

The phone rang, cutting across her thoughts and she clicked to take the call. Raymond.

'Couple of things,' he said. 'First of all, your farmer.'

Clare held her breath.

'No match for the hammer, I'm afraid.'

She sank back in her chair. Another dead end, unless it had been one of his farm workers. Then she gave herself a shake. *Stop trying to bend the facts to suit your theory*, she was fond of telling her officers. Time to take her own advice.

'You said a couple of things?'

'Yeah. The van. More luck there. Both Anthony Devine and Jack Sneddon's DNA match samples taken from the van and the contents.'

It was something. Not what she had hoped for – Maggie's killer. But at least they might have cracked the farm machinery thefts. There would be more than those two involved, though. She knew that. But one of them might talk – name names. She thought again about Paul Devine's three accomplices. 'Raymond, I'm sure you'll have checked this but the three men we arrested last Friday night...'

'Sorry, Clare. I did check. No matches.'

'Worth a shot,' she said.

'Don't forget you promised me dinner.'

'Soon as I've caught my killer.'

She ended the call, wondering what to do next. They had to look further into Maggie's private life. If her murder was nothing to do with the robbery or the farmer wanting her cottage, the killer had to be someone with a reason to want her out of the way. But who? And why?

A few minutes later a message arrived from Bill with a link to the jewellery shop CCTV. Her heart sank as she opened it and saw an array of files. She really couldn't spare the time. Sara, on the other hand, with her keen eye for detail…

She found her in the kitchen, chatting to Chris. 'Job for you,' Clare said, steering the PC towards a spare laptop. 'You're looking for anything unusual,' Clare said. 'Any customer behaving oddly, anyone who looks like a shoplifter and any change in Maggie – if she behaves differently. Also, watch for signs she was taking from the till or even helping herself to the stock. She must have come by that money somehow.'

Sara nodded. 'Might take a while, though.'

'Not necessarily. It seems to be motion activated so if there's no movement it'll skip forward to the next customer.'

Jim caught her eye. 'Maggie White's mother's on her way in. She arrived in the town this morning. Should be here anytime now.'

'Thanks, Jim. Maybe ask Max to rustle us up some coffee when she gets here?'

—

Jean White was lean and wiry, her face weather-beaten from a life spent on the road. Or outdoors, certainly. Clare thought she might be in her sixties but perhaps exposure to the sun had aged her skin. According to Jim, she'd spent the last few years travelling in Europe, and was hiking her way round Ireland when the Garda had tracked her down. In spite of an itinerant lifestyle her printed leggings and fisherman's rib jersey were clean and in good order, only her stout boots testament to the miles she'd doubtless covered. Her silver-grey hair was shoulder length and curly, held in check by two simple kirby grips.

She accepted the coffee Max had made but declined the offer of a biscuit. 'When can I see my daughter?' she asked.

Clare assured her she'd be taken to see Maggie as soon as possible.

She nodded at this. 'How did she die?'

Clare chose her words carefully. 'We believe she was hit on the back of the head when she was out in the garden.'

A spasm of pain crossed Jean's face.

'We don't think she suffered,' Clare said. 'She'd have been rendered unconscious quite quickly.'

A frown creased her features. 'I don't know who would do such a thing.' She met Clare's eye. 'Have you found him? The man who did this?'

Clare thought it interesting she assumed the attacker was a man. Admittedly most attacks on women were committed by men. But she wondered if there was anything to be learned from Jean's assumption. 'Not yet,' she said. 'In fact, we were hoping you might be able to tell us a bit more about Maggie. It's been difficult finding out who her friends were. Did she have a boyfriend? Or a girlfriend?'

'Not that I knew, although I'd not spoken to her for a while. I mean there had been boyfriends over the years,' she went on. 'One even looked serious for a bit but I think she's like me: a loner at heart.'

'What about her father?'

'Not around. I didn't tell him when I realised Maggie was on the way. It wouldn't have worked and I was quite capable of bringing her up myself.'

'How did you manage?' Clare said. 'For money, I mean – if you don't mind me asking.'

'Bit of this, bit of that. I'm good with a needle and thread. I made clothes for myself and for Maggie. People admired them and asked if I'd make for them. Word got around.' She paused, as if remembering. 'I was offered a job with a dressmaker,' she went on, 'but I preferred my independence. It wasn't always easy but we managed. Maggie was a great help.' She nodded. 'We were quite the little unit.' She picked up the coffee and sipped it. 'This is rather good.'

Clare smiled. 'My sergeant. Temporary sergeant, actually. He makes a decent cup.'

'I'd hang onto him,' Jean said.

Clare hesitated, then went on. 'I'm sorry to ask but can you think of anyone who might have wanted to harm Maggie?'

In spite of the circumstances, Jean's eyes widened, as though this hadn't occurred to her. 'I assumed,' she began, 'I thought it must have been a random attack. Someone – disturbed, you know?'

'It's possible,' Clare said. 'But we do need to check if there's anyone Maggie might have upset. Or someone who wished her harm.'

Jean shook her head. 'I honestly don't know. I've been away so much, you see?'

'Did you talk on the phone? Or message?'

'Now and then.'

'And did Maggie ever share anything about her private life or social engagements? Or any worries she might have had?'

Jean sighed. 'I wish I could help. But I really can't recall anything like that.' She glanced at Clare then away again, cradling her coffee cup. 'Sorry,' she said. 'You must think me a dreadful mother. It's just how we were.'

Clare smiled. 'Not at all. I'm sure you were a wonderful mother to Maggie.' She rose from her seat and took a card from her pocket. 'If you need anything at all,' she said, handing it to Jean, 'please give me a call.' She smiled. 'And now I'll ask one of my officers take you to see Maggie.'

Chapter 35

Clare sat on in her office after Jean White had left. Years of dealing with victims' relatives had pretty much inured her to grief but there was something in Jean's quiet demeanour she found particularly affecting. Then she gave herself a shake. There was work to be done and it didn't do to dwell.

She wondered idly how the insurance expert was getting on. Would she confirm the jewels were the ones taken in the Jardine's robbery? And then she remembered Gillian had been about to set up an alert for the couple's cars when the expert had arrived. She rose from her seat and went to the incident room. Janey was sipping a mug of coffee and looked up when Clare approached.

'Something I can do?'

'Please,' Clare said. 'I'd like to get in touch with the Jardines but it looks like they've gone away for a few days.'

'Mobiles?' Janey suggested.

'Not answering. The garage at the house is locked up, no windows, so I can't tell if they've taken the cars or not. Could you put out an alert for them please? I think Gill started to do it but I needed her for something else.'

Janey said she'd do that and Clare wandered back out to the main office. She was starting to think Maggie's attack might be random, as her mother had thought. There didn't seem to be anyone with a motive to kill her. Apart from the cash found in the shed, she wasn't particularly wealthy; and what she had would probably pass to her mother. She seemed to have few friends and, apart from the farmer wanting the cottage back, Clare could find no one who actually benefited from her death.

The door to interview room four opened and Gillian emerged. 'The insurance lady, boss – she'd like a word.'

Helen Cosgrove had spread her equipment out on the desk, but the jewels were back in the metal case when Clare entered the room. She glanced at it. 'You've finished?'

She pulled off a fine pair of gloves and put them in a small bag. 'For now,' she said. 'I presume you'll want to hang onto these until you conclude your investigations?'

'That rather depends on what you found.'

Helen smiled. 'As I said earlier it's not possible to carry out a full assessment here but I've seen enough to be fairly sure.'

Clare waited.

'I believe the contents of this case match the claim submitted by Mr Jardine in the number and type of items: the correct number of watches, rings and so on. However, there the similarities end.'

Clare's eyes widened. 'Meaning?'

'Meaning that Mr Menzies' assessment was correct. While some of the items are exactly as per Mr Jardine's claim, the vast majority do not match the claim and receipts he submitted.'

Clare stood for a moment trying to process this. Then she said, 'What does that mean?'

'Well, the receipts submitted were from reputable dealers so I don't doubt Mr Jardine purchased the items he claimed were stolen. But these,' she indicated the case, 'many of these are far lower in value.'

'Could Mr Jardine have mixed up his stock, in the panic of the robbery? Claimed for the wrong items?'

Helen shook her head. 'Unlikely. Mr Jardine has been a jeweller for almost thirty years. Plus our assessors did a full stock check following the robbery. The items claimed for were definitely missing.'

'So,' Clare said, speaking slowly, 'either these are not the items stolen in the Jardines robbery—'

'Or Mr Jardine's claim was fraudulent,' Helen finished. 'Either way, we'll certainly want to look further into this, once you release the jewels.' She began packing up her equipment. 'But I'm guessing you'd prefer to raise the matter with Mr Jardine yourself.'

‒

Clare called Chris and Max into her office and relayed the conversation she'd had with Helen Cosgrove.

'Could be a mistake,' Max said.

'It could be, but I don't think it is and I don't think Helen Cosgrove does either. I reckon he's bought that cubic whatever it is.'

'Cubic zirconia,' Max said.

'Yeah that. I reckon he's bought it from eBay, or the dark web, even. He buys it cheap, no questions asked. Probably pays with bitcoin so it can't be traced. Then he sells it in the shop for a bit more, offering a discount for cash. If it doesn't go through the till he doesn't pay tax on it. Neat little scam.'

'And he's given that cheap stuff to Devine?' Chris asked.

Clare angled her monitor so they could both see it and she clicked to view the CCTV footage from the day of the robbery again. 'Here's Maggie,' she said, 'in the window, rearranging things. Then see her react? Like she's seen the men get out of the car.'

They watched for a few seconds then Clare said, 'And now, here's Devine in the shop. See how Maggie goes to start putting things in the sack but Finlay moves forward.'

'Like he's protecting her?' Max suggested.

'You'd think, wouldn't you?' Clare said. 'But I reckon he's remembered the cheaper stuff under the counter; and he also knows a guy like Devine isn't likely to spot the difference.'

'So he claims for the expensive jewels that weren't actually stolen,' Chris said. 'But surely the assessors would have checked his stock and receipts. They wouldn't match with what's missing.'

Clare shrugged. 'He could have hidden the expensive stuff before they arrived. Kept it in his house – boot of the car, even.'

Chris rubbed his chin. 'Pretty quick thinking, though, going for the cheap stuff with a gun in your face. Almost like he knew he was going to be robbed.'

'I doubt it,' Clare said. 'I can't see someone like Finlay Jardine in cahoots with Paul Devine.'

Chris nodded. 'You're probably right.' He paused for a moment. 'Our murder victim – Maggie – do you reckon she was in on the fraud?'

Clare nodded. 'It's possible. It would certainly explain the stash of money found in her garden shed. Maybe being interviewed under caution will persuade Mr Jardine to tell us exactly what happened on the day of the robbery.'

'Want us to swing by the shop again?' Chris said. 'See if it's open now?'

'Yeah. Both of you go. Check the shop and the house. According to the note they left for the milkman they're likely to be away for another day or two but let's check anyway. And see if Janey's had any luck with their cars.'

'What about their credit cards?' Max asked.

Clare frowned. 'Need a warrant for that.' She reached for the phone then remembered she hadn't decided what to do about Ben's job offer. 'Erm, Max, could you phone DCI Ratcliffe please? Explain the situation and say we need a warrant for the Jardines' phones and bank accounts. House and shop too, while you're at it.'

Chris was looking at her, one eyebrow raised.

'I've other stuff to do,' she said, avoiding his eye.

She waited until they'd gone then she wandered through to the incident room. Sara was bent over the laptop watching the CCTV footage from the shop.

'Anything interesting?' Clare asked.

'Not so far, boss. I've been right through it once. Just checking again. There is one thing, though.'

'Yeah?'

'Monday – the day Maggie was killed. According to the shop website they're open until 5:30 p.m., Monday to Saturday. But,' she dragged the mouse forward until the time showed 2:30 p.m. 'See? He goes to the shop door and locks it and pulls down the blind.'

'He closed early. Maybe it was quiet.'

Sara shrugged. 'Suppose. It's probably that. All the same.'

Clare wandered across to Janey. 'Any luck with those cars?'

'Nothing so far. They've not pinged any ANPR cameras since I plugged the details in. But hopefully soon.'

'Maybe alert the traffic cars to look out for them,' Clare said. 'What do they drive anyway?'

Janey peered at the screen. 'He has a grey Audi Q5 and hers is a blue Megane.'

Clare stood for a moment taking this in. 'Megane?'

'Yeah. Why? Ring a bell?'

She searched her memory. 'It does. I can't think why, though.' And then she remembered. Tansy, the farmer's stepdaughter had spotted a blue Megane driving slowly up the Toll Road. 'There was a blue Megane near Maggie White's cottage the afternoon she died,' Clare said. 'Driving slowly, *as if it was lost*, according to the witness.'

Janey frowned. 'Sylvia Jardine was up near Maggie White's cottage the day she died?'

'Well, a car similar to hers certainly was. Quite a coincidence, if it wasn't her.'

'So we've got her, oh, wait – the DNA on the hammer, it was male, wasn't it?'

Clare nodded. 'It was, but if it was Finlay's hammer it would have his DNA on it.'

'And she could have worn gloves,' Janey said.

Clare stood thinking then she came to a decision 'Get on the radio, Janey. I want that car found and I want both Jardines detained on sight.' She was about to head back to her office when she felt the phone buzz in her pocket. A message from Mandy, the officer she'd asked to take Jean White to the mortuary. She stood, staring at the message. She read it over twice to make sure she'd understood. Then she turned and walked out of the station, clicking to unlock her car.

Chapter 36

'I don't know what else to say.' Jean White was pale but calm. 'The body in there is not my daughter.'

The staff had given them a private room and Clare invited Jean to sit. Then she spoke to Mandy, her voice low. 'You are sure the staff here haven't made an error? Brought out the wrong one?'

'Positive. But maybe you should look for yourself, boss. You were,' she hesitated, as if trying not to upset Jean. 'You were at the scene.'

Clare nodded and excused herself. She found the mortuary attendant waiting, paperwork in hand.

'It's all here,' he said. 'Feel free to check. That is definitely the woman who was brought in from Guardbridge on Tuesday.'

'I'd better see her.'

The attendant led Clare to the room where Jean and Mandy had viewed the body and she took her second look at the woman who, until tonight, they had thought was Maggie White. The body looked different now, removed from the horror of the garden shed, but she was pretty sure it was the same one.

'Were there any other women of around the same age brought in over the past week?'

The attendant shook his head. 'We only had three other females last week. The closest in age was a twenty-year-old and they were all brought in towards the end of the week. This one arrived on Tuesday after the pathologist examined her at the scene. It's definitely your body.'

Clare left him and returned to the room where Jean and Mandy were waiting. Jean looked up as she entered, her face lined with worry.

'I can only apologise,' Clare said, sinking down on a chair opposite. 'I'm so sorry to have distressed you. The body was discovered in the garden of your daughter's cottage and there was no sign of anyone else on the premises.'

Jean frowned. 'But did no one identify her? A neighbour perhaps?'

Clare thought back to Sylvia Jardine. She'd seemed fairly sure the body was Maggie's. Perhaps the upset of seeing a corpse had affected her judgement. From what Clare could recall of the shop CCTV there were similarities. But were the two women similar enough for Sylvia's mistake to have been a reasonable one? 'I'm sorry to have to ask this, Mrs White, but does the body you viewed resemble your daughter at all?'

Jean seemed to consider this. 'The hair, I suppose. Brown and curly, you know? She's not unlike Maggie but I think anyone who knew her well would realise. What made you think it was her?'

Clare hesitated. She was acutely conscious she'd put Jean through an unnecessarily distressing experience. Dragged her back from Ireland in the belief that her daughter was dead then faced her with the corpse of another woman. At the very least she owed her some sort of explanation. But she had no idea what was going on here – who the dead woman was and who had killed her. It would be safer to say as little as possible. 'We did have reason to believe the deceased person was your daughter,' she said, choosing her words carefully. 'But I'm truly sorry to have troubled you in this way.'

'I'm sure it wasn't deliberate,' Jean said, 'and it is a relief to know it's not Maggie.'

Clare rose and opened the door. 'Do you have somewhere to stay?' she asked, and Jean nodded.

'I have friends who I'm sure will help.'

Clare smiled. 'We'll drive you wherever you wish. But maybe you could give us a mobile number? Just in case we need to speak again.'

They stood outside the mortuary while Clare added Jean's number to her phone. Then they began walking towards the car. Clare clicked to unlock it then she stopped in her tracks as something occurred to her. 'Mrs White,' she said, 'if the body in the mortuary isn't Maggie, where is she?'

–

'No sign of the Jardines,' Chris said as Clare entered the station. 'Checked the house and the shop again. Both shut up tight.'

Clare nodded. 'Has Max had luck with that warrant?'

He laughed. 'Hah! Good joke.'

She fixed him with a steely gaze. 'Do I look like I'm joking? At the very least the Jardines are guilty of fraud and now they've disappeared. Plus I have a missing woman and a body I can't identify so howsabout you get on the phone to the DCI and ask *very nicely* if he's had time to sort out the warrant Max requested.'

He held up his hands. 'Okay, sorry. I'll give him a call.'

'And when you've done that, get back in here. God help me but I think two heads are better than one. Even yours.'

'None taken, Inspector.'

–

Max brought a cafetiere of coffee into Clare's office and Chris produced a pack of Wagon Wheels from his secret stash.

'I'm only handing these out 'cause you're in a mood,' he said.

'I should bite your head off more often.' She helped herself to one of the biscuits. 'Okay, let's try and make sense of this.'

'We have a body,' Chris began. 'Female, unidentified so far.'

'Found in Maggie's garden shed,' Max added.

'Who was she and why was she there?' Clare said.

'And why was she killed?' Chris added.

Max began pouring the coffee. 'Could be mistaken identity. The killer thought she was Maggie.'

'That would make sense,' Clare agreed. 'She was in Maggie's garden – why, we don't know – but she was there, our killer sneaks up behind, doesn't realise it's the wrong woman and hits her with the hammer.'

Chris pulled a Wagon Wheel out of the packet. 'Or someone's killed her and they're looking for a place to dump the body.'

Clare considered this. 'I'd say that's unlikely. But I'll bear it in mind.' She bit into a Wagon Wheel and chewed for a moment. 'Are we ruling out the Devines?'

Chris nodded. 'Think so. Anthony was up that road to steal the GPS unit. It's just his bad luck a murder was committed around the same time; and Paul was kept prisoner by the three men who ambushed the prison van. Plus, their DNA wasn't on the hammer.'

'Okay,' Clare said. 'Who does that leave?'

'The farmer?' Max suggested.

Clare shook her head. 'His DNA isn't a match either.'

'Doesn't mean it wasn't him,' Chris said. 'Could have used gloves. Come to that, anyone could have used gloves. Male or female.'

'Yes, it's a good point,' Clare said. She broke off another bit of Wagon Wheel and held it in her hand. 'I can't shake the feeling the Jardines are somehow involved.'

'Agreed,' Max said. 'Particularly if her car was up that road on the Monday afternoon.'

'And Finlay shut the shop early,' Chris added. Then he frowned. 'Both of them had the opportunity. But where's the motive?'

'Those jewels,' Clare said slowly. 'And the money in Maggie's shed.' She put down the Wagon Wheel and licked the melted chocolate off her fingers. 'Finlay lied about what was stolen in the robbery, agreed?'

They nodded and Clare went on.

'Suppose Maggie knew about it. Maybe she was in on it and the money we found was her share for keeping quiet.'

'Yeah, that works,' Chris said. 'Or maybe she was blackmailing him. She threatens to drop him in it, and he pays her off.'

'And he's had enough,' Clare went on. 'He's at the end of his tether. He goes to the cottage – maybe he means to reason with her, tell her he's had enough. Or maybe he just sees red. He's brought a hammer – or he finds one – and he waits.'

'There's that bit of hedge,' Max said. 'Perfect hiding place.'

'He sees her come outside,' Clare continued, 'follows her down the path and hits her from behind.'

Max was frowning. 'Hold on, though. Maggie worked for him for two years. Surely he'd realise it wasn't her in the garden.'

'Not necessarily,' Clare said. 'If it was later on, near dusk, it could've been hard to tell. The sun's low at this time of year. That garden would have been in the shade. And remember when we went to the house? Did you notice his glasses? Thick lenses. I'd say he's pretty near-sighted. Poor visibility, heat of the moment – if he approached her from behind he could easily have thought she was Maggie. The mother said the dead woman's hair was similar to hers.'

'And it was male DNA on the hammer,' Chris said. 'Any chance SOCO could isolate his DNA from those polymer notes?'

Clare shook her head. 'We were lucky to get the prints. Think how many hands those notes have been through? Better to get a fresh sample from him.'

Clare's office door flew open, and Sara came in.

'Just had a call through from the 999 service. It's the Jardines.'

Chapter 37

It took Chris three minutes to reach Donaldson Gardens, siren blaring. He pulled up outside the house and they jumped out of the car. Robbie had been stationed at the gate and he walked across to meet them.

'She's inside,' he said, his voice low. 'Arrived about half an hour ago. I was all set to call you when she came rushing back out in a right state.'

'And him?'

He shook his head. 'He's cold.'

'Has she said anything?'

'No.'

'Cautioned?'

'No. Thought I'd better wait.'

'Okay.' They crunched up the drive towards the front door. Clare tapped on it and entered without waiting for a reply. They found Sylvia in the front room, sitting on one of the teal sofas, her hands crossed in front of her. Her face was drawn and she eyed them as they entered, but she didn't speak.

Clare motioned to Chris and Max to look round the house then she took a seat opposite Sylvia.

'Your husband,' she began.

Sylvia raised her face to meet Clare's. 'I'm afraid he's dead.'

Clare nodded. 'Do you know what happened?'

She rubbed her head, as though she was having difficulty thinking. 'I've been away, you see. Just for a few days. Once we knew you'd caught the escaped prisoner I said to Finlay we should get away. Have a break, you know?'

'He didn't go with you?'

She looked down at her hands and began twisting her wedding ring. 'No.' Her voice was small. 'He said he'd rather stay. Catch up with the VAT.'

Clare could hear a siren, distant but coming closer, and she knew she had no more than a minute before the ambulance arrived.

'When did you last speak to him?'

She frowned. 'I, erm, yesterday morning I think.'

'And how did he seem?'

She shrugged. 'I can't think. I mean, I suppose he sounded pretty normal.' She hesitated. 'He did say he loved me.'

'Would he normally say that?'

'Sometimes. I can't think.'

The siren cut through the stillness of the room then died as the ambulance arrived.

Chris appeared at the door and motioned to Clare. She rose from her seat and followed him into the hall. Through the half glass of the vestibule door she could see the blue lights. A door slammed outside and she heard voices.

'Looks like an overdose,' Chris said, his voice low. 'Empty pack of pills at the bedside.'

'Any note?'

'Nothing.'

The vestibule door opened and two green-suited paramedics entered the hall. Max appeared at the top of the stairs and motioned to them to come up. Clare watched their progress then turned back to Chris. 'I want a family liaison officer up here as fast as you can. Then get onto her GP. And tea, Chris. Let's get her a cup of tea.'

–

Wendy Briggs, the family liaison officer, arrived an hour later and, after a brief conversation, Clare left her with Sylvia. Outside she spoke to Robbie.

'I'll send someone to relieve you as soon as I can. Wendy will see she doesn't leave the house but I don't want anyone calling at the door.'

'So, what now?' Chris said as they climbed back in the car.

Clare checked her watch. 'She won't be fit to be interviewed today. But I've asked the doctor if we can speak to her tomorrow.'

'It's pretty straightforward, though, isn't it?' Max said. 'He's heard about the arrests, probably heard we'd recovered the jewels and reckoned his time was up.'

Clare was quiet for a moment. 'It certainly looks that way.'

'Boss?' Chris said, one hand on the steering wheel.

She looked at him. 'She was very calm, Chris. Like she wasn't surprised.' She frowned. 'I need to think. Let's get back to the station.'

—

Jim arranged for a description of the woman found in Maggie's shed to be circulated to the press with an appeal for anyone who might be missing a friend or relative.

'And let's keep trying that number the mother gave us for Maggie,' she said. 'We have to get hold of her. She's the only person we haven't spoken to who might be able to shed some light on this mess.'

'Should we get a photo out too? Asking her to contact us?'

'Definitely. I'll speak to the mother again. See if she's remembered anything else.'

She left Jim and wandered through to her office, weary with the events of the day. Helen Cosgrove's analysis of the jewellery, Jean White's bombshell about Maggie and now Finlay Jardine's death. The bottle of pills and empty glass found at his bedside had gone off to the lab for fingerprints. Not that she expected anything unusual, but there was something so calm, so assured about Sylvia Jardine's reaction. Was she simply one of those buttoned-up women who kept their feelings to themselves? Or was there a lack of surprise about her reaction? Had she known he intended to kill himself? And, if so, did that mean Finlay had killed Maggie – or rather the woman they had all thought was Maggie? And, if he had killed her, had Sylvia known about it all along?

She rubbed her forehead, unable to think clearly any more.

Tomorrow.

She would interview Sylvia tomorrow when she'd had a night's sleep. Maybe it would all become clear then.

Out in the car park the air was still, the sky clear. She looked up at the carpet of stars and wondered if there might be a frost tonight. The first of the season. Suddenly she longed to be home, tucked up in front of the fire with Al and Benjy. With a wave to Chris and Sara who were heading off down Pipeland Road she climbed into her car and set off towards Daisy Cottage.

Wednesday

Chapter 38

Wendy called Clare about eleven the next morning. 'GP's been in again,' she said. 'He's prescribed her a low-dose diazepam but she's not keen to take it.'

'Can we interview her?'

'Yeah. He says she's fine. Come over anytime.'

Clare ended the call wondering how to approach the interview. Normally she would just take Chris with her but there was so much to this case she could do with another listening ear. It wasn't like she planned to record it. Not the morning after Sylvia's husband had been found dead. But why was she thinking about recording it? Was it just the jewellery? Or was it the fact that a blue Renault Megane had been spotted driving slowly past Motray Farm towards Maggie White's cottage? Maybe she would record it after all. Make it more formal. She called Wendy back to suggest Sylvia's solicitor was present and went to find Chris and Max.

–

Sylvia was finishing a sandwich when they arrived. A small dark-haired woman sat next to her on the leather club chair, a Pukka pad and pen on her knee. Sylvia introduced her as Rebecca Keith. 'My solicitor,' she added.

Rebecca nodded in acknowledgement but didn't speak.

'Can I offer you tea?' Sylvia went on. 'Or coffee perhaps?'

Wendy offered to make hot drinks and they sat down once more on the teal sofas. Clare explained that, as the circumstances of Finlay's death were not yet confirmed, she would be taping the interview. Sylvia said she understood, then Rebecca sat forward.

'Mrs Jardine has come to realise certain things over the past few days – things which she had no prior knowledge of, or involvement in. The sudden, shocking death of Mr Jardine has put a great strain on her, but she is willing to co-operate fully and to share what she has learned to assist your enquiries.'

Clare smiled at Sylvia. 'We're very grateful for your co-operation.' She chatted on, keeping the conversation light while Wendy made the drinks. 'This is a lovely room,' she said. 'Beautifully put together.'

Sylvia looked round, her brow creased, as if she was seeing it for the first time. 'I'm not sure what to do,' she said. 'The house...'

'It's early days,' Clare said. 'Don't look too far ahead.'

There was a light tap at the door and Max jumped up to open it. Wendy entered, bearing a large mahogany tray. She set this down on the coffee table and turned to leave. 'I'll be in the kitchen.'

When she'd closed the door Clare began the recording, introducing herself and the two sergeants. She assured Sylvia they could take a break any time and Sylvia thanked her.

'Perhaps we could go back to last Sunday night,' Clare began. 'I think you were aware we had arrested the other three men believed to have taken part in the robbery.'

'That's right,' Sylvia said. 'The officer who's been outside said the men were in custody and that you'd probably call off the watch on our house and shop.'

'How did you feel about that?'

She was quiet for a moment, as though trying to recall. 'Relieved, I suppose. Finlay had been in such a state since Paul Devine's escape. It was a huge relief to know he was back in custody. The others being detained was a bonus, I suppose. Gave us peace of mind.'

Clare could see Sylvia was relaxing. 'Then you decided to go away for a few days?' she said. 'But Finlay didn't join you.'

She nodded. 'As I said last night, I suggested a few nights away. A break for us both. Keep the shop shut for another week, recharge our batteries, you know?'

'You stopped the milk, I think,' Clare said, her tone light.

There was a flicker of something in Sylvia's eyes. *Aha*, Clare thought. *You'd forgotten that.* 'We saw the note at the door,' she explained.

Sylvia recovered her composure. 'Of course. I'd forgotten. I stopped it when I thought we were both going away. And after Finlay changed his mind he said not to bother changing it – that he'd pick up a pint at Tesco if he ran out.'

'What changed his mind?' Clare asked.

She sighed. 'The next morning we were chatting about it – trying to decide where to go; and then our cleaning lady arrived. She comes in every Monday to give us a tidy up and she was full of news about the arrests. I was keen for her to get on but she talked away. Then she said something about us hoping to get the jewels back. I asked what she meant. *Rumour is they've found the jewellery taken from the shop*, she said.'

Clare shot a glance at the other two. How did this kind of thing leak out?

'After that Finlay didn't seem so keen,' Sylvia went on. 'He said it was an ideal time to get on with his VAT; and that he'd better be here in case you needed to speak to him – about the jewels, you know? Or that's what he said.'

Clare was suddenly alert. 'You thought there was another reason?'

She looked down, examining her nails, shell pink and immaculately manicured. Then she spoke, her voice small. 'He didn't realise I knew.'

Clare sat forward. 'Knew what? What was it he thought you didn't know?'

289

She raised her head and met Clare's gaze. 'The jewels, of course. You must know by now. You'll have had them examined. You'll know they were vastly over-valued for the insurance claim.'

'Just to be clear,' Clare said, 'you are stating your husband made a fraudulent claim on his insurance policy, that he over-valued the items stolen in order to profit from the claim? Is that correct?'

'It is,' Sylvia said, her voice low. 'But you must believe me when I say I knew nothing about it.'

'Can you explain it to us?' Clare asked.

She nodded. 'I'll try. Finlay buys – I mean he bought – most of his stock from reputable merchants. All above board, receipts, certificates and so on. But he also buys other stock. Cheaper stuff, you know? Sometimes not real gems.'

'Where does he source this stock?'

'Some internet site,' Sylvia said. 'Not that I could find it.'

Clare glanced at Chris and Max. Did she mean the dark web? 'How did he pay for this stock?'

'Bitcoin. He'd buy some occasionally. Said it was handy to have.' She shrugged. 'Apparently it's perfectly legal. Anyway, he bought these items – rings mainly but the odd necklace. And if someone came into the shop looking for a cheaper item he'd bring them out.' She smiled. 'There really aren't enough wealthy customers to make a shop like ours pay, you know. Even in St Andrews. The cheaper stuff was popular so it helped.'

'Okay,' Clare said. 'And so the robbery?'

'Oh, that day,' Sylvia said. 'It caused so much…' She broke off, shaking her head. They waited and, after a moment, she continued. 'These men – they wouldn't know a diamond if it hit them in the eye. So Finlay gave them the rings that were at the front of the counter. Valuable ones, you know? Then he reached below and found the trays of cheaper stuff and he tipped in as many as he could. A minute later one of the others rattled the door and Devine picked up his sack and ran.'

'And the insurance claim?'

Sylvia shook her head. 'He always was a silly man. If I'd done it, we'd have been strictly honest. He didn't tell me, of course.

Just said we'd lost a lot of stock – worth a lot. He filled out the claim and sent it in. I can only guess he removed the rings and watches he claimed for from the shop when the insurers came to do a stocktake. Anyway, he had all the paperwork for the items claimed and it was settled.' Her shoulders drooped. 'And that's when the trouble started.'

Clare was watching her carefully. 'Can you explain what you mean by that?'

'Maggie,' Sylvia said.

'Maggie knew about the fraudulent claim?'

Sylvia nodded. 'She must have seen what Finlay had tipped into Devine's sack and she knew. She knew he was claiming for jewels that hadn't been stolen. So she told Finlay she wanted a cut.'

'Maggie White asked Finlay for some of the insurance money in return for keeping quiet about the fraudulent claim?'

'She did. I mean, Fin didn't tell me. Not in as many words. But I could read him like a book; and it didn't stop there. Every week there was something. She fancied a new coat, things for the house. Never done, asking Fin for money.' Her expression darkened. 'She was bleeding him dry and we both knew it had to stop.'

'So, to be clear,' Clare said, 'when you suggested Maggie was moody and that she might be dealing drugs, that wasn't true?'

Sylvia shook her head. 'No. I mean, I don't think so. It just seemed a way of explaining the money without telling you what Fin had done.'

'You believe the money found at Maggie White's home came from your husband?'

'Yes.' Sylvia's voice was small.

'Had you discussed it?' Clare asked.

'No. But I've been married for almost thirty years. I know when he's hiding something. And it wasn't hard to spot the money draining away.'

She broke off, head bent, and Clare wasn't sure for a moment if she'd finished her story or simply lost the will to continue. A carriage clock was ticking softly on the mantelpiece, the only sound breaking the quiet of the room. Clare looked round, her gaze resting on Rebecca Keith, sitting immobile at Sylvia's side, her long legs crossed at the ankle, pen poised to take notes. She felt almost as if she was part of a set piece in a theatre. It all seemed so staged – so managed. Was she being played? Was Sylvia putting on the performance of her life? And, more importantly, did she know the body in the shed was not actually Maggie's? She allowed the stillness to linger a little then she went on.

'Mrs Jardine, did you visit Maggie White's cottage on the Monday – the day Paul Devine escaped from custody?'

She nodded but didn't speak.

Rebecca Keith leaned forward, her hand extended. 'Sylvia,' but Sylvia waved it away.

'If you could confirm, for the tape,' Clare persisted.

'Yes,' Sylvia said, her voice barely above a whisper. 'I went to see Maggie. I wanted to speak to her. To tell her we'd had enough – that there would be no more money. I was going to threaten to report her for blackmail.'

Clare paused for a moment then she said, 'Did you kill Maggie White?'

She sighed and shook her head. 'No. I couldn't kill her. She was already dead when I got there.'

'You arrived at Maggie's cottage and found her dead?'

'Yes.'

'Where did you find her?'

'In the shed.' She closed her eyes as if recalling it. 'She was face down in the shed, the back of her head…'

'What time was this?'

She frowned, as though confused by the question. 'What difference does it make? I assure you, Inspector, she was dead. It was too late for an ambulance.'

'It'll help us work out what happened.'

'Of course. I think it was about four. Four thirty, maybe.'

This tallied with Tansy's account. 'What did you do next?' Clare asked.

Sylvia looked down, twisting the wedding ring on her finger. She swallowed, then raised her gaze to meet Clare's. 'I went looking for money.' Her shoulders sagged. 'It sounds awful now. So mercenary. But there was nothing I could do for Maggie and I thought maybe I could get some of it back.' She broke off for a minute then she went on. 'I put gloves on, of course. Left my shoes at the door. Didn't want to leave any evidence.'

'How did you get in?'

'Key. Under a plant pot.' She shook her head. 'Silly woman. Anyway, I had a quick look round – checked drawers and so on but I couldn't find anything; and I was worried someone would find me there.'

'You didn't take anything from the house?'

'No.'

'And then?'

'I let myself out again, put the key back under the pot and went home. Finlay was in a dreadful state. He wasn't making any sense but I think I knew what he'd done.'

'You believed your husband, Finlay Jardine, had murdered Maggie White that Monday afternoon.'

'Yes.'

'Did he admit it?'

'No. And I hadn't the courage to ask him outright. But I knew.' She paused for a moment, seemingly lost in thought. Then she said, 'You don't stay married for three decades and not know your husband inside out.'

Chris sat forward and cleared his throat. 'Mrs Jardine, what was your intention when you drove to Maggie's cottage?'

She considered for a moment, then she said, 'To be honest, I don't know. I suppose I thought I'd confront her with what I knew about the jewellery – the blackmail. As I said, threaten to report her.'

'But she would know,' Chris said, 'if you reported her you would have to report your own husband. That he might go to prison for fraud. Was that really your intention?'

'Mrs Jardine was clearly in a distressed state,' Rebecca Keith said. 'I'm not sure it's necessary for her to recall her intentions. She may not have been thinking straight.'

Chris nodded. 'Of course.' He sat back in his seat and gestured to Clare that he was finished.

Clare decided it was time to tell Sylvia about the body in the shed. 'Mrs Jardine, you volunteered to identify the body at the mortuary.'

Her eyes narrowed. *Ah*, Clare thought. *A question you weren't expecting.*

'I did.'

'Why did you do that? Surely Finlay would have been the obvious person, as her employer, I mean.'

Sylvia shrugged. 'I suppose I was trying to protect him. He'd been so upset. I wasn't sure what effect seeing Maggie's corpse would have on him.'

'So,' Clare went on, 'you saw Maggie in the garden shed and again at the mortuary; and you were quite clear about her identity?'

There was something in Sylvia's eyes. A first sign of doubt perhaps? 'Yes,' she said, at last. 'It was Maggie.'

Clare watched her for a moment then she said, 'I must tell you, Mrs Jardine, we believe the body found in the garden shed, the body you identified in the mortuary, was not that of Maggie White.'

'When did this come to light?' Rebecca asked. 'Mrs Jardine was not informed of this.'

Clare ignored the question. She was watching Sylvia who seemed to be struggling for the right words. 'I don't understand,' she said at last. 'Not Maggie? But I saw her in the shed.'

'Did you not recognise her? From the shop, I mean.'

She didn't answer. Her eyes flitted around as though she was trying to make sense of what she'd heard.

Clare waited. She was good at pauses. Particularly long pauses. *Let the suspect break the silence*, her old sergeant had said. *They'll blurt something out eventually.* She waited and her patience was rewarded.

'I'd seen her a couple of times,' Sylvia said. 'But I only worked at the shop on Maggie's days off, you see. Sometimes, if Finlay's car was off the road, I'd drive down at closing time and give him a lift home. If it was raining, that sort of thing. I'd seen her from a distance but not really close up.'

'Then why offer to identify her?' Clare said. 'Why would you do that when you barely knew her?'

Sylvia's face softened. 'I could see how this was going – for Fin, I mean. I knew you'd find out about the jewellery, about Maggie – or whoever it was. Finlay – he's not the brightest when it comes to these things. I was pretty sure he'd have left some trace at the scene. It would only be a matter of time before you came asking for his DNA. I suppose I wanted to spare him – for as long as I could.' She shook her head. 'Prison – it would have finished him. He'd never have coped.'

Clare watched her carefully. 'Mrs Jardine, did you give your husband an overdose of diazepam to end his life? To spare him the consequences of his actions?'

Sylvia's back stiffened and she met Clare's gaze, her face a mask. 'Of course not, Inspector. That would be a crime.'

Chapter 39

'Believe her about the diazepam?' Chris asked as they drove back to the station.

Clare raised a hand as a taxi waved her out into the stream of traffic. 'I'm honestly not sure.'

'I reckon she did it,' Max said. 'It's too convenient, her arranging to go away for a few days. She crumbles the pills in his coffee and when he gets sleepy she helps him up to bed. Once he's asleep she puts the glass and empty pills pack at his bedside and she leaves the house, knowing when she returns he'll be beyond help.'

'I agree,' Chris said. 'Plus the milk – she slipped up there. She must have stopped it so it didn't pile up at the door. Somebody would definitely have reported that, after all that's happened.'

'You're probably both right,' Clare said. 'The question is, can we prove it?'

Chris shook his head. 'She'd be a credible witness, that one. Easily convince a jury, especially with a top advocate on her side. And you can bet she'd have nothing but the best.'

'Doesn't mean we shouldn't try, though,' Clare said, pulling into the station car park. 'Max, can you work your usual miracle with the coffee please? We'll have a chat in my office.'

-

'Right,' Clare said, drawing her notepad across the desk. 'Let's do the jewellery first. Do we agree Finlay's insurance claim was fraudulent?'

They both nodded and Clare went on. 'Next question: do we think Sylvia knew about it?'

'She must have,' Chris said. 'The difference between the theft and the claim was vast. No way he could have kept that amount from her. Plus, where did he hide the stuff he claimed for while the insurers carried out their checks?'

'I agree,' Max said. 'But has she committed an offence?'

Clare frowned. 'I'm not sure. Failure to report isn't a crime. But, if she's an equal partner in the business, the insurers could claim she's benefited from the fraud.'

'Not knowingly, though,' Chris said. 'Remember she's claiming she *didn't* know.'

'Possibly not. I think they could take out a civil case for the return of the overpayment. As a partner, she'd be liable. But if we can't prove she was involved in the fraudulent claim we can't charge her.' Clare sat back, drumming absently on the desk with a pencil.

'You'll crack the lead,' Max said, indicating the pencil. 'Sorry,' he added seeing her face.

Clare inspected the pencil then set it down. 'You're probably right.'

'If I'd said that, you'd have bitten my head off,' Chris said.

'Yeah. But Max is nicer than you. So, what next?'

'Maggie,' Chris said. 'Or whoever she is.'

'That's a good point,' Clare said. 'Anyone come forward following the press appeal?'

He shook his head. 'Sara's working through a few. None looks likely, though.'

Clare frowned. 'Okay. Do we believe Sylvia? Did Finlay kill the woman in Maggie's shed?'

'He looked pretty shocked when we told him,' Max said.

Clare raised an eyebrow. 'He'd had at least a day to get his head round it, though. Time to perfect his reaction.'

They fell silent. Then Chris said, 'If it's his DNA on the hammer—'

'That only proves the hammer was his,' Max said.

Clare nodded. 'I agree. Sylvia could easily have used gloves. The question is: which of them's most likely to have committed a violent murder?'

'My money's on him,' Chris said. 'She's too cool a customer. I reckon she'd have found some other way to sort Maggie out. But him? He sounds like the type to panic. Maybe he went to see Maggie earlier in the day. Have it out with her then he saw her in the garden and rage took over.'

'You're forgetting the hammer,' Max said. 'He must have decided to take that with him.'

'And the car,' Clare added. 'Remember the farmer's daughter saw the blue Megane and the green van. She didn't say anything about an Audi Q5.'

'He could have come down the road,' Chris said. 'From the other end. If I was going to kill someone I wouldn't take the obvious route.'

Clare raised an eyebrow. 'I'll bear it in mind.' She fell silent for a moment. 'Sylvia told us she took her shoes off when she entered the cottage; but wasn't there a footprint in the bedroom?' She pulled the computer keyboard across the desk and began typing. 'I'm sure there was.'

She navigated her way to the SOCO report on Maggie's house. 'Yep. Here it is. Partial print.' She was silent for a moment as she scanned the report. 'Thought to be a man's shoe. Estimated between size nine and ten.' She read on then said, 'A small circular mark on the heel, not consistent with the sole pattern.' She looked up. 'Raymond says it could be a drawing pin or something similar, stuck on the heel. Could you two get back over there please? I want his shoes examined. Take gloves and evidence bags. Bear in mind he may have removed the drawing pin – or whatever it was. If so, you're looking for a tiny hole.'

Chris rose from his seat. 'What if she refuses?'

Clare considered this. 'Did Ben Ratcliffe ever get that warrant? Give him a call and check please. We might need it.'

Chris regarded her. 'Don't take this the wrong way, Clare, but have you fallen out with him?'

She turned back to her computer, feigning interest in the screen. 'Just practising the art of delegation, sergeant.'

–

They were back within the hour. 'Got the shoes,' Chris said. 'Dropped off at SOCO.'

'What do you reckon?'

'No sign of a drawing pin but there's definitely a hole where it might have been; and they're a size nine. Raymond wasn't in but one of his staff—'

'Samantha,' Max said.

'Yeah, her. She's looking at it now. Said she'll call as soon as she can.' His face darkened. 'She's an odd one, that Mrs Jardine.'

'How so?'

'I dunno. Cold, you know? I had a word with Wendy when we were upstairs looking at the shoes. Wendy says she hasn't shed a tear. Not one.'

Clare shrugged. 'She's maybe keeping it buttoned up until she's alone.'

'Even so,' Chris said, 'her reaction to your question about drugging the husband. No shock, no upset or outrage, even. Just *that would be a crime.*'

Clare nodded. 'Yeah. I think there's every chance she did drug him. Possibly out of compassion. As she said, he wasn't the kind who'd cope with prison. Maybe she felt it was easier this way.' She rose from her chair. 'But I doubt we'll be able to prove it.'

–

It was late afternoon when Samantha phoned from SOCO. 'There's a strong correlation between the footprint found in the victim's bedroom and the shoe brought in this afternoon. The tiny hole is at the centre of where the circular mark is and it's our view the print we took represents a shoe of this size and style with a drawing pin stuck in the sole.'

Clare thanked Samantha and ended the call. She went to find Chris and Max but as she crossed the front office a slim woman with brown curly hair entered the station. She stood uncertainly and Clare approached her.

'Can I help?'

The woman hesitated. 'I think you're looking for me. I'm Maggie White.'

—

They installed her in the interview room Ben Ratcliffe had recently vacated. Clare cautioned her and suggested she might want a solicitor present but Maggie waved this away.

'I've been on a retreat,' she said. 'Near Loch Rannoch.' A smile spread across her face. 'It was so restful.'

Clare recalled Maggie's car in the garage next to the cottage. 'You didn't drive?'

She shook her head. 'I'm trying to use the car a bit less. Takes longer but I was on holiday so there was no rush.'

'And you knew nothing about Paul Devine escaping custody?'

'Not a thing. I only switched my phone back on this morning. And then I saw the news; and I saw my own name! That you were looking for me. It was quite a shock.'

'I'm afraid you must prepare yourself for another shock,' Clare said, and she went on to explain a woman had been found dead in Maggie's garden shed. The colour drained from her face.

'Who is it – the dead woman?'

'We're not sure yet. We thought it was you to start with,' she said. 'Then your mother arrived from Ireland and—'

'My mother's here?'

'She is.'

'Goodness. I've not seen her for nearly two years. She went off travelling, you see? Said it was her last fling before she was too old. Where is she?'

'I'm not sure where she stayed last night but I do have her mobile number. But surely you have that?'

Maggie shrugged. 'She hasn't answered my last few messages so I assumed she'd changed her number. She is dreadful at keeping in touch.'

Clare couldn't help thinking how starkly this contrasted with her own mother who phoned at least twice a week. Sometimes she could do without the calls, particularly when she was busy at work. But to not see her mother for two years? 'I wonder if you could help us identify the woman found at your house.'

Maggie was silent for a moment. 'Do you mean look at the body? I'm not sure.'

'No,' Clare said. 'Nothing like that. We have a photo of her face and also photos of her clothes. If you wouldn't mind?'

Maggie agreed to view the images and Clare thanked her 'But before I show you them there is something else I would like to ask about; and I will remind you that you're still under caution.'

'Okay.'

'In the course of investigating the murder at your cottage our Scene of Crime Officers discovered a large sum of money in the garden shed. It was concealed in a bag of compost. I would like to ask how you came by that money.'

There was a pause. Maggie seemed to be considering her response. Then she said, 'Finlay gave it to me. Mr Jardine,' she added. 'My employer.'

'Why?'

She looked at Clare for a moment then said, 'I think I will have that solicitor, if you don't mind.'

While they waited for the solicitor to arrive, Clare showed Maggie the photos of the murder victim and her clothes. She watched as Maggie scrolled through the images, her eyes filling with tears. After a minute she sat back and reached in her pocket for a hankie.

'It's Freya,' she said. 'Freya Daniels. We've been friends for years.'

Clare frowned. 'We haven't had any reports of a woman missing. Why do you think that might be?'

Maggie thought for a moment. 'She is a bit of a loner, Freya. Doesn't have many friends.'

'Does she work?'

'She's an artist. She paints. Lovely watercolours. Doesn't make much money but she's happy doing it. She *was* happy,' she corrected. She turned to Clare. 'Where was she found?'

Clare decided there was no reason not to tell Maggie where the body had been left. 'In your garden shed. Do you know why she might have been there?'

Maggie nodded. 'My hedge trimmer. She asked to borrow it. I said I'd be away on the retreat but I'd leave the shed unlocked. I suppose that's why she was there.' She shook her head. 'I can't believe it. Poor Freya. She wouldn't harm a fly.'

Something was nagging away at Clare and then she remembered. 'Did Freya have a car? There wasn't one parked outside.'

Maggie shook her head. 'She'd have walked. She only lives in Guardbridge and she enjoys a walk.'

Clare nodded. It made sense. 'Let's take a break,' she said. 'We can chat again when your solicitor arrives.'

–

The duty solicitor arrived an hour later and, after he'd consulted with Maggie, the interview resumed.

'Miss White denies absolutely extorting money from her employer, Mr Jardine,' he said. 'She admits he made gifts of money to her but these gifts were tokens of his regard.'

'It's an awful lot of money for *tokens of regard*,' Clare said.

'He thought a lot of me,' Maggie said.

'Did Mrs Jardine know about these gifts?'

Clare thought Maggie was suppressing a smile.

'I doubt it,' she said. 'But they were loaded. She wouldn't even have noticed.'

The questioning continued but Maggie stuck firmly to her story that the money was a gift.

'Let's go back to the day of the robbery,' Clare said. 'What do you know about the jewellery the thieves made off with?'

Maggie shrugged. 'It's all a bit of a blur. I was pretty scared, to be honest. The man – Paul Devine – he told me to get stuff out of the glass cases. My hands were shaking and I struggled with the lock. I think he thought I was doing it deliberately and he yelled at me.' She shook her head. 'Horrible.'

The solicitor cleared his throat. 'Is it necessary to put Miss White through this?'

'Just a couple more questions,' Clare said. 'Did you see what Mr Jardine put in the sack?'

'Not really,' Maggie said. 'I could hear him under the counter, picking trays up. And Devine was yelling at him too. Telling him to hurry up. But I didn't see what he gave them.'

'And after the robbery – did you notice what was left? Anything Devine didn't get away with?'

'Sorry, I was too upset. I remember it was me who called 999, though. Then Finlay took me into the back shop and made me a hot drink. You guys came and I gave a statement. He called me a taxi and I went home.'

'Just one more thing, Maggie. When Mr Jardine put in the insurance claim, did you have any idea he might not have been strictly honest?'

'I don't see how Miss White could possibly know that,' the solicitor said. 'It seems an unreasonable question.'

'I don't mind answering,' Maggie said. She turned to Clare. 'I wasn't involved in the insurance claim. Mr Jardine shut the shop for the rest of the week. Gave me paid leave. He said he wanted peace to do the stocktake himself.'

Clare tried a few more questions but Maggie stuck firmly to her assertion that the money was a gift.

'We'll have to let her go,' Clare said to Jim when the interview was over. 'Released pending further enquiries. Could you do the needful, please? My head's burst with this case.'

She wandered into the kitchen and found Chris and Sara washing their mugs. 'Heading home?'

Sara nodded. 'We're looking at wedding venues tonight. Going to draw up a shortlist and book some visits.'

Chris rolled his eyes.

'Don't think I don't see you,' Sara said, drying the mugs. She put them back in the cupboard and went to fetch her coat.

'Sounds exciting,' Clare said.

'Frankly, I'd be okay with a couple of witnesses and a fish supper. But if it makes Sara happy...'

She patted his arm. 'You're a good lad, under that gruff exterior.' Then she said, 'How's your cousin – Alan?'

He was quiet for a moment. 'I think he's okay. Or he will be. Doc's signed them both off for two weeks. Alan says he's desperate to get back to work but Kim's not happy. Wants him to find another job.'

'I can understand that,' Clare said.

'She keeps crying. Cries all the time. Not keen to let Alan out of her sight, even now the Devines are in custody.' He shook his head. 'The odd thing is she's not heard from Debs. She keeps on at Alan to message Gav. But apparently Gav sent a message saying something had come up – that he'd be in touch soon and he's heard nothing since. Kim's convinced herself they've both been abducted again. She's in a right state.'

Clare's thoughts went back to Ben Ratcliffe introducing her to Gavin Gates and his warning that nothing was to go beyond the room. She couldn't tell Chris. Could she? Of course she couldn't. She'd already taken a risk, telling him Anthony Devine knew about the abduction. 'I'm sure she'll settle down,' she said. 'Just give it time.'

She wandered back into her office, mulling over Chris's words. It was so unfair. Kim Carter might never get over her experience and she didn't even know why it had happened. Something snapped in her head and she snatched up her coat and went out to the car.

–

Kim was washing the inside of her windows when Clare drew up outside. She stopped and peered out at the unfamiliar car. Then Clare emerged and her face cleared. She opened the door and stood back to let her in.

'Nothing wrong, is there?' she asked. She closed the door behind Clare and put the chain on.

'No, nothing like that.' Clare looked round. 'Is Alan in?'

'Gone for a pint,' she said. 'I didn't want him to go really but he needs to get out. Get away from me.' She smiled. 'I'm driving him mad, worrying all the time. Fancy a cuppa?'

'No thanks. I'm on my way home. I'll just stay a few minutes if you don't mind. There's something I think you should know.'

Chapter 40

'You told her?' the DCI said, uncorking a bottle of red. 'You told Kim Carter that Gavin had been working undercover?'

'Yup. She deserved to know.'

'Clare, that wasn't your information to tell. How do you know she won't go to the press? Splash it all over tomorrow's papers?'

Clare shrugged. 'She said she wouldn't.'

The cork came out of the bottle with a pop and he began pouring it into glasses. 'And you believe her? You think when she's processed this she won't get angry and find herself telling her tale to a tabloid journalist? A few quid for a shocking exclusive?'

'Chance I'll have to take.'

'It's a bloody stupid one, if you don't mind me saying so. You do realise you could be guilty of disclosure of protectively marked information, don't you? You could lose your job over this.'

Clare sipped her wine. 'To be honest, if this is the way the job's going, maybe I'm better off out of it.'

'You don't mean that.'

She sighed. 'No I don't. But this thing with Ben – it stinks. Two women's lives were put at risk all to pick up three armed robbers.'

The DCI took his wine through to the sitting room and Clare followed. 'Armed robbery's no joke,' he said. 'Remember a security guard died; and that gun could have gone off any time and killed your jeweller – or his assistant. Kim and Debbie probably weren't at risk. They assess these things to the last detail.'

She put her wine down on the coffee table and flopped back on the sofa. 'Yeah, I know, Al. But I was so bloody angry. Kim

Carter will never be the same again. Can you imagine what it was like for her and Debbie, being snatched from their homes, blindfolded, hands tied, thrown in a van, not knowing what the hell was happening? No undercover operation's worth that. If she did go to the papers, they'd have a field day, and quite right too.'

'Then let's hope she doesn't,' he said, his voice quiet. 'So, have you thought about Ben's job offer?'

She shook her head. 'Well obviously I can't take it, can I? How can I work with someone like that? Kim and Debbie – they're just collateral damage to him.'

'He has a job to do.'

'Yep. And so do I. In St Andrews.'

He took hold of her hand. 'You're absolutely sure?'

She nodded. 'I am,' She picked up her glass and sipped it. 'I think that's part of the reason I went to see Kim. Burn my boats in case I weakened and took the job.' She drained the glass. 'Fill 'er up, Al. I really need a drink tonight.'

They were relaxing later, starting on the second bottle of wine when an alert pinged on Clare's phone. She picked it up and squinted at the screen. 'Oh God,' she said.

'She's not been to the papers already?'

'Don't even joke about that.' She scanned the email. 'It's my Personal Development Conversation. Tomorrow morning. Ten thirty, God help me.'

He started to laugh. 'That'll teach you. Who's it with?'

'Penny Meakin,' she slurred. 'Never heard of her.'

'Lucky you. I'd have a few ideas for exciting initiatives up your sleeve. She's all about *initiatives*, that one.'

She swung her legs round and stood up, putting a hand out to steady herself. 'Better get the coffee on.'

Later, they lay in bed, the DCI stroking her hair. 'Were you serious?' he said, 'about being better off out of the job?'

'Probably not. But you have to admit, it is changing.'

'Everything does,' he said. 'It'll be the same on the outside.'

'You're so wise, Al Gibson.'

'I know.'

Thursday

Chapter 41

'I'll be out from half nine,' she told Jim as she entered the station. 'It's my PDC across in Dundee.'

He laughed. 'Lucky you. Should I have the wine ready for you coming back?'

'Definitely.' She turned to head for her office, but Jim forestalled her.

'These are for you,' he said, handing her a pile of glossy magazines. 'Max said to let you have them.'

'Really?' She took the magazines and set them down on the counter. Leafing through, she read, '*Home Building and Renovating, Grand Designs, Nordic Home Style.*' She looked back at Jim, shaking her head. 'I don't...' and then she remembered – the conversation she and Max had when they'd first walked up the Jardines' drive in Donaldson Gardens. He'd spoken about his architectural magazines at the time. And here they were, at least a dozen of them.

'Serves me right for humouring him,' she said. She scooped them off the counter. 'Suppose I'd better have a flick through – as he's gone to the trouble.'

'Better you than me.'

She headed for her office, glancing back as the station door opened. It took her a moment to recognise the schoolgirl who stood there. Then she walked across to greet her, arms still clutching the magazines. 'Tansy,' she said. 'Is everything okay?'

The girl nodded. 'Yeah. I'm back at school now. It was doing my head in being stuck at home all day.'

'Shouldn't you be in class?'

She shook her head. 'Got a study period. Till ten. I thought maybe I could have a look round. See what it's like, yeah?'

Clare's heart sank. She didn't want to put Tansy off. She'd been a huge help spotting Sylvia's car on the Toll Road and Clare was keen to do all she could to encourage youngsters into the job; but she really needed to prep for her PDC meeting. And then she spotted Sara, packing away laptops that had been used over the past couple of weeks. 'Tell you what,' she said, 'I'll introduce you to one of my uniformed officers and you can arrange a time to come in for a proper chat – when we're expecting you, yeah?'

Tansy's face lit up. 'That'd be great. Thanks.'

'But there's a catch,' Clare said. 'No more vandalism at the farm – or anywhere else.'

'It wasn't me!'

'But you know who it was.'

She shrugged but said nothing.

Clare studied her. 'How are things at home anyway?'

'Okay, I suppose.' She grinned. 'He's raging he can't have his GPS thing back. Said you were keeping it until the trial. Shuda heard him.'

Clare suppressed a smile. 'Come on. I'll introduce you to Sara.'

–

'You can go in,' Penny Meakin's secretary said, and Clare tapped on the door then entered. The *Conversation* consisted mainly of Penny going through the record of training courses Clare had attended and encouraging her to undertake further training. Then she put down her pen and removed her glasses.

'I'm particularly keen my officers play their part in the development of initiatives.'

Clare suppressed a smile at the mention of Penny's favourite word.

'Perhaps you'd like to tell me what you're involved in at the moment?'

She took a deep breath. 'I have an idea for a Youth Development Programme,' she said, thinking of Tansy. 'Bringing in the mid to late teens and showing them what life is like for our officers. In fact,' she went on, 'I was setting up the first meeting this morning before coming here.'

Penny smiled. 'This is exactly the kind of thing I want to see in place. Well done, Clare. You have my full backing.'

Saturday

Chapter 42

'That beef was delicious,' Raymond Curtice said. 'But I've eaten far too much.'

'Room for dessert?' Clare asked. 'It's a honey and ginger cheesecake.'

'Clare Mackay,' he said. 'You know your spells! Maybe just a sliver.'

'I've seen your slivers,' his partner Guy said. 'Save yourself some time, Clare, and give him a huge bit.'

'Go on, then,' Raymond said. 'I'll have a slice.'

Clare rose and went to the fridge to take out the cheesecake.

Raymond reached down to pat Benjy who was nuzzling his leg. 'You really do have the most adorable dog.'

She put the cheesecake down on the table. 'You wouldn't say that if he tore your oven gloves to bits.'

'I don't believe a word of it,' he said, and Benjy rewarded him with a lick on the hand. 'Did the Met charge those men with the Elzinga raid?' he went on.

'They did,' Clare said, cutting the cheesecake into slices. 'There was DNA linking two of the gang to the Elzinga shop but the real break came when Paul Devine agreed to testify against the other three.'

'Is that unusual?' Guy asked, taking a plate from Clare.

She nodded. 'It is. Often prisoners who give evidence against others can find themselves having a nasty accident. But, somehow, I don't see that happening to Devine. I reckon he can take care of himself.' She cut a large slice for Raymond and slipped it onto a plate. 'He's been moved, anyway. Single cell, the works.'

'Was he the one that struck the security guard?' the DCI asked.

Clare shrugged. 'They can't prove which of them did it. They were all dressed the same.'

'Is there not some way of analysing how a person moves?' Guy asked.

'Gait analysis?' Raymond shook his head. 'It's just not reliable enough. We did a bit of work on it but it's not there yet.' He loaded his spoon with cheesecake. 'Oh my, Clare. I'll need a whole week in the gym to make up for this.'

'Get it over your neck,' Clare said, cutting herself a slice. 'It's very light.'

'What about your dead jeweller?' Raymond went on. 'You reckon he did take an overdose? Or was it the wife?'

'My money's on the wife,' the DCI said.

'Yeah,' Clare said. 'I tend to agree. But we've not charged her. It has to be beyond reasonable doubt for a conviction and the Fiscal won't go for it. On the plus side,' she said, 'it looks like the insurance company are going after her for the return of the claim settlement.'

Raymond whistled. 'That'll be a fair bit. Wasn't it six figures?'

'So I believe. Again, we don't have enough evidence to charge her with fraud. She's a pretty sharp operator, that one. But, as a partner in the business, she's liable for the repayment.'

'What about the assistant?' the DCI asked. 'Maggie?'

Clare shook her head. 'Sylvia can't prove Maggie was black-mailing Finlay and we don't have enough evidence to charge her either. She could take out a private prosecution but I reckon she'll have her hands full fighting the insurance company.'

'Did you charge the brother?' the DCI went on.

'Anthony?' Clare nodded. 'Assisting an absconder, farm machinery thefts, to say nothing of an unauthorised burial.'

'I'm guessing they wouldn't have granted an application to bury a pile of house bricks,' the DCI said, laughing.

'You deserve a promotion for cracking that one,' Guy said. 'Raymond said you were working all hours.'

'She has a shiny new sergeant, though.' Raymond winked at Clare. 'Is he the new Chris? Is our Christopher moving on to bigger and better things?'

'Better than me?' Clare said. 'I don't think so! Anyway, he did a bloody good job on the farm machinery thefts. Thousands of pounds' worth of stuff recovered. The young lad's been charged with reset which panicked him into naming a few names.'

'So Max'll be heading back to Dundee, then?' the DCI said.

Clare shook her head. 'I'm hanging onto Max. He makes the *best* coffee.' She began cutting another slice of cheesecake for Raymond whose plate was now empty. 'I'll make a case for keeping both of them,' she said. 'Tie it in with my shiny new youth initiative.' She held out her hand for Raymond's plate, but he shook his head.

'Honestly, Clare, I couldn't. 'I'll burst.'

'Let's have a break,' the DCI said. He uncorked another bottle of wine and began topping up glasses. 'I need to get Clare drunk enough to agree to put in a wood burner.'

Raymond turned and regarded the open fire. It was dying down a bit now and he held out a hand as if testing how warm it was. 'You do know most of the heat—'

'Goes up the chimney,' Clare said, 'yes, thank you Raymond. I've had that pointed out to me more than once.'

'If you order it now,' he went on, 'you could have it in for Christmas.'

Clare shook her head. 'Honestly, it's like having a parrot. If I've heard it once.' She shoved her wine glass across the table. 'Go on then,' she said to the DCI. 'Top me up and you can order your stove.'

Acknowledgements

The opening scene in *Old Bones Lie* came from a conversation with my good friends Lisbeth, Mary (aka Marydoll) and Winda who introduced me to the wonder that is *Alexa*! Alan Rankin and Andy Jones kept me on track with police procedure and the lovely Rebecca Alston's insight into police intelligence work was invaluable. Peter Darbyshire was my go-to person for farming information, Lisa Wallace kept me right on optometric matters and Ally Todd, as usual, helped with the guns! Any errors in these matters are entirely mine.

The team at Canelo are quite wonderful. In particular, I am in awe of Louise Cullen and Siân Heap's skill as editors. Ladies, you really are the best in the business – thank you! Francesca Riccardi and her colleagues work tirelessly and pretend never to tire of my stupid questions. For Deborah Blake's skilled copy editing and Abbie Headon's eagle-eyed proof reading I'm so grateful. I promise, ladies, I will try to sort out my dashes! James Macey's stunning cover has captured the spirit of the book and generated so much interest; and Hannah Weatherill, my utterly wonderful agent, is the best support a writer could ask for. Thank you for everything, Hannah, I'd be nowhere without you.

My Caledonia Crime Collective chums deserve a special mention for being the best group of writers I could ever hope to meet. To Emma, Debs, Gareth, Allan, Andy and Jonathan, thanks for all the laughs and support. And finally, to the many book bloggers, reviewers, booksellers and (most importantly) readers, thank you for your unending support. I hope this book goes some way to repaying the debt I owe you all.

Do you love crime fiction and are always on the lookout for brilliant authors?

Canelo Crime is home to some of the most exciting novels around. Thousands of readers are already enjoying our compulsive stories. Are you ready to find your new favourite writer?

Find out more and sign up to our newsletter at canelocrime.com

Also by Marion Todd

Detective Clare Mackay

See Them Run
In Plain Sight
Lies to Tell
What They Knew
Next in Line
Old Bones Lie

Old Bones Lie

A native of Dundee, Marion Todd studied music with the Open University and worked for many years as a piano teacher and jobbing accompanist. A spell as a hotel lounge pianist provided rich fodder for her writing and she began experimenting with a variety of genres. Early success saw her winning first prize in the *Family Circle Magazine* short story for children national competition and she followed this up by writing short stories and articles for her local newspaper.

Life (and children) intervened and, for a few years, Marion's writing was put on hold. During this time, she worked as a college lecturer, plantswoman and candle-maker. But, as a keen reader of crime fiction, the lure of the genre was strong, and she began writing her debut crime novel. Now a full-time writer, Marion lives in North-east Fife, overlooking the River Tay. She can often be found working out plots for her novels while tussling with her jungle-like garden and walking her daughter's unruly but lovable dog.